CONCISE DI

of

HOUSE BUILDING TERMS

(Arranged by Trades)

FRENCH-ENGLISH   ENGLISH-FRENCH

Compiled by

A. S. LINDSEY

HADLEY PAGER INFO

Second Edition 2001
Reprinted 2003
Reprinted 2004
ISBN 1-872739-11-3

(First Published 1994 ISBN 1-872739-02-4)

Printed and bound in Great Britain by Antony Rowe Ltd., Chippenham

HADLEY PAGER INFO
Leatherhead, Surrey, England

FOREWORD TO FIRST EDITION

This dictionary is a completely new publication which has been prepared over a period of more than three years following the successful publication of the "French-English Glossary of Legal, Financial and Building Terms Relating to House Purchase" in 1990.

In Britain the building trade has evolved its own special and often trade-oriented vocabulary. Similarly in France the building trade has developed its own range of specialised and technical terms, the meanings or equivalents of which in English are not readily accessible, the more so since the building materials and building techniques used in France often differ from those traditionally used in Britain. It is hoped that this Concise Dictionary of Building Terms in French and English will help to ease the future path of the translator of building literature, specifications, estimates, architectural plans, survey reports and other similar documents.

Often the French terms used in a particular building trade are applicable only to that trade, and where the same word or phrase is used in different trades its meaning may well differ, being determined by the particular context. For this reason the dictionary has been compiled on the basis of the separate trades which should make it easier to look up a given word. The terms and phrases included in the dictionary are essentially those in present usage and wherever possible have been checked against currently available technical textbooks, manuals, glossaries, dictionaries and catalogues relating to the building trade, both in French and in English. An attempt has been made to include the broad majority of terms used in the building trades covered by the dictionary but it is not claimed to be comprehensive.

The terms included have been essentially restricted to those of a technical or trade specific nature, and commonly used French or English words have not been included. The number of word or phrase entries present in either language section (French-English or English-French) of the Concise Dictionary is in excess of 10,000 providing an overall total of more than 20,000 entries.

The Concise Dictionary should prove of value to English speaking builders operating in France as well as to those owners of French property, whose vocabulary is not strong on building terms, and who may be faced with the task of understanding estimates provided by French building contractors. English-speaking property owners in France should therefore find this dictionary useful when arranging renovation, decoration or modification of their property.

I am greatly indebted to my wife Hazel Lindsey for her untiring assistance in the preparation of the text, as well as with the proofreading. I also thank C. F. Lindsey for his considerable help in tracking down and verifying some of the more difficult technical terms, and for assistance with the proofreading. All errors and omissions which might be found are mine alone and I would ask users of the dictionary to let me know of any faults that they may note so that these can be rectified in later editions.

A. S. L.

FOREWORD TO SECOND EDITION

The need for a second edition of the Concise Dictionary of House Building Terms has prompted a revision of all sections of the book. Further clarification of many entries has been made and known errors corrected. Most sections have been augmented with additional terms. A list of the principal information sources utilised has been included. Suggestions for the improvement of future editions will be welcomed.

A. S. L.

PRINCIPAL INFORMATION SOURCES ACCESSED
IN THE PREPARATION OF THE DICTIONARY

1. Dictionary of Electrical Engineering, Telecommunications, and Electronics, German-English-French, 1966
   Goedecke, W. (pub. Pitman)
2, Harrap's New Standard French and English Dictionary, 1970
   Mansion, J.E., Revised by Ledésert D.M. and Ledésert, R.P.L. (pub.Harrap & Co)
3. Technologie d'Électricité, Volume 1,1974
   Merlet, R. (pub. Dunod)
4. Glossary of Timber Construction, Swedish-English-French-German, 1975
   Swedish Centre of Technical Terminology. Publication TNC 60
5. French-English Science and Technology Dictionary, 1975 (4th Edition)
   DeVries, L., & Hochman, S. (pub. McGraw-Hill Book Co.)
6. Dictionnaire Technique Général, Anglais-Français, 1978 (2nd Edition),
   Belle-Isle, J-G. (pub. Routledge & Kegan Paul)
7. Dictionary of Technical Terms and Phrases, French-English and English-French, 1980
   Ketteridge, J.O. and Arden, Y.R. (pub. Routledge & Kegan Paul)
8. Lexique Technique General, Français-Anglais, 1983
   Côté, J-M., & Collaborateurs (pub. Presses de l'Université du Quebec)
9. Elsevier's Dictionary of Building Tools and Materials, English-French-Spanish-German-Dutch, 1982
   Chaballe, L.Y., & Vandenberghe, J-P. (pub. Elseviers Science Publishers)
10. Collection "Concevoir et Construire": Maçonnerie; Charpentes; Électricité; Plomberie; Toitures; Menuiseries; Béton Armé; Le Permis de Construire, 1991
    Matana, M. (Editor). (pub. Syros-Alternatives, Paris)
11. Dictionnaire Technique du Bâtiment et des Travaux Publics,, 1992 (11th Edition)
    Barbier, M., Cadiergues, R., Delefosse, J., Flitz, J., Stoskopf, G., Venien, J. (pub Eyrolles)
12 La Plomberie, 1992
    Gallauziaux, T., Fedullo, D., Jacquelot, M. (pub. Eyrolles)
13. Routledge French Technical Dictionary, French-English and English-French, 1994
    Arden, Y.R., Clements, N. & Collaborators. (pub. Routledge)
14. Dictionary of Building and Civil Engineering, English-French and French-English, 1996. Montague, D. (pub. E. & F.N. Spon)

ARRANGEMENT AND USE OF DICTIONARY

The dictionary is arranged into fourteen sections corresponding approximately with the services or trades required in each phase of building a house. Each section is self-contained within its subject matter but overlaps to some degree with other sections. Therefore if the word sought is not found in the expected section a check should be made in allied sections.

The sections 'MAÇON' and 'BUILDER' which are the largest of the individual sections have the greatest overlap with the others and these should be searched for the required word if not found elsewhere. It should be noted that the sections 'ARCHITECTE' and 'ARCHITECT' also cover terms associated with surveying, drawing plans, and building regulations; the sections 'TERRASSEMENTS ET FONDATIONS' and 'EARTHWORKS AND FOUNDATIONS' also cover excavation work and concreting; the sections 'PEINTRE-DÉCORATEUR' and 'PAINTER AND DECORATOR' cover painting, tiling and wallpapering. Terms for tools are included in the individual sections.

It should be noted that the definitions given in this dictionary have no legal or statutory basis. Entered words which the author has reason to believe are registered trade names or marks, or which have been used as trade names or marks are indicated by the symbol ™. However, the presence or absence of such a symbol should not be regarded as affecting the legal status of any trade mark or name.

ABBREVIATIONS USED

abb	abbreviation	agric	agricultural
adj	adjective	archit	architectural
adv	adverb	const	construction
adv phr	adverbial phrase	elect	electrical
f	feminine noun	geol	geological
m	masculine noun	mech	mechanical
pl	plural form	™	Trade Mark or Name
suff	suffix		
v	verb		

FRENCH-ENGLISH

1. ARCHITECTE

accès *m* access

acheter *v* **une maison sur plan** buy a house at the plan stage (to)

achever *v* finish (to); end (to); complete (to)

agent *m* **immobilier** estate agent

alimentation *f* supply (eg of gas, water)

alimentation *f* **en eau** water supply

alimentation *f* **en électricité** electricity supply

alimentation *f* **en énergie** power supply

alimentation *f* **en gaz** gas supply

aménagement *m* fitting-out; converting; conversion; developing

aménagements *mpl* **paysagers** landscaping

aménager *v* fit out (to); equip (to); lay out (to); convert (to); plan (to); develop (to)

▪ **à aménager** = for conversion

annexe *f* annexe; extension (to a building); schedule (to a contract); appendix

architecte *m* architect

architecte *m* **d'intérieur** interior designer

architecture *f* **moderne** modern architecture

are *m* 100 square metres

aréage *m* area of land measured in ares

arpentage *m* land surveying

arpenteur *m* surveyor (land)

artisan *m* craftsman; artisan

aspect *m* aspect

assurance *f* **dommage-ouvrage** insurance against building faults

avant-projet *m* draft project; proposed plan; preliminary study

avenant *m* additional clause; endorsement; rider; amendment (to a contract)

bâtir *v* build (to); construct (to); erect (to)

bien fonds *mpl* real estate

biens *mpl* **immeubles; biens** *mpl* **immobiliers** real estate; property

bornage *m* boundary marking; demarcation

borne *f* boundary stone or marker; limit

bruit *m* noise; sound

cadastre *m* land registry; cadastral register; cadastral survey

cahier *m* **des charges** specification; schedule of conditions

cahier *m* **des charges détaillés** detailed specification; detailed conditions

cahier *m* **des charges techniques** technical specification

certificat *m* **d'origine** certificate of origin

certificat *m* **d'urbanisme** certificate issued by local authority stating planning and building requirements to be met for specified property

certificat *m* **de conformité** certificate of conformity

cession-bail *f* sale and leaseback

chaine *f* **d'arpenteur** chain (surveyor's); chain measure

chantier *m* building site; roadworks

chantier *m* **de construction** building site

chauffage *m* **central** central heating

clause *f* clause; article; provision; stipulation

clause *f* **pénale** penalty clause

clôture *f* fence; fencing; hedge; wall; enclosure

clôture *f* **de bornage** boundary fence

coloris *m* colour; shade

commune *f* commune; town; village; district; parish

commune *f* **rurale/urbaine** rural/urban district

compte-rendu *m* report; progress report

compte-rendu *m* **de séance** minutes

condition *f* condition; stipulation; term of contract

conformer à (se) *v* conform to (to)

▪ **conformément aux regléments** = according to regulations

constat *m* certified report

constat *m* **parasitaire** professional report on whether property is free of parasites (eg termites etc)

constructeur *m* builder; constructor

constructeur *m* **de maisons** house-builder

constructible *adj* physical conditions and official authorisation permits construction on site

construction *f* building; construction; structure

construction *f* **en éléments préfabriqués** prefabricated construction

construire *v* build (to); construct (to)

contenance *f* capacity (eg volume of

reservoir); size (of land area)

contrat *m* contract; agreement

contrat *m* **d'entreprise** business contract (eg building work contract); company contract

contrat *m* **de construction** construction contract

contrat *m* **passé à une entreprise** contract placed with a contractor/company

contrat *m* **principal** main contract

convertir *v* convert (to); transform (to)

couleur *f* colour; shade

coupe *f* section; cross-section

coupe *f* **longitudinale** logitudinal cross-section

coupe *f* **transversale** transversal cross-section

cuisine *f* **équipée** fitted kitchen

déclaration *f* **d'achèvement des travaux** notification (to local authority) that permitted building work has been completed (see also 'certificat de conformité')

défaut *m* defect; fault; flaw

défaut *m* **caché** latent/hidden defect

défaut *m* **d'entretien** lack of upkeep

défrichement *m*; **défrichage** *m* clearing; surface clearing (of ground, wood etc.)

dégagement *m* passage (in appartment); backdoor; exit

dégagement *m* **d'entrée** private entrance

délai *m* time limit; delay; deadline

délai *m* **de livraison** delivery delay; delivery date

délai *m* **de réflexion** time for consideration; cooling-off time

demande *f* **de sursis** request for deferment

démolir *v* demolish (to)

déplacer *v* move (to); shift (to); displace (to)

déplacer (se) *v* be moved (to)

déroulement *m* progress; development

déroulement *m* **des travaux** progress of building work

déroulement *m* **du contrat** progress of the contract

dessin *m* drawing; design; sketch

dessin *m* **de coupe** sectional drawing

dessinateur *m*; **dessinatrice** *f* draughtsman; draughtswoman; designer

dessiner *v* draw (to)

destination *f* **du local** intended usage of premises/dwelling (eg private or commercial)

devis *m* estimate

devis *m* **descriptif** detailed estimate; specification

devis *m* **estimatif** preliminary estimate

devis *m* **préliminaire** outline specification

devis *m* **quantitatif** bill of quantities

disposition *f* **d'urbanisme** planning provision; planning requirement

disposition *f* **des lieux** requirements for installation

document *m* document

dommage-ouvrage *m* building fault; construction fault or damage

dossier *m* file; dossier; documentation

dossier *m* **de permis de construire** application documents and plans required for the 'permis de construire'

dossier *m* **de plans** set of architectural/ building plans

droit *m* **de passage** right of way

droit *m* **de puisage** right to draw water (eg from well)

ébauche *f* outline drawing; rough sketch

ébaucher *v* sketch out (to)

échantillon *m* sample

échantillon *m* **pour essai** test sample

échelle *f* 1 ladder; 2 scale (of map; of charges, etc)

échelle *f* **de sauvetage** fire escape

échelle *f* **proportionnelle** proportional scale

édifier *v* build (to); construct (to); erect (to)

élément *m* unit; element; component

élément *m* **de cuisine** kitchen unit

éléments *mpl* **compris dans le contrat** items covered by contract

éléments *mpl* **de rangement** storage units

emprise *f* **au sol** appropriation of ground

énoncer *v* express (to); state (to)

énoncé *m* statement; wording; terms

enregistrement *m* registration; registering

ensemble *m* housing scheme; housing development

entrepreneur *m* **de constructions** building

contractor
entreprise *f* enterprise; company; firm
entreprise *f* **de service public** public utility
company
entreprise *f* **priveé** private company
équerre *f* **à/en T** T-square
esquisse *f* sketch; rough sketch; outline (of
a project)
établir *v* establish (to); fix (to) (a price);
draw up (to) (a document)
établir *v* **un projet d'accord/de contrat**
produce a draft agreement/contract (to)
étage *m* level; stage; storey
étape *f* stage
étape *f* **de la construction** construction
stage
exemplaire *m* copy
expert *m* expert; specialist; professional
expert *m* **géomètre** surveyor
expertise *f* expert valuation/appraisal;
survey; surveyor's report
expertise *f* **d'un bien** valuation of a property
exposé au sud/au nord/à l'est/à l'ouest
facing south/north/east/west
exposition *f* exposition; aspect (of a building)

façade *m* front; facade
facture *f* invoice
faire *v* **un procès-verbal** draw up a report (to)
fonds *m* land; estate; fund(s); capital
fonds *m* **de terre** piece of land
fonds *m* **dominant** dominating land (of
easements on other land)
formulaire *m* form
fouille *f* excavation

garage *m* garage
garantie *f* guarantee
gazon *m* lawn; turf
gazon *m* **anglais** smooth, well-kept, lawn
gazonnage *m*; **gazonnement** *m* turfing;
planting with grass
gazonner *v* turf (to); plant with grass (to)
géomètre *m* surveyor; geometrician;
geometer
géomètre *m* **du cadastre** ordnance surveyor
grand ensemble *m* high-density housing
development
gros œuvre *m* foundations and walls; shell

(of a building)

haie *f* hedge
hauteur *f* height; elevation; altitude
hectare *m*; **ha** *abb* hectare (10,000 sq.
metres = 2.4711 acres)
honoraires *mpl* fee
honoraires *mpl* **de l'architecte** architect's fee

immeuble *m* building; block of flats;
premises
immeuble *m* **de rapport** block of flats
immeuble *m* **sans servitudes ni hypothèques**
estate free from encumbrances
immobilier *m* property; real estate
immobilier, -ière *adj* property
implantation *f* setting out; introduction;
setting up; siting; locating
instruction *f* **de la demande de permis de
construire** examination of the request for
permission to build

jalon *m* surveyor's pole or rod; range pole
jardin *m* garden
jardin *m* **d'hiver** winter garden; conservatory
jardin *m* **paysagé** landscaped garden
jouissance *f* use; possession of; tenure

lac *m* **d'agrément** ornamental lake
levé *m* survey; surveying; survey report
levé *m* **de terrain(s)** land-survey; land
surveying
longueur *f* length
longueur *f* **hors-tout** overall length
lotissement *m* plot or parcel of land;
housing estate or site; housing development

main-d'œuvre *f* labour; manpower
mairie *f* town hall; council offices; office of
mayor
maison *f* **individuelle** detached house
maître *m* **d'œuvre** project manager
maître *m* **d'œuvre qualifié** qualified
building supervisor (eg architect, builder)
maître *m* **d'ouvrage** owner (commissioning
building work)
malfaçon *f* fault; defect (due to bad
workmanship)
matériaux *mpl* **de construction** building

materials
menuiserie *f* joinery; woodwork; carpentry
mesurage *m* measurement; measuring
mesure *f* measure; measurement
mesure *f* à ruban measuring tape
metallerie *f* metalwork; metal items
méthode *f* d'isolement method of insulation
méthode *f* de construction method of construction
métrage *m* measurement; measuring; quantity surveying; surveying
métrè *m* quantity surveying; measurement; estimate of costs
mètre *m* metre; metre rule
mètre *m* à ruban measuring tape (one metre)
mètre *m* carré square metre
mètre *m* cube cubic metre
métreur *m*; **métreuse** *f* quantity surveyor; surveyor
métreur-vérificateur *m* quantity surveyor
miroiterie *f* mirror items; mirror trade
mise *f* putting; setting
mise *f* au point developing; perfecting; fine-tuning; finalising/settling (business); restatement
mise *f* en demeure summons; formal demand; formal notice
mise *f* en œuvre implementation (of a regulation); using; marshalling; employing; preparation; construction
mise *f* hors d'air (à la) building stage with doors and windows completed
mise *f* hors d'eau (à la) building stage with roof completed
modalité *f* form; mode; method; modality; means; way
modalités *fpl* de mise en œuvre details of implementation
modalités *fpl* de paiement methods/terms of payment
mode *m* de répartition du partage des honoraires way the fees are allocated
modèle *m* réduit scale model
modifier *v* modify (to); alter (to)
modifier (se) *v* alter (to); be modified (to)
motte *f* de gazon (une) turf, a

négocier *v* negotiate (to)
niveau *m* level; storey

niveau *m* de bruit noise level
notaire *m* notary; notary public; solicitor (conveyancing)

œuvre *f* work; piece of work
offre *f* de prix quotation
ordre *m* association; professional association; order
ordre *m* de service architect's instruction to builder
Ordre *m* des Architectes Association of Architects
orientation *f* exposition; aspect (of a building)
origine *f* origin; source
origine *f* de propriété vendor's title to property
ouverture *f* de chantier start of building work
ouvrage *m* work; building work

papier-calque *m*; **papier** *m* à calquer tracing paper
papier *m* à dessin drawing paper
papier *m* translucide tracing paper
parc *m* à l'anglaise landscaped garden or park
parc *m* paysager landscaped garden
parcellaire *adj* divided into plots
parcelle *f* parcel (of land)
parcelle *f* de terre plot of land
partie *f* party; person signing a contract; part; amount
parties *fpl* contractantes contracting parties
passage *m* way; passage; change; changeover
passation *f* signing (a contract, deed); drawing up (a contract); entry (into accounts ledger); placing (an order)
passation *f* de l'acte signing the deed of sale
passation *f* des marchés signing business contracts
paysage *m*; **paysager, paysagère** *adj* landscape; scenery
permis *m* de construire planning permission; building permit
permis *m* de démolir permit to demolish a building

perron *m* front steps (of house)
photocalque *m* **bleu** blueprint
pièce *f* room (of house); part; component;
piece; document
piscine *f* swimming pool
placard *m* cupboard
plan *m* plan; scale drawing; plane
plan *m* **d'ensemble** housing development
plan
plan *m* **d'implantation** site plan
plan *m* **d'installation** installation plan
Plan *m* **d'Occupation des Sols; POS** plan
of local land use
plan *m* **de chaque niveau** architectural
diagram of each storey
plan *m* **de construction** building plan
plan *m* **de la maison** house plan
plan *m* **de masse** solid mass plan; aerial plan
of mass
plan *m* **de situation** location plan
plan *m* **des facades** plan of elevations
planche *m* **à dessin** drawing board
plomberie *f* plumbing materials; plumbing
pondération *f* **des bruits** noise rating
pont *m* **thermique** heat bridge
préavis *m* prior notice; advance notice
given before contract or agreement is
broken
préciser *v* specify (to); give precise details
(to); stipulate (to)
prescription *f* prescription; order; item in
contract; specified item; statute of
limitations
prescriptions *fpl* regulations; instructions
prescriptions *fpl* **techniques** technical
regulations; specifications
prix/coût *m* **de la main-d'œuvre** labour
cost(s)
procès-verbal *m*; **procès-verbaux** *mpl*
minutes; report; statement
projet *m* project; plan; scheme
projet *m* **d'acte** draft conveyance document
projeter *v* plan (to); consider (to); project
(to)
prolongation *f* **de temps** extension of time
promoteur *m* **immobilier** property developer
propriétaire *m* owner; proprietor; landlord
propriété *f* property; estate; ownership;
possession; characteristic

propriété *f* **bâtie** developed property
propriété *f* **foncière** real estate; property
ownership
propriété *f* **non bâtie** undeveloped property
publicité *f* **de la demande de permis de
construire** public notice of request for
building permit
pylône *m* pylon

quartier *m* **résidentiel** residential area
quincaillerie *f* ironmongery; ironmonger's
(shop)

rapport *m* report
rapport *m* **d'expertise** survey report
réception *f* receipt; reception
réception *f* **des ouvrages/travaux** final
verification and acceptance that building
work has been satisfactorily completed to
specification
rédaction *f* wording; drafting (of a document); drawing-up
rédaction *f* **de bail** drawing-up a lease
rédiger *v* write (to); draft (to) (a document);
draw up (to) (a contract)
réduction *f* **de bruit** noise reduction
règlement *m* regulation(s); settlement;
payment (eg of an invoice)
règlement *m* **intégral** regulation(s);
settlement; payment (eg of an invoice)
règlement *m* **intérieur** rules and regulations;
bye-laws
règlement *m* **par chèque** payment by cheque
règlementation *f* regulation(s); control
règlementation *f* **des changes** exchange
controls
règlementation *f* **en vigueur** regulations in
force
remise *f* delivery; handing over; postponement; discount
remise *f* **en état** reconditioning; restoration;
refurbishment
remise *f* **à neuf** restoration; renovation
rénovation *f* renovation; modernisation;
restoration; redevelopment
renover *v* renovate (to); modernise (to);
restore (to) (a building)
réparation *f* repairing; restoring
réparer *v* repair (to); mend (to)

répartition *f* distribution; sharing out; allocation

réprendre *v* **en sous-œuvre** underpin (to)

résiliation *f* termination; cancellation; rescinding

résiliation *f* **d'un contrat** cancellation of a contract

restauration *f* restoration

restaurer *v* restore (to)

rez-de-chaussée *m*; **rdc** *abb* ground floor; street level

robinetterie *f* taps and fittings; tap trade

rompre *v* break off (to) (a contract)

route *f* road; roadway; route

route *f* **nationale/départementale** main/ secondary road

route *f* **non goudronnée** unmade road; unmetalled road

S.A.F.E.R.(Société d'Aménagement Foncier et d'Établissement Rural) French Land Commission

saisie *f* distraint (legal); foreclosure; seizure

schèma *m*; **schéme** *m* diagram; plan; scheme; sketch

serre *f* conservatory

servitude *f* easement; charge; encumbrance; constraint

servitude *f* **de passage** right of way

servitudes *fpl* **privées grevant le terrain** private easements attached to the land/site

signature *f* signature; signing

signer *v* sign (to)

sous-estimer *v* undervalue (to)

sous-œuvre *m* underpinning; substruction

soussigné *m*; **soussignée** *f*; also *adj* undersigned (the)

spécification *f* specification

standing *m* standing (situation and condition)

stipulation *f* stipulation; item in contract; specified item

stipulations *fpl* **d'un contrat** specifications of a contract

style *m* style

superficie *f* surface; surface area

superficie *f* **de plancher hors œuvre nette** overall net floor area

surestimer *v* overvalue (to)

surface *f* surface; surface area

surface *f* **habitable** habitable surface area of dwelling

surface *f* **hors œuvre brute** gross area of house; gross habitable floor area

surface *f* **hors œuvre nette** basic area of house; habitable floor area (see also 'superficie')

système *m* **de chauffage** heating system

système *m* **de drainage** drainage system

terrain *m* land; plot (of land); piece of land; building land/site; ground; terrain

terrain *m* **à bâtir** building land/site

terrain *m* **avec/sans viabilité** site with/ without services laid on

terrain *m* **boisé** wooded land

terrain *m* **clos** enclosed land

terrain *m* **constructible** land on which technically and legally one can build

terrain *m* **viabilisé** site with services laid on

terrasse *f* terrace

terrassement *m* excavation

tiers *m* third party

traçage *m* marking out; drawing; tracing

transformer *v* transform (to); change (to); alter (to)

transmission *f* passing on; forwarding

urbanisme *m* town planning

verger *m* orchard

viabiliser *v* service (to) (eg a building plot)

■ **entièrement viabilisé** = fully serviced

viabilité *f* practicability; availability of services (eg water etc)

vice *m* fault; defect; flaw

vice *m* **caché** latent or hidden fault/defect

vice *m* **de construction** construction fault/ defect

vice *m* **de forme** legal flaw or irregularity

visite *f* **d'expert** house survey

vitrerie *f* glazing; glass items

voie *f* **de dégagement** slip road

zone *f* **bâtie** built-up area

abaissement *m* subsidence; sinking; lowering (eg temperature)

accélérateur *m* accelerator

accélérateur *m* **de prise** setting accelerator (for cement/mortar)

acier *m* steel; steel rod; steel reinforcement

acier *m* **à haute adhérence (HA)** high-adherence steel (rod) (for reinforcement)

acier *m* **crénelé** ribbed or deformed steel bar

acier *m* **de construction** structural steel

acier *m* **de répartition** distribution steel

aciers *mpl* **de la semelle** reinforcement steel in the foundations or footings

additif *m* additive

adjuvant *m* additive

affaissement *m* subsidence (ground, foundations); sag (eg roof); slump; collapse

affouillable *adj* liable to wash away

affouiller *v* undermine (to); erode (to)

agrégat *m* aggregate

alignement *m* alignment

alimentation *f* **en eau** water supply

ancrage *m* anchorage; anchoring

ancrer *v* anchor (to); fix (to)

▪ **bien ancré** = well-anchored

angle *m* **de frottement** angle of friction

angle *m* **de talus** angle of slope

angle-dozer *m* angledozer

angle *m* **droit** right angle

antigel *m* antifreeze additive for concrete

antigélif *m* additive to prevent disintegration of concrete by frost

aplanir *v* level (to); smooth out (to)

aplanir *v* **un terrain** level a piece of land (to)

appareillage *m* equipment

apprêter *v* make ready (to); prepare (to)

approvisionnement *m* **d'eau** water supply

appui *m* **béton** concrete sill; concrete support

arase *f* **étanche** impervious levelling layer; damp-proof layer

araser *v* level (to) (eg a wall)

argile *f* clay

argileux,-euse *adj* argillaceous; clay; clayey

armature *f* reinforcement; steel rod reinforcement (for concrete); framework

armer *v* reinforce (to)

asséchement *m* drying out; drainage; draining; emptying

assemblage *m* **des armatures par ligature** joining reinforcements by tying with wires

assise *f* bed; course; foundation; stratum (geol)

bâche *f* tarpaulin; tank

banche *f* form (work); shuttering panel

barre *f* **d'acier** steel bar

battage *m* **de pieux/pilots** pile driving

bêche *f* spade

bêcher *v* dig (to)

benne *f* dump truck; skip; tipper lorry; bucket (of earthmover)

béton *m* concrete

béton *m* **armé; B.A.** *abb* reinforced concrete

béton *m* **armé sollicité** stressed reinforced concrete

béton *m* **banché** formed concrete; concrete moulded in timber or steel formers

béton *m* **cellulaire** cellular concrete

béton *m* **courant** ordinary concrete

béton *m* **de masse** mass concrete; plain concrete

béton *m* **de propreté** bedding concrete; blinding concrete

béton *m* **précontraint** prestressed concrete

béton *m* **réfractaire** refractory concrete

béton *m* **routier** road concrete; highway concrete

béton *m* **universel** universal concrete

bétonnage *m* concreting; adding concrete by pouring

bétonner *v* concrete (to)

bétonnière *f* concrete mixer

blindage *m* shoring up; sheeting (wood or metal); timbering (eg of excavation)

blindage *m* **par caissons** shoring up with coffers; casing; coffering

blindage *m* **par panneaux préfabriqués** shoring up with prefabricated boards

blindage *m* **par planche horizontale/ verticale** shoring with horizontal/ vertical planking

blinder *v* shore up (to); timber (to)

bloc *m* block; lump; mass; piece

bloc *m* **de béton** block of concrete

blocage *m* 1 clamping; locking; blocking;
2 rubblework; cement block foundation;
3 filling-in or packing of wall
blocageux, blocageuse *adj* rubbly
blocaille *f* ballast; hardcore; rubble
boisage *m* timbering; timberwork; cribbing
bouchardage *m* bush hammer finish;
roughening
boucharde *f* bush hammer
boucharde *f* **de cimentier** cementer's
patternmarker roller
bourrage *m* packing; stuffing; filling
(material); backfilling
brouettage *m* barrowing
brouette *f* barrow; hand-barrow; wheel-
barrow
brouettée *f* barrowful; barrowload
bulldozer *m* bulldozer
burin *m*; **burin** *m* **à froid** chisel; cold-chisel
burin-bêche *m* scaling chisel (for
hammer-drill)
burinage *m* chipping; chiseling

cadre *m* frame(work); packing case
cage *f* carcass (of house); shell (of building)
caillou *m* pebble; stone
caillouteux,-euse *adj* pebbly
calage *m* 1 wedging; 2 keying; 3 adjustment;
4 chocking up
cale *f* wedge; choc; prop; strut
cale *m* **en béton** concrete blocking piece
camion *m* lorry
camionage *m* cartage; carting
canal *m* **d'écoulement** drainage channel
carotte *f* **d'enchantillon** core test sample (of
soil)
chaise *f* **d'angle** corner profile board
chaise *f* **d'implantation** 1 profile board;
level board; 2 support frame
chantier *m* building site; roadworks
chantier *m* **de construction** building site
chape *f* coating; screed
chape *f* **adhérente** adherent screed (opposed
to floating screed); monolithic screed
chape *f* **ciment** cement covering; screed
chape *f* **d'arase** levelling layer of screed
chape *f* **d'usure** screed laid as floor surface
chape *f* **de revêtement** screed laid as base

for floor covering
chape *f* **flottante** floating screed
chape *f* **incorporée** adherent screed;
incorporated screed; monolithic screed
charge *f* load
charge *f* **admissible** permissible load
chargement *m* loading; load
charger *v* load (to); fill (to)
chargeur *m* loader
chargeuse *f* loading shovel; mechanical
shovel; front-end loader
chaux *f* lime
chaux *f* **éteinte** slaked lime
chaux *f* **grasse** fat lime
chaux *f* **gris** grey lime
chaux *f* **hydraulique** hydraulic lime
chaux *f* **vive** quick lime
chevillette *f* **de maçon** bricklayer's pin; line
pin
CHF *abb* see 'ciment de haut fourneau'
ciment *m* cement
ciment *m* **à prise lente** slow-setting cement
ciment *m* **à prise rapide** quick-setting
cement
ciment *m* **armé** reinforced cement
ciment *m* **blanc** white cement
ciment *m* **de haut fourneau**; **CHF** blast-
furnace slag cement
ciment *m* **de laitier** slag cement
ciment *m* **de laitier au clinker** Portland
blast-furnace cement; CLK
ciment *m* **de Portland** Portland cement
ciment *m* **fondu** high alumina cement
ciment *m* **gris** grey cement
ciment *m* **hydraulique** hydraulic cement
cimentier *m* cementer (person); cement
manufacturer
ciment *m* **joint** jointing cement
ciment *m* **Portland** Portland cement
ciment *m* **Portland artificiel** artificial
Portland cement; CPA
ciment *m* **Portland au laitier** Portland
blast-furnace cement
ciment *m* **Portland pur** Portland cement
ciment *m* **pouzzolanique** pozzolana cement
ciment *m* **prompt** rapid setting cement
cimentage *m* cementation; cementing
cimentation *f* cementation; cementing
cimenter *v* cement (to)

cimentier *m* cementer (person); cement manufacturer

ciseau *m* ; **ciseaux** *mpl* chisel

ciseau *m* **à froid** cold chisel

ciseau *m* **de maçon** mason's chisel

classification *f* **des terrains** classification of terrain

clinker *m* clinker

CLK *abb* see 'ciment de laitier au clinker'

coffrage *m* coffering; form; formwork; framing (for concrete work); lining; shuttering

coffrage *m* **de plafond** ceiling formwork; ceiling boarding

coffrage *m* **en tôle** sheet metal casing/formwork

coffre *m* case; form (for concrete)

coffrer *v* place a frame/form (to) (for concrete)

coffreur *m* **(pour béton armé)** formwork carpenter

cohésion *f* **de sol** soil cohesion (soil resistance to movement)

colonne *f* column

colonne *f* **de béton** concrete column

combler *v* fill (to); fill up (to)

compactage *m* compaction

compacter *v* compact (to); roller (to)

compacteur *m* **à pneu** rubber-tyred roller

compresseur *m* compressor

compressibilité *f* **de sol** soil compressibility

comprimer *v* compress (to)

concasser *v* break (to); crush (to)

COPLA *abb* Commission permanente des liants hydrauliques et des adjuvants du béton French Permanent Commission overseeing the usage of binders and additives in concrete

couche *f* coat; layer

couche *f* **d'approche** initial layer (of plaster or mortar)

couche *f* **d'étancheité** damp-proof course

couche *f* **d'usure** layer ready for use (eg concrete path)

couche *f* **de finition** finishing coat; finishing layer; setting coat (plaster); skimming coat; top coat

couche *f* **de revêtement** layer ready for covering (eg with tiles)

couche *f* **isolante** insulating layer; damp-proof layer

couche *f* **isolante imperméable** damp-proof course

coulage *m* pouring (eg concrete)

couler *v* pour (to) (eg concrete, asphalt)

CPA *abb* see 'ciment portland artificiel'

CPJ *abb* see 'ciment portland composé'

crépi *m* rendering; masonry paint; textured paint; roughcast

crépir *v* cover with masonry paint (to); render with cement (to); roughcast (to)

crépissage *m* rendering; roughcasting

creusage *m*; **creusement** *m* digging

creuser *v* dig (to); dig out (to); sink (to) (a well)

creuser *v* **au marteau-piqueur** drill (to)

crochet *m* hook

dallage *m* flagging; pavement; paving

dalle *f* **de béton** concrete slab

dalle *f* **de compression** topping slab; structural topping slab; concrete layer

dalle *f* **en béton armé** reinforced slab floor (concrete)

dalle *f* **flottante** floating slab floor

damage *m* ramming; tamping

dame *f* beetle; earth-rammer; earth compacter

damer *v* ram (to); tamp (to); slope (to)

débarrasser *v* clear (to); remove (to); get rid of (to)

déblai *m* clearance; cutting; excavation; levelling a site by earth removal; clearing

déblais *mpl* excavated material; spoil; waste

déblayage *m* **déblaiement** *m* clearing; levelling off

déblayer *v* clear away (to); level off (to); cut (to) (earthworks)

décapage *m* clearing; scouring; cleaning; rubbing (eg with pumice); clearance of ground to about 20cm depth before levelling out

déchet *m*; **déchets** *mpl* waste; waste material eg slag

décintroir *m* **à talus** mattock

décoffrage *m* removal of shuttering; removal of formwork

décombres *mpl* building rubble; debris

défrichage *m;* **défrichement** *m* clearing; surface-clearing (of ground)

dégel *m* thaw

dégeler *v* thaw (to); melt (to)

dégradation *f* **des fondations** deterioration of the foundations

délai *m* **de durcissement** hardening interval

délayer *v* mix (to) (to required consistency); thin down (to); add water to (to) (eg cement)

demoiselle *f* beetle; rammer; earth-rammer

dernière *f* **assise** last course; top course

désordre *m* disorder

déterrer *v* dig up (to); uproot (to)

dispostif *m* **d'étaiement** shoring arrangement; shoring contrivance

dressage *m;* **dressement** *m* drawing up; setting up; dressing; levelling; preparing

dresser *v* prepare (to); set up (to); level (to); dress (to); draw up (to) (eg plan)

dumper *m* dumper; dump-truck

durcissement *m* hardening (eg of cement); tempering

eau *f* **de gâchage** mixing water (for concrete, etc)

eaux *fpl* **de surface** surface waters

eaux *fpl* **superficielles** surface water

éboulement *m* 1 caving in; collapsing; 2 rockfall

échafaud *m* scaffold(ing); staging

échafaudage *m* erecting a scaffold; scaffolding

échelle *f* ladder

effondrement *m* caving in; collapse; falling-in; subsidence

élément *m* **sollicité** stressed member

en forme de talus sloped; sloping

enfoncement *m* driving; driving in (eg pile); giving way; sinking (eg foundation)

engin *m* appliance; gear; machine

engin *m* **d'excavation** excavator

engin *m* **de compactage** motorised compacter; motorised roller

engin *m* **de damage** rammer

engin *m* **de nivellement** earth-levelling machine

engin *m* **de terrassement** earth-mover

engin *m* **de transport** earth transporter

engins *mpl* **de levage** hoisting equipment

engins *mpl* **de terrassement** earth-moving equipment

entraineur *m* **d'air** air-entraining agent

épaisseur *f* thickness

épingle *f* pin

étai *m* prop; shore; stay; support

étai *m* **de maçon tubulaire** mason's tubular stay

étai *m* **réglable** adjustable stay/support

étaiment *m* propping up; supporting; shoring up

étaiment *m* **des constructions voisines** shoring of adjoining constructions

étanchéité *f* waterproofing; waterproofness; impervious layer; imperviousness; water-tightness

étançon *m* shore; stanchion; stay

étayage *m;* **étayement** *m* shoring; propping

étayer *v* prop (to); shore (to); stay (to); support (to); underpin (to) (wall); prop up (to); shore up (to)

étrésillon *m* brace; strut

étrésillon *m* **hydraulique** hydraulic brace

étrier *m* stirrup; joist hanger

étude *f* **géotechnique** geotechnical survey

évacuation *f* **des terres** removal of (excavated) earth

excavation *f* digging; excavating; excavation

faire *v* **des travaux de terrassement** carry out earthworks (to)

ferraillage *m* introduction of steel reinforcement

filler *m* filler (eg used in cement)

film *m* **plastique étanche** plastic film damp-proof membrane

fines *fpl* filler; fines (eg aggregate)

fluidifiant *m;* also *adj* plasticizer

foisonnement *m* expansion in bulk; swell; swelling

foisonner *v* increase in bulk (to); swell (to)

fonçage *m* **au poussage** sinking by piling

fond *m* base; bottom; primary coat of paint

fondation *f* foundation; base

fondation *f* **"hors-gel"** frost-free foundation

fondation *f* **en redans** stepped foundation

fondation *f* **par semelle** strip foundation
fondation *f* **sur pieux/pilotis** pile foundation
fondation *f* **sur puits** pier foundation; pile foundation
fondation *f* **sur radier** raft foundation; mat foundation
fondation *f* **sur remblais** foundation on refilled or embanked sites
fondation *f* **sur semelle continue** continuous strip foundation
fondation *f* **sur semelle isolée** single strip foundation
fondations *fpl* **d'un bâtiment** foundations of a building
fondement *m* base; foundation
fondements *mpl* **d'une maison** foundations of a house
force *f* **portante d'un terrain** bearing capacity of a terrain (see also 'taux de travail admissible du sol')
forme *f* levelling layer of cement or sand below paving or flagstones; form; shape
forme *f* **en béton** concrete bed
fosse *f* pit
fossé *m* ditch
fouille *f* excavation site; pit; excavation; hole; trench; digging; trenching
fouille *f* **à ciel ouvert** open excavation
fouille *f* **de fondation** foundation excavation
fouille *f* **de rochers** excavation of rock
fouille *f* **en déblais** open excavation (levelling)
fouille *f* **en excavation** horizontal passage excavation; underground excavation
fouille *f* **en "excavation superficielle"** shallow excavation
fouille *f* **en galerie** horizontal passage excavation; underground excavation
fouille *f* **en puits** shaft excavation; well excavation
fouille *f* **en rigole** foundation trench; narrow trench excavation
fouille *f* **en sous-œuvre** excavation under existing construction
fouille *f* **en terrain rocheux** excavation in rocky ground
fouille *f* **en tranchée** trench excavation; deep trenching
fouille *f* **non-blindée** unlined excavation

fouille *f* **pour fondation** foundation excavation
fouille *f* **souterraine** underground excavation
fouiller *v* dig (to); trench (to); excavate (to)
fouilles *fpl* **en pleine masse** general excavations
fouilleur *m*; **fouilleuse** *f* excavator; digger
fourche *f* fork
frottement *m* friction; rubbing

gâchage *m* tempering; mixing
gâcher *v* mix (to) (mortar/concrete); temper (to) (plaster)
gel *m* frost; freezing
geler *v* freeze (to); ice over (to)
glace *f* ice
glaise *f* clay soil
glissement *m* sliding; slippage; slipping
glissement *m* **de la fondation** foundation slippage
godet *m* bucket; cup (of loader, etc)
gonflement *m* inflation; swelling
gonfler *v* inflate (to); swell (to)
granulat *m* aggregate (eg sand, gravel, stone)
granulat *m* **léger** light aggregate (eg pumice, expanded slag)
granulat *m* **lourd** heavy aggregate (eg iron shot)
grattoir *m* **de coffrage** shuttering scraper; formwork scraper
gravats *mpl*; **gravois** *mpl* rubble
gravier *m* gravel; grit
gravière *f* gravel pit
gravillon *m* gravel
gravillon(s) *m (mpl)* chippings
gravilloner *v* gravel (to)
gravois *m* rubble (see 'gravats')
gros œuvre *m* basic structure; shell (of a building); foundations , walls and floors etc; outer walls
gypse *m* gypsum

hauteur *f* depth (eg excavation); height; hill
hérisson *m* foundation of next-to-earth compacted layer of stones; flagging laid on compacted stones

hérissonnage *m* laying of stone etc bedding
hydrofuge *m*; also *adj* water-repellant; water-resisting

imperméabiliser *v* render impermeable (to); waterproof (to)
imperméable *adj* damp-proof; impermeable; impervious; waterproof
implantation *f* setting out; layout
implantation *f* **des terrassements** setting out of the earthworks
implanter *v* peg out (to); set out (to); mark out (to) (site)
inaffouillabilité *f* **d'ouvrage** non-erodability by water of the ground carrying the building
inclinaison *f* inclination; pitch; tilt; slope
incliner *v* incline (to); slope (to)
isolateur *m* insulator
isolation *f* insulation; damp-proofing

jalon *m* surveyor's pole or rod; range pole; levelling rod
jet *m* 1 jet; 2 cast; throw; throwing
jet *m* **de pelle** shovel's cast
jet *m* **horizontal** horizontal cast
jet *m* **sur banquette** cast to bench, at higher level
jet *m* **sur berge** cast to the bank (eg of an excavation)

laitier *m* slag
laitier *m* **concassé** *m* crushed slag
largeur *f* breadth; width
levier *m* crowbar; handspike; lever; prise
levier *m* **à pied-de-biche et à pointe** pick-and-claw crowbar
limon *m* mud; silt
lit *m* **de béton** bed of concrete
lit *m* **isolant** damp-proof course
longueur *f* length

mâchefer *m* clinker; slag aggregate
malaxage *m*; **malaxation** *f* mixing; blending; malaxage

malaxage *m* **du béton** mixing of concrete
malaxeur *m* mixer
malaxeur,-euse *adj* mixing
marne *f* marl; calcareous clay
marteau *m* **électrique** electric hammer-drill
marteau piqueur *m*; **marteaux-piqueurs** *mpl* pneumatic drill
marteau *m* **pneumatique** pneumatic drill
marteau *m* **à deux mains** sledge hammer
marteau m perforateur hammer drill
marteau-pilon *m* power hammer
masse *f* sledgehammer; beetle
masse *f* **couple** sledgehammer
masse *f* **surface d'un terrain** total area of a piece of ground
massette *f* club-hammer; lump hammer
massette *f* **de casseur de pierres** stone breaker's hammer
massif *m* **de fondation** foundation block
massif *m* **de maçonnerie** block of masonry
matériel *m*; **matériels** *mpl*; also *adj* appliances; equipment; material; plant; stock
membrane *f* membrane
membrane *f* **d'étanchéité** damp-proof membrane
mesure *f* **de compression** measurement of resistance to compression
moellon *m* rubble; rubble-stone; small (handsize) building stone
mortier *m* mortar
mortier *m* **bâtard** lime-cement mortar
mortier *m* **de chaux** lime mortar
mortier *m* **de ciment** cement mortar
mouiller *v* moisten (to); wet (to)
moule *m* mould, form (eg for concrete)

nappe *f* **phréatique** water table
nivellement *m* levelling; levelling out
nivelleuse *f* earth levelling machine; grader
niveau *m* **d'eau** water level

œuvre *f* work; piece of work; task
ossature *f* framework
outil *m* tool
outillage *m* equipment; plant; tools
ouverture *f* gap; hole; opening
ouvrabilité *f* workability

ouvrier *m*; ouvrière *f* workman; worker
ouvrier *m* de chantier labourer
ouvrier *m* de construction construction
worker

panneau *m* de coffrage shuttering panel
parcelle *f* parcel (of land)
pare-gel *m* frost protecting additive for
concrete
passer *v* au bulldozer bulldoze (to)
pelle *f* shovel; spade
pelle *f* forgée en acier au carbone shovel of
forged carbon steel
pelle *f* mécanique mechanical shovel
pelleter *v* shovel (to); shovel (up) (to)
pelleteur *m* digger (workman)
pelleteuse *f* excavator (machine); mechanical
digger
phénomène *m* de retrait phenomenon of
contraction
pied-de-biche *m* claw-bar; clawed
spike-lever
pieu *m* pile; post; stake
pilon *m* rammer; tamper
pilonner *v* ram (to); tamp (to)
pilot *m* pile; spike
pilotage *m* pile-driving; piling
piloter *v* drive in piles (to); pile (to)
pilotis *m* pile; piling
pince *f* à décoffrer dismantling crowbar
pince(s)-monseigneur *m* crowbar
pioche *f* hammer-pick; pick; mattock
pioche *f* ordinaire pick-axe
pioche *f* à défricher mattock
piquage *m* thrusting concrete; rodding
concrete
piquet *m* picket; post; stake
piquet *m* repére de nivellement levelling
marker post
piquetage *m* marking out with stakes;
staking out
plan *m* de construction building plan; site
plan
plan *m* de situation du terrain
drawing/plan of situation of site
planche *f* floorboard; plank
planéité *f* flatness; planeness
plastifiant *m*; also *adj* plasticizer

platoir *m* finishing trowel; laying-on trowel
(cement or plaster)
plâtras *m* plaster debris; rubble
pompage *m* pumping out; pumping
pompe *f* pump
pompe *f* électrique electric pump
pomper *v* pump (to); pump out (to)
poser *v* fix (to); lay (to); place (to); set (to)
poser (se) *v* to be set, etc
poser *v* les fondements d'une maison lay
the foundations of a house (to)
poussée *f* des terres thrust of the ground
pouzzolane *f* pozzolana (see also puzzolane)
précontraint,-e *adj*; also *m* prestressed
(concrete)
prédalle *f* 1 thin prestressed concrete slab
forming base of final cast slab; 2 precast
concrete slabs forming permanent shuttering
pression *f* de contact contact pressure
prise *f* setting (eg of cement)
prise *f* lente slow setting
prise *f* rapide fast setting
profondeur *f* depth
puits *m* shaft; well
puits *m* artésien artesian well
puits *m* perdu soak away
puits *m* profond deep well
puzzolane *f* pozzolana

radier *m* apron; foundation apron; raft;
oversite concrete; mat foundation
ragrément *m* cleaning down; finishing off;
smoothing; making good
ragréage *m* 1 finishing; trimming; making
good; 2 cleaning building facade; 3 cement
mortar used for screeding or rendering
rampant *m* slope; rise
rampe *f* rise; slope; incline; gradient
rampe *f* d'accès approach ramp
rapidité *f* de prise speed of setting
râteau *m* rake
ratisser *v* rake (to)
ravalement *m* cleaning; restoration; cutting
back (agric); resurfacing; refacing work;
rough-casting; levelling (soil)
reconnaisance *f* des sols examination of the
ground; soil survey
refouler *v* drive in, down (etc) (to); force in

(to); tamp (to) (earth)

remblai *m* backfill; banking up; embankment; filling up (eg ditch)

remblai *m* **et déblai** *m* cut and fill

remblaiement *m*; **remblayage** *m* filling up; backfilling; banking up

remblayer *v* backfill (to); fill up (to); bank up (to)

remplissage *m* filling; filling up

reprendre *v* repair (to); take back (to)

reprendre *v* **en sous-œuvre** underpin (to) (building)

reprendre *v* **les travaux** restart work (to)

reprise *f* **en sous-œuvre** underpinning

résistance *f* **de béton** compression resistance of concrete; compressive strength of concrete

retardateur *m*; also *adj* retardant

retrait *m* contraction; shrinkage

rétrécissement *m* contraction; narrowing; shrinkage

revêtment *m* **impermeable** waterproof coating

rigole *f* channel; foundation trench; trench (small)

risque *m* **d'éboulement** risk of caving in; risk of earth-fall

risque *m* **d'enfoncement** risk of giving way; risk of sinking (eg foundation)

risque *m* **de glissement** risk of land-slip; risk of slippage

roche *f* rock

roche *f* **concassée** crushed rock; crushed stone

rond *m* **lisse d'acier** smooth steel rod (for reinforcement)

roue *f* **de brouette** wheel of barrow

rouleau *m* roller; roll

rouleau *m* **à pneus** rubber-tyred roller

rouleau *m* **compresseur** roller (road)

rouleau *m* **leger** light roller

ruissellement *m* rilling; running down; running-off (of water) over the surface

sablage *m* sand blasting; sanding

sable *adj* sand-coloured

sable *m* sand

sable *m* **à bâtir** building sand

sable *m* **doux** sand, soft

sable *m* **grossier** sand, coarse

saignée *f* groove; trench; ditch

scie *f* **de coffreur** formworker's saw

scraper *m* mechanical scraper; bowl scraper

seau *m* bucket; bucketful; pail; pailful

seau *m* **en tôle galvanisée** galvanized- iron bucket

séchage *m* drying

semelle *f* footing; base-plate; foundation (load distributing element); base-slab

semelle *f* **de répartition** load-spreading footing or plate

skip *m* skip

sol *m* earth; ground; ground floor; soil

sol *m* **argileux/glaiseux** clay soil

sol *m* **de fondation** subsoil

sol *m* **en béton** concrete floor

sol *m* **inaffouillable** non-erodable ground (by water)

soubassement *m* base; basement

soulever *v* lift up (to); raise (to)

sous-œuvre *m* substruction; underpinning

sous-sol *m* basement; subsoil; substratum

souterrain *m*; also *adj* subterranean; underground

subsidence *f* subsidence

superficie *f* surface; surface area

surcharge *f* overloading

surface *f* surface

surface *f* **d'appui** support surface

surface *f* **de portée** bearing surface

surface *f* **des étages** floor surface (of building)

surface *f* **lisse** smooth surface

surface *f* **portante** bearing surface

surprofondeur *f* excess depth

talochage *m* surface finshing with a float; floating; floated work

taloche *f* float; darby; hawk; laying on trowel

taloche *f* **à pointes** devil float; scratch trowel

taloche *f* **plastique** plastic float

talocher *v* float (to); roughcast (to)

talus *m* slope; bank; batter (eg of a wall)

talus, en forme de sloped; sloping

taluter *v* batter (to) (embankment, etc); slope (to) (side of an embankment)

tamis *m* sieve
tamis *m* bois sieve with wooden frame
tamis *m* métallique wire gauze; gauze; metal sieve
tamisage *m* sieving; sifting
tamiser *v* sieve (to); sift (to)
tas *m* heap; pile
tassement *m* 1 packing; ramming; 2 settlement; settling; subsidence
tassement *m* du remblai settlement of the backfill
tassements *mpl* differentiels differential settlements
taux *m* de travail admissible du sol loading strength of a terrain; permissible loading stress (see also 'force portante d'un terrain')
temps *m* de séchage drying time
terrain *m* building land/site; ground; land; plot (of land); terrain
terrain *m* à bâtir building site
terrain *m* boisé wooded land
terrain *m* clos enclosed land
terrain *m* cohérent coherent ground
terrain *m* constructible land on which one can technically and legally build
terrain *m* de fondation subsoil
terrain *m* détritique detrital ground
terrain *m* en palier level ground
terrain *m* en pente sloping ground
terrain *m* ferme firm ground
terrain *m* instable unstable ground
terrain *m* pierreux stony ground
terrain *m* pulvérulent powdery ground
terrain *m* solide firm ground
terrain *m* vague waste land
terrasse *f* terrace; bank; flat roof
terrassement *m* earthwork(s); embankment; excavation; groundwork(s)
terrassement *m* à découvert open excavation

terrassement *m* en surface surface earthwork
terrasser *v* excavate (to); dig out (to)
terrassier *m* earthworks labourer; navvy
terre *f* earth; ground; land; soil
terre *f* argileuse clayey soil
terre *f* calcaire chalky soil
terre *f* sableuse sandy soil
terre *f* végétale soil (ordinary)
terre-plein *m* earth platform; raised strip of land; solid earth
tilt-dozer *m* tiltdozer
toile *f* à bâche tarpaulin
toile *f* goudronnée tarpaulin
tolérance *f* d'exécution permitted tolerance
tourbe *f* peat
tranchée *f* cut; surface cut; trench
travail *m* préparatoire preparatory work
travaux *mpl* de terrassement earthworks
treillis *m* soudé welded steel trellis (for reinforcement)
treuil *m* crab; hoist; winch
treuil *m* électrique electric hoist
trou *m* hole
truelle *f* trowel
truelle *f* dentelée toothed trowel
truelle *f* ronde round trowel
tuf *m* tufa

vase *f* mud; silt
vérin *m* hydraulique hydraulic jack; hydraulic ram
vidanger *v* drain off (to); empty (to); empty out (to)
vider *v* clear (to); drain (to); empty (to)
voie *f* d'accès access road
voile *m* shell

about *m* butt; butt-end
■ **en about** = abutting
aboutement *m* abutting; abutment
abouter *v* abut (to); butt (to); butt-joint
(to)
abri *m* cover; protection; shed; shelter
abri *m* à vélos bicycle shed
abri *m* pour la voiture carport
ABS *m* (plastique) ABS (plastic)
(acrylonitrile,butadiene,styrene copolymer)
absorber *v* absorb (to)
acajou *m* mahogany
■ **en acajou** = made of mahogany
accélérateur *m* accelerator
accélérateur *m* de prise setting accelerator
(eg for cement/mortar)
accessoire *m* accessory
accrochage *m* key; keying; adhesion
achever *v* complete (to); end (to); finish
(to)
acier *m* steel
acier *m* cementé case-hardened steel
acier *m* chromé chrome steel
acier *m* de construction structural steel
acier *m* doux mild steel
acier *m* galvanisé galvanized steel
acier *m* inoxydable stainless steel
acier *m* noir black steel
acrotère *m* parapet of a roof terrace; acroter
(archit)
additif *m* additive
adhérence *f* adhesion
adhérer *v* adhere (to); stick (to)
adjuvant *m* additive
AFNOR: Association *f* Française de Normalisation AFNOR: French National
Standards Association
aggloméré *m*; **agglo** *abb* breeze block;
concrete block (parpaing); chipboard
aggloméré *m* creux hollow concrete block
aggloméré *m* plein solid concrete block
agrafe *f* clamp; hook; wall tie; casement
fastener; staple
agrafe *f* à T T cramp (archit)
agrafer *v* staple (to); fasten (to); hook (to)
agrafeuse *f* staple gun
agrégats *mpl* aggregate
alcôve *f* alcove; recess
aléa *m* hazard

alêne *f* awl
alignement *m* alignment
alignement *m* au cordeau alignement by
cord; bricklaying line
aligner *v* align (to)
alimentation *f* feed; supply
alimentation *f* en eau water supply
alimentation *f* en électricité electricity
supply
alimentation *f* en énergie power supply
alimentation *f* en gaz gas supply
allège *f* breast (section of wall between
window sill and floor)
alliage *m* alloy
aluminium *m* aluminium
alvéolé,-e *adj* alveolate; honeycombed
aménagement *m* arrangement; conversion;
converting; fitting-out
aménagements *mpl* extérieurs/intérieurs
exterior/interior fixtures
aménager *v* convert (to); develop (to); equip
(to); lay out (to)
■ **à aménager** = for conversion
aménager *v* du bois cut up wood (to)
amiante *m* asbestos
amorcer *v* prime (to) (a pump); start (to)
(building, etc)
ancien, ancienne *adj* ancient; old
ancrage *m* anchor(age)
ancre *f* anchor
ancre *f* de maintien fixing anchor
ancre *f* en forme d'un S S-shaped anchor;
S-plate
ancrer *v* anchor (to); fix (to)
■ **bien ancré** = well-anchored
année *f* de construction year of construction
antirouille *adj* antirust
aplanir *v* level (to); smooth out (to)
■ **aplanir** *v* un terrain level a piece of land
(to)
aplanisseur *m*; **aplanisseuse** *f* planer;
leveller
appareil *m* apparatus; appliance; bond
(of brickwork, or wall components);
machinery; plant
appareil *m* anglais English bond
appareil *m* à carreau stretcher-bond
(stone)

appareil *m* **en besace** bond used at corners (with alternate courses showing the header); toothing

appareil *m* **en boutisses** heading-bond

appareil *m* **en long** stretcher bond

appareil *m* **en opus incertum** stone bond-ing according to natural shape; irregular bonding

appareil *m* **en panneresse** stretcher bond

appareil *m* **en travers** header bond

appareil *m* **flamand; appareil** *m* **hollandais** Flemish bond

appareil *m* **français** French bond

appareil *m* **sanitaire** bathroom appliance

appareillage *m* bonding (eg brickwork); equipment; fittings

appareillage *m* **de pierre** stone bonding (wall)

appareiller *v* bond (to); dress stone (to)

appareilleur *m* fitter

appartement *m* apartment; flat

appentis *m* lean-to; shed; sloping roof; penthouse

apport *m* contribution; provision; supply

apprêt *m* priming; size; sizing (sealing)

apprêter *v* make ready (to); prepare (to)

approvisionnement *m* **d'eau** water supply

appui *m* support; rest; window ledge or sill; balustrade

appui *m* **à oreilles** lug sill

appui *m* **béton** concrete sill; concrete support

appui *m* **de fenêtre/porte** window/door sill

arase *f* levelling course (of a wall)

■ **les arases** = levelling stones

arase *f* **de pose** levelling course

arase *f* **étanche** impervious levelling layer; damp-proof layer

arasement *m* levelling; levelling course

arasement *m* **(des briques/pierres)** final levelling course (of bricks/stones)

araser *v* level (to) (eg a wall); make even (to); plane down (to); cut off (to) (level)

arbre *m* axle; shaft; spindle; tree

arc *m* arch

ardoise *f* slate (roof)

ardoiser *v* slate (to)

are *m* one hundred square metres (see below)

■ one hectare = 100 ares = 10,000 square

metres = 2.471 acres

aréage *m* area of land measured in ares

arête *f* arris; edge; ridge; hip

arête *f* **de bris** edge of break

arêtier *m* hip rafter; arris rafter; corner rafter

argile *f* clay

armature *f* reinforcement (for concrete, cement); fastening; strap

armature *f* **à toit** roof truss/trussing

armature *f* **de chainage** reinforcement cage

armoire *f* cupboard; wardrobe

armoire *f* **à linge** linen cupboard

arrêté *m* administrative order or decree; order

arrêté *m* **de compte** settlement of account

arrêté *m* **municipal** bye-law

arrière *m* back; rear

arrière-cour *f* backyard

arrière-cuisine *f* pantry; scullery

artisan *m* artisan; craftsman

asbeste-ciment *m* asbestos cement

aspérité *f* roughness; unevenness

asphalte *m* asphalt

asphalter *v* asphalt (to)

■ **asphalté,-e** *adj* = asphalted

aspirateur *m* extractor; aspirator; vacuum cleaner

aspirateur *m* **statique pare-pluie** chimney cowl with rain protector

assainissement *m* cleansing; draining; drainage; sewage disposal

assainissement *m* **d'habitation** house drainage

asséchement *m* draining; drainage; drying out; emptying

assemblage *m* assemblage; assembling; joining; joint; jointing

assembler *v* assemble (to); join (to); joint (to)

assise *f* bed; course; foundation

■ **dernière assise** = last course

assise *f* **à joints croisés** broken course

assise *f* **de boutisses** heading-course

assise *f* **de carreaux** stretching-course

assise *f* **de niveau** level course

assise *f* **de retombée** springing-course (of an arch)

assurance *f* **dommage-ouvrage** insurance

against building faults

astreinte *f* constraint; daily fine for delay; penalty

atelier *m* workshop; workroom; studio

âtre *m* hearth

attache *f* fastener; tie (to hold reinforcement)

attache *f* **de fixation** fixing clip

attacher *v* clip (to); fasten (to); fix (to)

auge *f* **plastique** plastic mixing trough

auget *m* plaster filling between ceiling joists

auvent *m* canopy (over a porch); weatherboard

avaloir *m* throat of fireplace

avaloir *m* **de chaussée** road gully

avant-projet *m* draft scheme; preliminary plan; preparatory study of constructional project

avant-toit *m* eave

bac *m* sink; tray; trough

bac *m* **à gâcher** mixing tray (eg for mortar)

bac *m* **de douche** shower tray

bâche *f* tarpaulin; tank; cistern

badigeon *m* distemper; whitewash

badigeonner *v* distemper (to); whitewash (to)

bague *f* ring; washer

bague *f* **d'étanchéité** joint ring; sealing ring

baie *f* opening; window; bay

baie *f* **de fenêtre** window opening

baie *f* **de porte** door opening

baie *f* **vitrée** picture window; bay window

baignoire *f* bath; bathtub

baignoire-douche *f* shower bath

baignoire *f* **sabot** hip-bath

bain *m* bath

bain *m* **de mortier** bed of mortar

■ **à bain de mortier** = bedded in mortar; with full mortar

bain *m* **soufflant de mortier** bed of pasty mortar

balai *m* broom

balai *m* **coco** garden broom

balai *m* **de bouleau** besom

balai *m* **de piste** yard broom

balai *m* **paille de riz** besom

balcon *m* balcony

balèvre *f* lip (projecting irregularity); fin (mortar)

ballon *m* **d'eau chaude** hot water tank

banche *f* form(work); shuttering panel

bande *f* band; strip

bande *f* **à joint** joint tape; scrim

bande *f* **de mousse** band of foam rubber

bande *f* **de recouvrement** cover strip; covering plate

bandeau *m* string course (masonry)

bandelette *f* fillet; strip

barbotine *f* cement grout (cement and fine sand (1:1) mixture)

bardage *m* cladding (eg with shingles)

bardage *m* **à clin** weatherboard cladding

bardeau *m* shingle; weatherboard

barre *f* **transversale** crosspiece; strut

base *f* base

bassin *m* pond; ornamental pond

bâti *m* frame; framework; framing

bâti *m* **dormant** fixed frame (door or window)

bâtiment *m* building; house

■ **le bâtiment** = the building trade

bâtiment *m* **restauré** restored building

bâtiments *m* **d'exploitation** farm buildings or sheds

bâtiments *m* **d'élevage** livestock buildings

bâtir *v* build (to); construct (to); erect (to)

bâtisse *f* building; masonry

battage *m* **de pieux/pilots** pile driving

batte *f* mallet

bêche *f* spade

benne *f* skip; dump truck; tipper lorry; bucket (of earth mover)

besace see 'appareil en besace'

béton *m* concrete

■ **sol en béton** = concrete floor

béton *m* **armé sollicité** stressed reinforced concrete

béton *m* **armé; B.A.** *abb* reinforced concrete

béton *m* **banché** concrete cast in situ; concrete cast in forms; rammed concrete

béton *m* **cellulaire** aerated concrete; cellular concrete

béton *m* **courant** ordinary concrete

béton *m* **de propreté** bedding concrete; blinding concrete

béton *m* **gras** concrete rich in cement

béton *m* **hydrofuge** waterproofed concrete
béton *m* **maigre** concrete poor in cement
béton *m* **précontraint** prestressed concrete
béton *m* **precoulé** precast concrete
béton *m* **préparé** ready-mixed concrete
béton *m* **prêt à l'emploi** ready-mix concrete
béton *m* **réfractaire** refractory concrete
béton *m* **universel** universal concrete
bétonnage *m* concreting
bétonner *v* concrete (to)
bétonnière *f* concrete mixer
bi-couche *f* double coat; double layer
biberon *m* **de poudre bleu** small bottle of
   blue powder (mason's marking powder)
bilan *m* appraisal; assessment; statement of
   accounts
billes *f* **de polystyrène** polystyrene pellets
biseau *m* bevel; bevel edge; bevelled;
   feather-edge; side chisel; skew chisel
biseau (en) bevelled
biseautage *m* bevelling
biseauter *v* bevel (to)
bitume *m* bitumen; asphalt; pitch; tar
bitumineux,-euse *adj* bituminous
blindage *m* sheeting (wood or metal);
   shoring up; timbering; screening (elect)
blindage *m* **par caissons** casing; coffering;
   shoring up with coffers
blindage *m* **par panneaux préfabriqués**
   shoring up with prefabricated boards
blindage *m* **par planche verticale** shoring
   with vertical planking
blinder *v* shore up (to); timber (to); screen
   (to) (elect)
bloc *m* block; lump; mass; unit
bloc *m* **courant en béton** standard concrete
   block
bloc *m* **creux en béton** hollow concrete
   block
bloc *m* **d'about** end block; butt-end block
bloc *m* **d'angle** angle block; corner block;
   L-shaped block
bloc *m* **de/en béton** concrete block
bloc *m* **de/en béton cellulaire** cellular
   concrete block
bloc *m* **de terre cuite** fired clay block; brick
bloc *m* **en U** U-shaped block
bloc *m* **ISECO™** concrete-polystyrene
   block; ISECO™ block

bloc *m* **léger** light block; low-strength block
bloc *m* **linteau** lintel block
bloc *m* **lourd** heavy block; high-strength
   block
bloc *m* **multifonction** multifunctional block;
   insulating block
bloc *m* **perforé, bloc B2** perforated block
bloc *m* **plein de granulats (courants ou
   legers)** solid aggregate block (standard or
   light)
bloc *m* **plein en béton** solid concrete block
bloc *m* **poteau** corner block; pillar block
bloc *m* **pour chainage horizontal/vertical**
   block for horizontal/vertical reinforcement
bloc *m* **pour linteau** lintel block
bloc *m* **SIPOREX™** cellular concrete block;
   SIPOREX™ block
bloc-cuisine *m* kitchen unit
bloc-douche *m* shower unit
bloc-evier *m* sink unit
bloc-porte *m* prefabricated door unit
blocage *m* method of constructing wall from
   randomly placed stones (moellons); clamping; locking; filling; rubble; rubble-stone;
   blocking (eg road)
blocageux, blocageuse *adj* rubbly
blocaille *f* ballast; hardcore; rubble
bois *m* timber; wood; woodland
bois *m* **blanc** deal; whitewood
bois *m* **contreplaqué** plywood
bois *m* **de charpente** timber
bois *m* **massif** solid wood
bois *m* **vermoulu** worm-eaten wood
bois *m* **vert** green wood; unseasoned wood
boiser *v* panel (to) (in wood)
boiserie *f* panelling; wainscotting; woodwork
boisseau *m* flue block; drain tile
boisseau *m* **avec alvéoles** perforated flue
   block
boisseau *m* **de terre cuite** fired clay flue
   block
boisseau *m* **en béton** concrete flue block
boisseau *m* **plein** solid flue block
boîte *f* **à suie** soot box (of flue)
bomber *v* bulge (to) (eg wall)
bord *m* border; edge; rim; verge (road)
bornage *m* boundary marking; demarcation
borne *f* boundary stone or marker; limit;

terminal (elect)

bossage *m* boss; building block/stone with embossed face

botte *f* boot (eg rubber)

bouchage *m* obstruction; plugging; plugging up; sealing; stoppage; stopping up

boucher *v* plug (to); plug up (to); seal (to); stop up (to)

bouchon *m* bung; cork; plug; stopper

bouchon *m* à vis screwed plug/cap

boucle *f* buckle; loop

boucle *f* d'amarrage ring-bolt

boucle *f* de levage lifting loop

bourrage *m* packing; ramming; tamping

bourrage *m* au plâtre et filasse packing with plaster and tow

bourrelet *m* d'étanchéité angle bead

boutisse *f* header

branchement *m* branch-pipe; branching; connecting-up; connection; installation; junction; plugging-in; tapping

branchement *m* sur le secteur connection to local electricity supply

bretelle *f* brace; strap; suspender

bridage *m* clamping; fastening together

bride *f* flange; collar cramp; clamp

bride *f* à capote clamp; G-clamp

brider *v* clamp (to); connect up (to) (flange)

brique *f* brick

brique *f* "graissée" buttered brick (ie coated with mortar or plaster on three sides before positioning)

brique *f* à alvéoles G-brick; hollow brick; perforated brick

brique *f* à alvéoles horizontales/verticales brick with horizontal/vertical air holes

brique *f* à couteau arch brick; feather-edged brick

brique *f* à deux quartiers bat; half-brick

brique *f* blanche fire brick; white brick

brique *f* creuse hollow brick; perforated brick

brique *f* creuse de terre cuite hollow fired clay brick

brique *f* creuse à rupture de joint hollow brick with break joint

brique *f* d'appoint closer

brique *f* de laitier slag brick

brique *f* de parement facing brick

brique *f* de terre cuite brick; fired clay brick

brique *f* de type courant ordinary type brick

brique *f* de ventilation air brick; ventilation brick

brique *f* évidée air brick

brique *f* fabriquée à la filière wire-cut brick

brique *f* fabriquée à la presse pressed brick

brique *f* G G-brick; insulating brick

brique *f* hollandaise dutch clinker brick; engineering brick

brique *f* moulée pressed brick

brique *f* perforée perforated brick

brique *f* pilée brick dust

brique *f* platrière plasterer's brick

brique *f* plein solid brick

brique *f* réfractaire fire-brick; refractory brick

brique *f* rustique textured brick

brique *f* vitrifiée vitrified clinker brick

briquetage *m* bricklaying; brickwork

briqueter *v* brick (to); build with bricks (to); face in imitation brickwork (to); lay bricks (to)

briqueterie *f* brick-making; brickfield; brickyard

briqueteur *m* bricklayer

briqueteuse *f* bricklayer's trowel

briquetier *m* brick merchant; brickmaker; brickyard worker

briqueton *m* bat; half-brick

briquette *f* briquette; small brick

brisis *m* lower and steeper slope of Mansard roof; angle between two planes of a curb roof

broche *f* drift; locking-pin; driftpin; driver; spike; spike-nail; tommy-bar; tommy-lever

broche *f* conique taper drift; taper driftpin

broche *f* de maçon mason's point; drift; (see also 'pointerolle de maçon')

broche *f* imperdable pin and chain (scaffolding)

brosse *f* brush; paintbrush

brosse *f* à goudronner tar-brush

brosse *f* en fil de fer wire brush

brosse *f* métallique wire brush

brosser *v* brush (to); scrub (to)

brouette *f* barrow; hand-barrow; wheel-

barrow
bruit *m* noise; sound
buanderie *f* laundry room; utility room
bureau *m* office; study (room)
burin *m* chisel; cold chisel
burinage *m* chipping; chiselling
buse *f* **d'entrée** nose-piece; nozzle; vent pipe
between boiler and flue
butée *f* abutment; prop; shore
buter *v* prop (to); shore (to); shore up (to);
butt (to)

cabinet *m* closet; office
cabinet *m* **d'étude** study
cabinet *m* **de débarras** boxroom; lumber
room
câblage *m* **de circuit** circuit wiring
câble *m* cable; heavy-duty flex
câble *m* **de mise à la terre** earthing cable
câble *m* **enterré** buried cable
câble *m* **multifilaire** multi-wire cable
câble *m* **métallique** stranded wire; wire rope
câble *m* **électrique** electric cable
cadre *m* frame; framework; framing
cage *f* **d'une batisse** shell of a building
caillasse *f* large heavy stone; road metal
caillou *m* pebble; stone
cailloutage *m* pebble paving; metalling
(road); gravelling; pebble work
caillouter *v* metal (to) (path, road)
cailloutis *m* gravel
calage *m* wedging; packing; blocking
cale *f* block; needle (shoring); packing-
piece; wedge; shim
cale *f* **imputrescible** non-decayable
packing-piece/wedge
calfeutrage *m*; **calfeutrement** *m* draughtproofing; filler; filling; stopping up
calfeutrer *v* draughtproof (to); fill (to); stop
up (to)
calicot *m* calico
calorifuge *m*; also *adj* therrmal insulator;
(heat) insulating
calorifère *m*; also *adj* heater; stove
calorifère *m* **à air** hot-air heater
calorifère *m* **à eau** hot-water heater
canalisation *f* canalisation; pipes; ground
level pipework; pipework; cables (elect);

conduit (wiring/cable)
caniveau *m* gutter (road); service duct
canne *f* cane
canne *f* **PVC** PVC cane
caractéristiques *fpl* **thermiques**. thermal
characteristics
carcasse *f* shell (of building)
carneau *m* flue
carneau *m* **de chaudière** boiler flue
carreau *m* tile; tiled floor; pane (window
glass); stretcher (masonry); square file
carreau *m* **au mur** wall tile
carreau *m* **de carrelage** floor tile
carreau *m* **de faïence** ceramic tile
carreau *m* **de plâtre** plaster tile or block
carreau *m* **de terre cuite** terra cotta tile
carreau *m* **de verre** pane of glass
carreau *m* **par terre** floor tile
carrelage *m* tiled floor; tiles; tiling
carrelage *m* **de sol** floor tiling
carrelage *m* **en briques** brick paving
carreler *v* tile (to)
carrière *f* stone quarry
carton *m* **bitumé** roofing felt; tarred felt
cartouche *f* cartridge
cave *m* cellar; store room; vault
cave *m* **voûtée** vaulted cellar
caveau *m* small cellar
cavité *f* cavity
ceinture *f* belt; surround; ring support
(pipe)
cellier *m* storeroom
céramique *adj* ceramic
certificat *m* **d'urbanisme** certificate stating
planning and building requirements to be
met
certificat *m* **de conformité** certificate of
conformity
chai *m* shed; vat room; wine and spirit store;
wine cellar
chaînage *m* bonding beam; bonding girder;
reinforcement; chaining
chaînage *m* **béton** concrete bonding beam
chaîne *f* chain
chaîne *m* **à maillons** chain-link
chaîne *f* **d'arpenteur** measuring chain;
surveyor's chain
chaînette *f* **d'angle** corner chain bonding (of
alternate courses)

chambranle *m* architrave; frame (door, window); jamb-lining; door post
chambre *f* bedroom
chambre *f* **d'amis** spare/guest room
chambre *f* **à coucher** bedroom
chant *m* edge
chantier *m* building site; roadworks
chantier *m* **de construction** building site
chape *f* coating; screed
chape *f* **adhérente** adherent screed (opposed to floating screed); monolithic screed
chape *f* **ciment** cement covering; screed
chape *f* **d'arase** levelling layer of screed
chape *f* **d'usure** screed laid as floor surface
chape *f* **de revêtement** screed laid as base for floor covering
chape *f* **flottante** floating screed
chape *f* **incorporée** adherent screed; incorporated screed; monolithic screed
chape *f* **rapportée** non-adherent screed; detached screed
chapeau *m* cap; capping; corbel course
chaperon *m* coping
chaperonner *v* cope (to) (a wall)
charge *f* load; stress; charge (elect)
charge *f* **de rupture** breaking load
charnière *f* butt-hinge; hinge
charpente *f* frame(work) (of house, building); roof structure; skeleton
charpente *f* **en bois** carpentry
charpentier *m* carpenter (usually roof timbers); (see also 'menuisier')
chasse *f* **d'eau** flushing cistern of WC
châssis *m* frame (eg of window); framework
châssis *m* **de charpente** open framework (timber); outer frame
châssis *m* **vitré** skylight
chaudière *f* boiler
chaudière *f* **à eau chaude** hot-water boiler
chaudière *f* **cylindrique** cylindrical boiler
chauffage *m* heating
chauffage *m* **central** central heating
chauffage *m* **à air chaud** hot-air heating
chauffe-bain *m* geyser
chauffe-eau *m* water-heater
chauffe-eau *m* **à élément chauffant** immersion water heater
chauffe-eau électrique *m* electric water heater
chaufferie *f* boiler room
chaumière *f* cottage; thatched cottage
chaumine *f* small thatched cottage
chaux *f* lime
chaux *f* **aérienne** non-hydraulic lime
chaux *f* **aérienne éteinte pour le bâtiment**; **CAEB** *abb* slaked lime (for building work)
chaux *m* **blanche** high-calcium lime; white lime
chaux *f* **éteinte** slaked lime
chaux *f* **grise** grey lime
chaux *f* **hydraulique** hydraulic lime
chaux *f* **vive** quicklime
chef *m* **d'équipe** foreman
chef *m* **de chantier** site foreman
cheminée *f* chimney; chimney piece; fireplace; mantlepiece
chemisage *m* deposition of coating on interior wall of a flue; pargetting; lining
chéneau *m* gutter (roof); eaves gutter
chevêtre *m* joist trimmer-beam; trimmer
chevêtre *m* **sous la marche palière** landing-trimmer (staircase)
chevêtrier *m* trimming-joist
cheville *f* bolt; pin; plug; spike; dowel; wallplug
cheville *f* **de moise** clamp nail
chevillette *f* peg; pin
chevillette *f* **carrée** square pin
chevillette *f* **de maçon** mason's pin; line pin
chevillette *f* **ronde** round pin
chevron *m* rafter
chevronnage *m* raftering
chromage *m* chromium plating
chrome *m* chromium
chromé,-e *adj* chromium plated
chute *f* downfall; drop; fall; pitch; slope
chute *f* **d'eau** head of water; waterfall
chute *f* **de comble** pitch of roof
chute *f* **en fonte** downpipe in cast iron
ciment *m* cement
ciment *m* **à prise lente** slow-setting cement
ciment *m* **à prise rapide** quick-setting cement
ciment *m* **armé** reinforced cement
ciment *m* **blanc** white cement
ciment *m* **colle** mortar fixative; tile adhesive

ciment *m* **fondu** high alumina cement
ciment *m* **gris** grey cement
ciment *m* **joint** jointing cement; grouting (for tiles)
ciment *m* **Portland** Portland cement
ciment *m* **pouzzolanique** pozzolana cement
ciment *m* **prompt** rapid setting cement
cimentage *m* cementation; cementing
cimentation *f* cementation; cementing
cimenter *v* cement (to)
cintrage *m* arching; bending (of pipes)
cintre *m* arch; centre; centering; curve
cintrer *v* bend (to); curve (to); shape (to)
circuit *m* circuit
▪ **circuit électrique** = electric circuit
ciseau *m*; **ciseaux** *mpl* chisel(s)
ciseau *m* **à brique** brick bolster
ciseau *m* **à froid** cold chisel
ciseau *m* **de maçon** bolster; pitcher
ciseau *m* **de maçon poignée pare-coups** brick bolster with shock-protector handle
ciseler *v* chase (to); chisel (to)
citerne *f* cistern; rain-water tank; tank; water tank
claire-voie *f*; **claires-voies** *fpl* lattice; open-work; open-work fence; opening; skylight
clause *f* article; clause; provision; stipulation
clause pénale *f* penalty clause
clavette *f* cotter; feather; key; pin; spline
clavette *f* **d'échafaudage** scaffold tie
clavette *f* **de serrage** locking pin
clavette *f* **fendue** split pin
clé *f*; **clef** *f* frog (of brick); key; keystone; spanner
clé *f* **à douille** box-spanner
cloison *f* partition; partition wall; wall; division
cloison *f* **à âme alvéolée** partition with honeycomb core
cloison *f* **de distribution** dividing partition
cloison *f* **de doublage** liner; partition liner; wallboard; double partition
cloison *f* **de bois** wood partition
cloison *f* **mitoyenne** partition wall
cloison *f* **vitré** glass/glazed partition
cloisonnage *m* partitioning

cloisonner *v* partition (to)
clôture *f* enclosure; fence; fencing; hedge; paling; wall
clôture *f* **de bornage** boundary fence
clou *m* nail
clou *m* **à patte** holdfast
clou *m* **à deux pointes** staple
clouer *v* nail (to)
coefficient *m* **G** G coefficient; thermal loss factor
coffrage *m* coffering; form; formwork; shuttering
coffrer *v* coffer (to); place shuttering (to); place a frame for (to) (eg concrete)
coin *m* corner; key; wedge
coin *m* **à fendre le bois** timber-splitting wedge
coin *m* **éclateur** splitting wedge
coinçage *m* wedging
collage *m* gluing
colle *f* cement; glue; paste; wallpaper paste
collecteur *m* collector; receiver (tank)
▪ **grand collecteur** = main sewer
collecteur *m* **principal** main sewer
collecteur *m* **à l'égout** main drain (sewage); main sewer
collier *m* **de fixation** fixing collar
colombage *m* half-timbered
colonne *f* column; pillar
colorant *m* colouring material
coloris *m* colour; shade
comble *m* roof; roof timbers; roof trussing
▪ **les combles** = the attic; the loft; roof space
comble *m* **d'un bâtiment** roof (of building)
comble *m* **mansardé** French roof; mansard roof
combler *v* fill (to); fill up (to) (eg well)
comprimer *v* compress (to)
compte *m* **rendu** progress report; report
compteur *m* counter; meter
compteur *m* **à eau** water meter
compteur *m* **à gaz** gas meter
compteur *m* **électrique** electricity supply meter
concasser *v* break (to); crush (to)
condensation *f* condensation
condensation *f* **par surface** surface condensation

condensation *f* **superficielle** surface condensation

condition *f* condition; stipulation; term of contract

conditions *fpl* **générales**. general conditions

conduit *m* cable duct; conduit; pipe

conduit *m* **accolé** flue unified with supporting wall along full height

conduit *m* **adossé** flue, self-supporting but tied to independent wall

conduit *m* **de cheminée** flue

conduit *m* **de fumée** flue; smoke-pipe

conduit *m* **de ventilation** ventilation conduit

conduit *m* **en amiante ciment** asbestos cement flue

conduit *m* **en béton armé** reinforced concrete flue

conduit *m* **en grés** earthenware drainpipe

conduit *m* **isolé** flue, completely self-supporting

conduit *m* **metallique** metal flue pipe

conduit *m* **monocombustible** flue for single fuel burner

conduit *m* **polycombustible** flue for burners of multiple fuels

conduite *f* conduct; conduit; duct; ducting; pipe

confort *m* **acoustique** acoustic comfort

confort *m* **thermique** heat comfort

constructeur *m* builder; constructor

constructeur *m* **de maisons** house-builder

constructible *adj* construction possible (physical conditions and official authorisation)

construction *f* building; construction; structure

construire *v* build (to); construct (to)

contenance *f* capacity (eg volume of reservoir); size (of land area)

contrat *m* agreement; contract

contre-cloison *f* partition liner; lining partition; wall lining

contre-feu *m* fireback

contre-fil *m* against the grain (wood)

contre-linteau *m* internal lintel

contre-mur *m* outer wall; lining wall

contrecœur *m* fire back

contrefiche *f* brace (of truss); strut

contremaître *m*; **contremaîtresse** *f* foreman/forewoman

contremarche *f* riser (of staircase)

contrevent *m* brace or strut; shutter; windbrace

convergent *m* combining tube

convertir *v* convert (to); transform (to)

convertir *v* **en** convert into (to)

coquille *f* spandrel (staircase); underpart of spiral staircase; soffit; shell

corbeau *m* corbel; pipe hook

cordeau *m* cord; line

cordeau *m* **traceur** setting-out line

cordon *m* cordon; string course

corniche *f* cornice; cove; coving

cornière *f* angle-iron; angle-piece; L-iron

corps *m* body; head (of a hammer); substance

corps *m* **de l'enduit** second or middle coat of mortar/plaster

costière *f* shoulder; upstand (on roof)

couche *f* coat (eg of paint); layer

▪ **première couche** = priming coat

▪ **sous-couche** *f* = undercoat (paint)

couche *f* **d'accrochage** keying coat; keying layer; scratch coat (see also 'gobetis' or 'couche d'approche')

couche *f* **d'air** air cushion; air gap (cavity wall)

couche *f* **d'approche** initial layer of plaster or mortar

couche *f* **d'étanchéité** damp-proof course

couche *f* **d'impression** priming coat

couche *f* **d'usure** layer ready for use (eg concrete path)

couche *f* **de désolidarisation** separation layer; insulating layer

couche *f* **de finition** finishing coat; finishing layer; setting coat (plaster); skimming coat; top coat

couche *f* **de glissement** isolation layer; non-adherent layer; slip layer

couche *f* **de revêtement** layer ready for covering (eg with tiles)

couche *f* **étanche** damp-proof course

couche *f* **isolante** insulating layer; damp-proof course

couche *f* **isolante imperméable** damp-proof

course
coude *m* bend; elbow
coude *m* **prolongé** long bend; long elbow
coulage *m* pouring (eg of concrete)
couler *v* pour (to) (eg concrete, asphalt)
coulis *m* grout; jointing mortar
coupe-circuit *m* cut-out (elect); fuse-box
coupe-circuit *m* **à fusible** fuse
couper *v* cut (to); cut-off (to); switch off (to) (elect)
cour *f* court; courtyard; yard
cour *f* **de ferme** farmyard
cour *f* **empierrée** stone courtyard
cour *f* **intérieure** inner courtyard
courant *m* current; power (elect)
courant *m* **alternatif** alternating current
courant,-e *adj* ordinary; standard
courette *f* small courtyard
couronnement *m* cap; coping; crowning; flue crown
couverture *f* cover; roof; roofing
couverture *f* **de chaume** thatched roofing
couverture *f* **en tuiles** tiled roofing
couvre-joint *m* butt strap; butt strip; cover strip; covering plate; joint cover
couvreur *m* roof tiler; roofer; slater
coyau *m* furring; furring-piece (of a roof); eaves board
crampon *m* cramp; cramp-iron; dognail; spike; staple
cramponner *v* clamp (to); cramp (to); fasten (to)
craquelure *f* crackle; fine cracks
crépi *m* cement or plaster rendering; masonry paint; rendering; roughcast; textured wall paint; pargeting
crépir *v* apply masonry paint (to); parget (to); render with cement (to); roughcast (to)
crépissage *m* rendering; roughcasting; pargeting
crête *f* coping (of wall); comb; crest; ridge (of roof); ridge tile
creuser *v* dig (to)
croisée *f* casement window
croupe *f* hip
cuisine *f* kitchen
cuisine *f* **équipée** fitted kitchen
cuisinière *f* cooker; kitchen range; stove

cuisinière *f* **électrique** electric cooker
cuisinière *f* **à charbon** coal-fired cooker; solid-fuel stove
cuisinière *f* **à gaz** gas cooker or stove
cuivre *m* copper
cuve *f* bowl (of sink unit); cistern; tank
cuve *f* **à mazout** fuel-oil tank
cuvelage *m*; **cuvellement** *m* lining (eg of a cellar); casing; base and walls of cellar
cuvette *f* bowl; wash-basin
cuvette *f* **de WC** WC basin; WC pan
cuvette *f* **rotule** ball-socket

dallage *m* flagging; pavement; paving
dallage *m* **en ardoise** paving with slate slabs
dalle *f* flag; flagstone; paving stone; slab (concrete)
dalle *f* **de compression** topping slab; structural concrete topping slab; concrete layer
dalle *f* **en béton armé** reinforced concrete slab floor
dalle *f* **flottante** floating slab floor
daller *v* pave (to)
dallette *f* small flag; small slab
dame *f* beetle; earth-rammer; rammer
■ **une dame de 10Kg** = 10Kg rammer
damer *v* ram (to); tamp (to)
dans-œuvre *adv* in the clear (measurements); inside (measurement) (opposite to hors-œuvre)
débarras *m* box room; lumber room
débit *m* discharge; flow; sawing up
débiter *v* saw up (to); cut up (to)
déblai *m* clearance; cutting; excavation
déblais *mpl* spoil; waste; excavated material
débouchage *m* unblocking
décalage *m* displacement forward or backward; gap; interval
décapage *m* burning off; cleaning; clearing; sandblasting; scouring; stripping
décharge *f* discharge; outlet; receipt; refuse tip; rubbish dump; release of debt; unloading
décharge *f* **des eaux usées** discharge/disposal of waste water
déchet *m*; **déchets** *mpl* loss; refuse; wastage; waste; waste material
décintroir *m* **de maçon** cutting-hammer;

mason's cutting-hammer

décintroir *m* **à talus** mattock; pick-mattock

déclaration *f* **d'achèvement des travaux** notification that permitted building work has been completed

décoffrage *m* removal of formwork; removal of shuttering

décombres *mpl* building rubble; debris

décorateur *m*; **décoratrice** *f* decorator (interior)

décorer *v* decorate (to)

défaut *m* default; defect; fault; flaw

défaut *m* **caché** latent/hidden defect

défaut *m* **d'entretien** lack of upkeep

défaut *m* **de paiement** failure to pay

déformation *f* deformation; strain

défrichement *m*; **défrichage** *m* clearing; surface-clearing (of ground, wood etc.)

dégagement *m* back-door; exit; passage (in appartment)

dégagement *m* **d'entrée** private entrance

dégradation *f* raking out (mortar joints)

dégradation *f* **des fondations** deterioration of the foundations

délai *m* deadline; delay; time limit; waiting period

délai *m* **de durcissement** hardening interval

délai *m* **de livraison** delivery date

délayer *v* mix (to) (with water to required consistency); thin down (to) (plaster, etc)

démarche *f* procedure; step

démarches *fpl* **nécessaires** necessary steps

démarrage *m* starting up (eg machine)

démarrer *v* start (to); start up (to); switch on (to) (electrical appliance)

demi-bloc *m* half-block

demi-brique *f* bat; half-brick

demoiselle *f* **de paveur** beetle; earth-rammer; rammer

démolir *v* demolish (to); pull down (to)

densité *f* density

dépendance *f* dependence; outbuilding;

déperdition *f* **calorifique** heat loss

déplacer *v* displace (to); move (to); shift (to)

déplacer (se) *v* be moved (to)

déposer *v* deposit (to) (money); dump (to) (rubbish); lay down (to); lodge (to) (a document)

déroulement *m* development; progress

déroulement *m* **des travaux** progress of building work

déroulement *m* **du contrat** progress of the contract

descente *f* downpipe; rainwater downpipe

dessin *m* design; drawing; sketch

dessin *m* **à l'échelle** scale drawing

dessin *m* **de coupe** sectional drawing

destination *f* **d'un bâtiment** intended use of a building; purpose for which building is to be used

détails *mpl* details

détritus *mpl* refuse; rubbish

détritus *mpl* **de jardin** garden rubbish

déviation *f* deflection; deviation

devis *m* estimate; quotation; specification

devis *m* **descriptif** detailed estimate; detailed specification

devis *m* **estimatif** preliminary estimate

devis *m* **préliminaire** outline specification

devis *m* **quantitatif** *f* bill of quantities

dévoiement *m* bend; turn (in chimney, etc)

diamètre *m* diameter

dilatation *f* expansion

dilater *v* expand (to)

dimension *f* dimension; measurement; size

dispositif *m* arrangement; contrivance; device

dispositif *m* **d'étaiement** shoring arrangement; shoring contrivance

dispositif *m* **de sécurité** security device

disposition *f* arrangement; disposition; layout

disposition *f* **d'urbanisme** planning provision /requirement

dommage *m* damage; harm; injury; loss

dommage-ouvrage *m* building fault; construction fault or damage

dommages et intérêts/dommages-intérêts *mpl* damages (see 'assurance dommage-ouvrage')

dormant *m* casing; door-frame; frame; window-frame

dosage *m* **de mortier** proportional composition of mortar mix

dossier *m* documentation; dossier; file

doublage *m* lining; doubling; laying double;

plating
double *m* **mètre bois** wooden two-metre rule
double *m* **vitrage** double glazing
double équerre *f* T-square
doubleau *m* beam; double floor joist
doublis *m* double row of tiles/slates forming
eaves
douche *f* shower; drenching; soaking
drain *m* drain
drain *m* **collecteur** main drain
drainage *m* drainage; draining
dresser *v* **les plans de** make plans for (to)
(eg a house, garden)
droit *m* **de passage** right of way
droit *m* **de puisage** right to draw water (eg
from a well)
durcissement *m* hardening (eg of cement);
tempering

eau *f* water
eau *f* **buvable/potable** drinking water
eau *f* **de distribution** tap water
eau *f* **de source** spring water
eau *f* **de ville** town/mains water
eau *f* **douce** fresh water
eau *f* **douce/dure** soft/hard water
eau *f* **froide/chaude** cold/hot water
eaux *fpl* **d'égout** sewage
eaux *fpl* **ménagères** household waste water
eaux *fpl* **pluviales; EP** rain water; run-off
water
eaux *fpl* **résiduaires** industrial effluent;
sewage
eaux *fpl* **usées; EU** sullage; waste water
eaux *fpl* **vannes; EV** foul water; sewage
éboulement *m* caving in; fall; falling in
écart *m* deviation; difference; variation; gap;
spacing
écart *m* **au/de feu** fire gap
écartement *m* gap; movement apart; space
between; clearance
échafaud *m*; **échafaudage** *m* scaffold;
scaffolding; stage; staging
échafaudage *m* erecting a scaffold
échafauder *v* erect a scaffold (to)
écharde *f* splinter
écharpe *f* brace (timber frame)
échelle *f* ladder

échiffre *m* partition wall of staircase
éclairage *m* illumination; lighting
éclat *m* chip(ping); fragment; splinter
éclats *mpl* **de pierre** stone chippings
éclisse *f* butt strap; fishplate
éclisse *f* **cornière** angle bead
écoulement *m* drainage; flow; outflow
écoulement *m* **d'électricité** flow of electricity
écoulement *m* **naturel** natural drainage
écran *m* screen; barrier
écran *m* **d'indépendance** independent
screen; unattached screen
écrasement *m* crushing
E.D.F; Électricité de France French
Electricity Board
édifice *m* building; edifice
édifice *m* **public** public building
édifier *v* build (to); construct (to); erect (to)
efflorescence *f* efflorescence
effondrement *m* caving in; collapse;
falling-in; subsidence
égout *m* drain; drainage; sewer; eaves; slope
(of roof)
égout *m* **collecteur** main sewer
égout *m* **du bord du toit** eaves
égout *m* **pluvial** storm drain/sewer
électricien *m* electrician
électricité *f* electricity
élément *m* component; element; unit
élément *m* **de cuisine** kitchen unit
élément *m* **porteur** loadbearing element;
loadbearing section
éléments *mpl* **compris dans le contrat** items
covered by the contract
éléments *mpl* **de rangement** storage units
élevation *f* elevation; lifting; raised plan (of
building)
emboîtement *m* boxing; housing; jointing;
socketing; spigot joint (pipework)
emmarchement *m* tread width (stairs)
empattement *m* footing; foundation; joining
of timbers
empierrer *v* gravel (to); metal (to)
emprise *f* **au sol** expropriation or
requisitioning of ground/land
en forme de talus in a slope form; sloped
en plus in addition
en sous-face underface; underside

encastrement *m* embedding; flush fitting; building; in-housing; tailing

encastrer *v* embed (to); fit flush (to); build in (to); tail in (to)

enchevêtrer *v* **des solives** trim joists (to)

enchevêtrure *f* tail trimmer

encorbellement *m* cantilever

enduit *m* coat; coating; rendering (plaster, mortar); size/sizing

enduit *m* **d'application à chaud; EAC** *abb* hot application coat (eg of bitumen)

enduit *m* **de façade** exterior coating; facade rendering

enduit *m* **de goudron** coating of tar

enduit *m* **de jointoiement** grout (pointing)

enduit *m* **de ragréage** final rendering; finishing screed

enduit *m* **en trois couches** three-coat plastering/rendering

enduit *m* **étanche** sealant; waterproof coating

enduit *m* **extérieur** exterior coating

enduit *m* **intérieur** interior coating; interior rendering

enduit *m* **lisse de plâtre** fair-faced plaster

enduit *m* **pelliculaire** skim coat

enduit *m* **prêt à gâcher** ready-mix plaster/mortar

enfoncement *m* driving; driving in (eg pile); giving way; sinking (eg foundation)

engins *mpl* **de levage** hoisting equipment

engins *mpl* **de terrassement** earth-moving equipment

enlever *v* lift (to); remove (to)

enrobage *m*; **enrobement** *m* coating; encasing; enclosing

enrober *v* coat (to); encase (to); enclose (to)

enrobé *m* **bitumineux** bitumen coated

ensemble *m* housing development; housing scheme

entonnoir *m* funnel; hollow

entrait *m* tie-bar; tie-beam; tie-rod; roof beam

entrepreneur *m* contractor

entrepreneur *m* **de constructions** building-contractor; builder

entreprise *f* company; contractor; enterprise; firm; undertaking

entreprise *f* **privée** private company

entretoise *f* brace; strut; cross-bar; cross-beam; spacer; spacing piece

entrevous *m* masonry, etc filling space between floor joists; filler block; interjoist space (floor);

entrée *f* entrance; entry; hallway

enveloppe *f* casing; cover; jacket; lagging

enveloppe *f* **de cylindre** cylinder-jacket

épais *m*; also *adj* thick; thickness

épaisseur *f* thickness; depth

épaufrure *f* chip; spalling; splinter

équarrir *v* square (to); broach (to)

équerre *f* set square; square; L-iron; right angle bracket; T-iron

équerre *f* **à dessin** set-square

équerre *f* **à lame d'acier** try square

équerre *f* **d'angle** angle-plate; corner-plate

équerre *f* **de maçon** mason's set square

équerre *f* **en T**; **équerre** *f* **à T**; **équerre** *f* **en té** T-square

équipe *f* gang; shift; team

équipement *m* equipment; fitments; fittings; fitting out; plant

▪ **les équipements** = facilities/amenities

équipement *m* **extérieur** exterior fittings

équipement *m* **électrique** electrical fittings

équiper *v* equip (to); fit (to); install fitments (to)

escalier *m* staircase; stairs; stairway; steps

escalier *m* **de dégagement** private or back staircase

escalier *m* **en colimaçon** spiral staicase

escalier *m* **tournant** spiral staircase

espace *m* space; gap

esquisse *f* outline (of a project); rough sketch; sketch

essai *m* test; attempt; trial

esse *f* hook; S-shaped pipe connector

établir *v* draw up (to) (document); establish (to); fix (to) (a price)

établir *v* **un projet d'accord/de contrat** produce a draft agreement/contract (to)

étage *m* stage; storey; floor

étagère *f* shelf

étai *m* prop; shore; stay; support

étai *m* **de maçon tubulaire** mason's tubular stay

étai *m* **incliné** raking shore

étai *m* **réglable** adjustable stay/support
étai *m* **vertical** dead shore; vertical shore
étaiement *m* shoring
étaiement *m* **des constructions voisines**
shoring of adjoining constructions
étaler *v* lay (to); spread (out) (to)
étanchéité *f* impervious layer; imperviousness; water-tightness; waterproofing;
waterproofness; airtightness
étançon *m* shore; stanchion; stay
étape *f* stage
étape *f* **de la construction** construction stage
étayage *m*; **étayement** *m* propping; shoring;
staying; supporting (see also 'étaiement')
étayer *v* shore (to); shore up (to); support
(to)
étrésillon *m* strut between joists; brace
étrésillon *m* **à verin; étrésillon** *m* **à vis**
adjustable prop (Acrow™ type)
étrésillon *m* **hydraulique** hydraulic brace
évacuation *f* discharge; evacuation; removal
évacuation *f* **d'air** removal of air
(ventilation)
évacuation *f* **des terres** removal of
(excavated) earth
évier *m* kitchen sink; sink
évier *m* **à un bac/deux bacs** single/double
sink
évier *m* **simple/double** single/double sink
éviter *v* avoid (to)
excavateur *m* excavator; mechanical digger
excavation *f* digging; excavating; excavation
exécuter *v* accomplish (to); carry out (to);
execute (to)
exécution *f* **courante** normal tolerance of
execution
exécution *f* **soignée** higher-care tolerance of
execution
expert *m* expert; professional; specialist;
valuer
expert *m* **géomètre** surveyor
expertise *f* expert valuation/appraisal;
survey; surveyor's report
expertise *f* **d'un bien** valuation of a property
extérieur *m*; also *adj* exterior; outside

façade *f* façade; face; front (of building)
façade *f* **abritée** protected façade

façade *f* **arrière** back (of building)
façade *f* **latérale** side wall
faïençage *m* small cracks (appearing on the
surface of a coating or rendering)
faïence *f* earthenware (glazed)
faïencerie *f* earthenware factory
faire *v* **des réparations** make repairs (to);
repair (to)
faire *v* **le bilan de** take stock of (to)
faire *v* **masse** act as earth (to) (elect)
faire *v* **surface** surface (to)
faîtage *m* ridge (roof)
faîtière *m* ridge tile
fausse *f* **équerre** bevel (square)
faux-plafond *m* false ceiling; suspended
ceiling; intermediate ceiling
fendre *v* cleave (to) (eg wood); shear
through (to) (eg metal)
fente *f* crack; fissure; split
fenêtre *f* window
fenêtre *f* **mansardée** mansard dormer
window
fenêtre *f* **ordinaire** casement window; French
window
fenêtre *f* **à guillotine** sash window
fenêtre *f* **à tabatière** skylight
fente f fissure; crack; shake; split
fer *m* bit; iron
fer *m* **à joint demi-lune** half-round pointing
trowel
fer *m* **à joint plat** flat pointing iron
fer *m* **cornière** angle iron; L iron
fer *m* **d'angle** angle iron; L iron
fer *m* **de fonte** cast iron
fer *m* **forgé** wrought iron
ferme *f* roof timbers; truss (roof);
girder
ferraillage *m* iron framework; preparation
and placing of steel frames; steel frame
reinforcement for concrete
feuillard *m* strap; strip (eg of iron, steel)
feuille *f* sheet
feuille *f* **d'aluminium** aluminium foil
feuille *f* **de placage** veneer
feuille *f* **de plomb** lead sheet
feuille *f* **de PVC** PVC sheet
feuille *f* **de sauge** cross-file; double
half-round file
feuille *f* **de scie** saw-blade

feuille *f* **de verre** sheet of glass
feuiller *v* rabbet (to); rebate (to)
feuillure *f* rebate; rabbet; fillister; sash fillister; groove
feutrage *m* felting
feutre *m* felt; felting
feutre *m* **bitumisé** bitumised felt
fibragglo *m* woodwool slab; agglomerate of wood fibres and cement
fibre *f* **de bois** wood fibre
fibre *f* **de verre** glass fibre
fibre *f* **minérale** mineral fibre
fibrociment *m* fibrocement
fiche *f* hinge, cabinet; peg; pin; plug
fil *m* cord (of electric appliance); cutting edge (of a tool); filament (of electric bulb); grain (of wood); thread; wire
fil *m* **à plomb** plumb-line
fil *m* **sous tension** live wire (elect)
filasse *f* tow
file *f* **d'étais** line of supports
filière *f* wire gauge; purlin; side-timber; ledger (scaffolding); threading die
filler *m* filler
fillerisé,-e *adj* filled
film *m* **plastique étanche** plastic film damp-proof membrane
film *m* **polyester** polyester sheet/membrane
finition *f* finish; finishing
fissuration *f* cracking
fissure *f* crack; fissure
fixation *f* fixation; fixing; fastening
flèche *f* bending; flexing/flexure; sagging
flèche *f* **d'une dalle** deflection of slab/slab floor
foisonnement *m* expansion in bulk; swell; swelling
foisonner *v* increase in bulk (to); swell (to)
fonçage *m* **au poussage** sinking by piling
fondation *f* base; foundation
fondation *f* **sur pieux/pilotis** pile foundation
fondations *fpl* **d'un bâtiment.** foundations of a building
fondement *m* base; foundation
fondements *mpl* **d'une maison** foundations of a house
fonte *f* cast iron; pig iron; casting; melting
fonte *f* **brute** pig iron

fonte de fer *f* cast iron
forme *f* levelling layer of cement or sand below paving or flagstones; form; shape
fosse *f* pit
fosse *f* **d'aisances** cesspool
fosse *f* **septique** septic tank
fossé *m* ditch
fossé *m* **collecteur** drainage ditch
fossé *m* **d'irrigation** irrigation channel
fouille *f* digging; trenching; excavation; hole; trench
fouille *f* **de rochers** excavation of rock
fouille *f* **en "excavation superficielle"** shallow excavation
fouille *f* **en déblais** open excavation (levelling)
fouille *f* **en excavation** horizontal passage excavation; underground excavation
fouille *f* **en galerie** horizontal passage excavation; underground excavation
fouille *f* **en puits** shaft excavation; well excavation
fouille *f* **en rigole** foundation or service trench
fouille *f* **en sous-œuvre** excavation under existing construction
fouille *f* **en terrain rocheux** excavation in rocky ground
fouille *f* **en tranchée** trench excavation
fouille *f* **pour fondation** foundation excavation
fouille *f* **souterraine** underground excavation
fouilleur *m* **fouilleuse** *f*; (also *adj*) digger; excavator; excavating
foyer *m* furnace; hearth; grate; fireplace
frottement *m* friction; rubbing
frotter *v* rub down (to); scrub (to)
fruit *m* batter (wall); inclination; rake

gabarit *m*; **gabari** *m* gauge; template
gâchage *m* mixing; tempering (eg plaster); wasting
gâche *f* box-staple; lock-staple; staple; strike (plate); striking plate (lock); plasterer's trowel
gâcher *v* mix (to) (mortar/concrete); temper (to) (plaster); waste (to); botch (to)

galet *m* pebble; pebble-stone; cobble
galvaniser *v* galvanize (to)
▪ **galvanisé** = galvanized
garage *m* garage
garage *m* **à bicyclettes** bicycle shed
garnir *v* decorate (to); fit out with (to);
  garnish (to); lag (to); line (to); pack (to)
garnissage *m* lagging; lining; packing
garniture *f* fitments; fittings; jacket;
  lagging
gaz *m* gas
G.D.F. Gaz de France French Gas Board
gaz *m* **de ville** mains gas
gaz *m* **en bouteille** bottled gas
gaz *m* **propane/butane** propane/butane gas
génie *m* **civil** civil engineering
génie *f* **sanitaire** public health engineering
gentilhommière *f* manor house (small)
géomètre *m* geometer; geometrician;
  surveyor
géomètre *m* **du cadastre** ordnance surveyor
gestion *f* administration; management
glissement *m* sliding; slippage; slipping
gobetis *m* initial plaster or mortar coating;
  render coat; pointing
gorge *f* groove (eg beading, pulley); throat
gorge *f* **anti-refoulante** anti-backflow throat
  (fireplace)
goulet *m* neck opening (flue); neck gutter (of
  roof)
goutte *f* **d'eau** drip throat; drip; weep groove
gouttière *f* gutter
graisser *v* butter (to) (eg a brick with
  mortar); grease (to)
grand *m* **collecteur** main sewer
grand *m* **ensemble** high-density housing
  development
▪ **les grands ensembles** = high-rise flats;
  tower blocks
grange *f* barn
granit *m* ; **granite** *m* granite
granulats *mpl* aggregate (eg sand, gravel,
  stone)
granulat *m* **lourd** heavy aggregate (eg iron
  shot)
granulat *m* **léger** light aggregate (eg pumice,
  expanded slag)
granulométrie *f* granulometry
gratton *m* devil float

gravats *mpl*; **gravois** *mpl* rubble
gravier *m* gravel; grit
gravier *m* **de filtrage** filter gravel
gravillon *m* chippings; gravel
gravilloner *v* gravel (to) (eg road, path)
grenier *m* attic; loft
grès *m* sandstone; grit; stoneware; earthenware
grès *m* **cérame** vitrified clay tile; stone-ware
grès *m* **émaillé** ceramic floor tile
grès *m* **siliceux** ragstone
grésage *m* sanding; polishing; buffing
grillage *m* wire mesh; wire mesh fencing;
  wire netting; grille (of a door)
grille *f* bars (window); gate (metal); grating;
  grid (electricity); grille; railings
grille *f* **d'aération** air grille; ventilation grille
grille *f* **de clôture** surrounding railing
gros œuvre *m* basic structure; foundations,
  walls and floors etc; outer walls; shell (of a
  building)
groupe *m* **d'habitations** block of flats
gypse *m* gypsum

habillage *m* assembly; casing (machine);
  lagging (eg boiler)
habitation *f* dwelling; house
habitation *f* **principale** main residence
hachette *f* hatchet
hachette *f* **de charpentier** axe-hammer;
  carpenter's hammer
hachette *f* **de plâtrier** lath hammer;
  plasterer's hammer
haie *f* hedge
harpe *f* toothing (in masonry)
hauteur *f* elevation; height
hauteur *f* **au-dessus du niveau de la mer**
  height above sea-level
hectare *m*; **ha** *abb* hectare (10,000 sq.
  metres = 2.4711 acres)
hérisson *m* chimney sweep's brush; flue
  brush; foundation of next-to-earth
  compacted layer of stone; flagging laid on a
  stone foundation; spikes on top of wall
hérissonnage *m* flagging laid on compacted
  stone foundation; laying a foundation of
  next-to-earth compacted stones
hérissonner *v* roughcast (to)

hors d'aplomb out of plumb; out of true

hors d'équerre out of square

hors *m* **d'œuvre** annexe; outwork

hors-œuvre *adj*; **hors d'œuvre** *adj* external (measurement); (opposed to 'dans-œuvre'); annexed; projecting

hotte *f* hood; head (eg of drain-pipe); hopper-head

hotte *f* **refractaire** refractory hood

hourdage *m* pugging; rough-walling

hourder *v* deaden (to); deafen (to); pug (to) (frame) ; roughcast (to); render (to)

hourdis *m* deadening material; pugging; sound-proofing material (placed between sub-floor and floorboards)

huisserie *f* frame (door or window)

humidification *f* damping; humidifying; wetting

hydrofuge *m*; also *adj* water-repellant; water-resisting (compound)

ignifuge *m*; also *adj* fire-proofing agent; fire-retardant; fire-proofing

imperméabiliser *v* render impermeable (to); waterproof (to)

imperméable *adj* damp proof; impermeable; impervious; waterproof

implantation *f* introduction; locating; setting out; siting; layout

imposte *f* fanlight; transom (window)

inclinaison *f* inclination; pitch; slope; tilt

incliner *v* incline (to); slope (to)

infiltration *f* infiltration; rising damp

inflammable *adj* inflammable

ingénieur *m* engineer

inoxydable *adj* stainless

installation *f* **sanitaire** bathroom plumbing

interrupteur *m* switch (elect); circuit-breaker (elect)

intérieur *m*; also *adj* inside; interior

isolant *m* insulation material; insulator

isolateur *m* insulator

isolation *f* insulation; damp-proofing; isolation

isolation *f* **acoustique** sound insulation

isolation *f* **par panneaux composites** insulation with composite panels

isolation *f* **par projection** insulating material introduced by projection (eg spraying)

isolation *f* **phonique** sound insulation

isolation *f* **polyester/polyuréthane** insulation with polyester/polyurethane

isolation *f* **thermique** thermal insulation

isolement *m* insulation; isolation; separation

isorel™ *m* hardboard

jambage *m* jamb; jamb-post; foundation wall; stone pier

jambage *m* **d'une baie de port** jamb-post of a doorway

jambage *m* **d'une cheminée** jamb of a fire-place

jambage *m* **de force** strut/prop

jardin *m* garden; vegetable garden; yard

jardin *m* **d'hiver** conservatory; winter garden

jardin *m* **de rocaille** rock garden; rockery

jet *m* **de pelle** shovel's cast

jeu *m* action; clearance; play; slack; set (eg of tools); blowing (of a fuse)

joint *m* connection; coupling; joint; pointing (eg brickwork)

joint *m* **d'étanchéité** waterproof joint

joint *m* **de dilatation** expansion joint; slip joint

joint *m* **résilient** resilient joint

jointoiement *m* pointing (masonry); grouting

jointoyer *v* point (to); grout (to)

joints *mpl* **au cadre** mortar joints laid using metal former

joints *mpl* **croisés** vertical mortar joints staggered from row to row

joue *f* cheek; flange

jouée *f* reveal; cheek of dormer window

jour *f* stair well; gap; day; daylight

kit *m* **de débouchage** drain clearing kit

kit *m* **de ramonage** chimney sweeping kit

laine *f* **d'acier** steel wool

laine *f* **de verre** glass-wool

laine *f* **minerale de roche** rock wool

laine *f* **minerale de verre** glass wool

laitier *m* slag

laitier *m* **concassé** crushed slag

laitier *m* granulé granulated slag
laiton *m* brass
laiton *m* fondu cast brass
lambris *m* ceiling board, tongued and grooved; cladding; lining; panelling; wainscoting
lambris *m* d'appui dado (wall)
lambrissage *m* panelling; wainscoting
lambrisser *v* line (to); panel (to); wainscot (to)
lame *f* blade; lath; strip
lame *f* d'air air gap; layer of air
lame *f* de parquet floorboard; strip of parquet flooring
laminé,-e *adj* laminated
languette *f* feather; tongue
languette *f* de bois cleat; strip of wood
laque *f* shellac
laquer *v* shellac (to)
largeur *f* breadth; width
largeur *f* hors-tout overall width
larmier *m* dripstone (archit); coping
latte *f* lath
lauze *f* roofing stone; flat paving stone
lavabo *m* washbasin
lé *m* length/strip (of wallpaper); width (of cloth)
levé *m* de géomètre surveyor's report
levier *m* crowbar; handspike; lever; prise
levier *m* à pied-de-biche et à pointe pick-and-claw crowbar
lézarde *f* chink; crack; crevice
liant *m* binder; binding material; flexibility (of a metal)
liaison *f* bonding; connection
liaisonnement *m* des parois tying walls
liaisonner *v* bond (to)
liège *m* cork
lier *v* bind (to); fasten (to); join together (to) (with tie, strap)
lime *f* file
limon *m* mud; silt; stringer (staircase)
lingerie *f* linen room
linteau *m* lintel; transom
linteau *m* continu lintel tied to a bonding beam; continuous lintel
linteau *m* de grande portée long span lintel
linteau *m* de petite portée short span lintel
linteau *m* filant lintel tied to a bonding beam

linteau *m* isolé *m* isolated lintel
linteau *m* préfabriqué prefabricated lintel
linteau-botte *m* lintel with boot
lissage *m* smoothing
lisse *f* hand-rail; smoothness
lisser *v* smooth (to)
lissoir *m* à tuyau pipe-slick; pipe-smoother
lit *m* bed; layer
lit *m* de béton bed of concrete
lit *m* de carrière natural bed (of stone)
lit *m* isolant damp-proof course
lité,-e *adj* bedded
liteau *m* batten; bracket (for shelf)
logement *m* apartment; flat; housing; socket
logement *m* en ancien old house; no longer a new house
longueur *f* length
longueur *f* hors-tout overall length
louer *v* hire (to); rent (to)
lucarne *f* dormer window; skylight

mâchefer *m* clinker
machine *f* à couper tile-cutting machine
machine *f* à crépir masonry paint appli-cator
maçon *m* bricklayer; mason; stone-mason
maçonner *v* brick (to); brick up (to); lay bricks (to)
maçonnerie *f* masonry; stonework
madrier *m* beam
madrier *m* de faîtage ridge beam
maillet *m* mallet
maillet *m* caoutchouc rubber mallet
maillet *m* de calfat caulking mallet
main-d'œuvre *f* labour; labour force; manpower; workmanship
mairie *f* council offices; office of mayor; town hall
maison *f* house; firm
maison *f* à colombage half-timbered house
maison *f* à deux étages three-storeyed house
maison *f* à toit de chaume thatched cottage (see also 'chaumière')
maison *f* d'habitation dwelling house; private house
maison *f* de 5 pièces five-roomed house
maison *f* de commerce business firm
maison *f* de/en pierre(s) stone-built cottage or house

maison *f* en ancien old house; previously owned house

maison *f* en neuf new house

maison *f* individuelle detached house

maître *m* d'œuvre project manager; architect in charge

maître *m* d'œuvre qualifié qualified building supervisor (eg architect, builder)

maître *m* d'ouvrage owner (commissioning building work)

malaxage *m* blending; mixing

malfaçon *f* defect (due to bad workmanship); fault

mansarde *f* attic; mansard roof

manteau *m* mantle; mantlepiece

marbre *m* marble

marbrier,-ière *adj* marble

marouflage *m* stuck-on layer; sticking on a layer (eg PVC sheeting)

marquage *m* category specification (Norme Française); marking

marteau *m* à briques bricklayer's hammer

marteau *m* à dent claw hammer

marteau *m* à deux mains sledge hammer

marteau *m* à pioche pick-hammer

marteau *m* à piquer pick hammer; scaling hammer

marteau *m* américaine avec arrache-clous adze-eye hammer; claw hammer

marteau *m* d'ajusteur fitter's hammer

marteau *m* électrique electric hammer-drill

marteau *m* piqueur; marteaux-piqueurs *mpl* pneumatic drill

marteau *m* pneumatique pneumatic drill

marteau-matoir *m* caulking hammer

marteau-perforateur *m* hammer drill

marteau-pilon *m* drop-forge; drop-hammer (for pile driving); power hammer

martelette *f* small hammer

martelette *f* à pic pick hammer

masse *f* mass; massive structure; earth (elect); sledge-hammer

masse *f* couple sledge-hammer

masse *f* de l'édifice massive structure of the building

massette *f* club hammer; lump hammer

massette *f* de casseur de pierres stone-breaker's hammer

massette *f* de maçon club hammer; mason's hammer

massif *m* de fondation foundation block

massif *m* de maçonnerie block of masonry

mastic *m* cement; putty; mastic

mastic *m* calfeutrement stopping putty

mastic *m* de fer iron putty

mastic *m* de vitrier glazier's putty

mastic *m* à la chaux *m* lime putty

mastiquer *v* putty (to); cement (to); grout (to)

matériau *m* ; matériaux *mpl* material; materials

matériau *m* de revêtement cladding; coating material; covering material; lining material

matériaux *mpl* de construction building/construction materials

matériaux *mpl* en vrac loose materials; non-packaged materials

matériel *m*; matériels *mpl*; also *adj* appliances; equipment ; material; plant

matériel *m* de brasage brazing/hard soldering equipment

membrane *f* membrane

membrane *f* d'étanchéité damp-proof membrane

meneau *m* mullion; transom

menuiserie *f* joinery; carpentry; joiner's workshop; piece of joinery/carpentry

menuisier *m* joiner; carpenter

menuisier *m* d'art cabinet-maker

merlin *m* cleaver

métallerie *f* metal grilles etc; metal items; metalwork

métrage *m* measurement; measuring; quantity surveying; surveying

mètre *m* metre; metre rule

mètre *m* carré square metre

mètre *m* cube cubic metre

mètre *m* à ruban measuring tape

métreur *m*; métreuse *f* quantity surveyor; surveyor

métré *m* estimate of costs; measurement; quantity surveying

mettre (se) *v* à l'ouvrage start work (to)

meuler *v* grind (to) (eg tool)

meuleuse *f* angulaire angle grinder

meulière *f* stone; grindstone; buhrstone

meulière *f* piquée stone with dressed face

meulière *f* **plaquette** stone with almost parallel faces

mezzanine *f* mezzanine; mezzanine floor

mirette *f* **de maçon** mason's jointer

mise *f* **au point** clarification; developing; finalising/settling (business); fine-tuning; perfecting; restatement

mise *f* **en œuvre** employing; implementation (of a regulation); marshalling; preparation; using; laying (a floor)

modifier *v* alter (to); modify (to)

modifier (se) *v* be modified (to)

moellon *m* ragstone; rubble; quarry-stone; rubble-stone; small irregular-shaped stone

moellon *m* **traité** dressed moellon; dressed stone

moellonage *m* rubble; rubble-work; stone wall construction

moellons *mpl* **bruts** roughly dressed small stones (moellons)

moellons *mpl* **smillés** lightly dressed small stones (moellons)

moisissure *f* mildew; mould

molette *f* **au carbure de tungstène** tungsten carbide cutter

monocouche *f* **prêt à l'emploi** ready-to-use single coat rendering

montage *m* **d'un mur** raising a wall

montant *m* jamb-post; post; stud; upright

montant *m* **d'angle** corner-post

montant *m* **de porte** door-post; gate-post

mortier *m* mortar

mortier *m* **bâtard** lime-cement mortar

mortier *m* **blanc** white mortar

mortier *m* **colle pour béton cellulaire** cement/mortar for cellular concrete blocks

mortier *m* **de chaux** lime mortar

mortier *m* **de ciment** cement mortar

mortier *m* **de liaison** bonding mortar

mortier *m* **fin** fine mortar; finishing mortar

mortier *m* **gras** fat mortar

mortier *m* **hydraulique** hydraulic mortar

mortier *m* **maigre** lean mortar

mortier *m* **moyen** average mortar; medium mortar

mortier *m* **normal** masonry mortar; ordinary mortar

mortier *m* **rapide** rapid setting mortar

mortier *m* **refractaire** refractory mortar

mortier *m* **riche** fat mortar

mortier *m* **universel** universal mortar

mouiller *v* moisten (to); wet (to)

moule *m* mould (eg for concrete); form-work

moulure *f* moulding; trunking (elect)

mousse *f* moss; foam

mousse *f* **de caoutchouc** foam rubber

mousse *f* **expansée** foam rubber

mulot *m* queen-closer; half-header; half of brick cut along length

multicouche *adj* multiple layer; multilayer

mur *m* wall

mur *m* **à double cloison/paroi** hollow wall

mur *m* **bombé** bulged wall

mur *m* **bouclé** bulged wall

mur *m* **composite** composite wall

mur *m* **creux** cavity wall

mur *m* **d'appui** breast-high wall

mur *m* **d'enceinte** surrounding wall; outer wall

mur *m* **d'échiffre** wall carrying a stairway

mur *m* **d'écran** baffle wall; screen wall

mur *m* **de brique alvéolé** honeycomb wall; perforated brick wall

mur *m* **de cloison** partition wall

mur *m* **de clôture** enclosing wall; outer/surrounding wall

mur *m* **de face** front wall

mur *m* **de façade** façade wall; front wall

mur *m* **de parapet** breast-high wall; parapet

mur *m* **de refend** cross wall; interior load-bearing wall

mur *m* **de remplissage** exterior non-load-bearing wall

mur *m* **de retenue** retaining wall

mur de revêtement *m* retaining wall

mur *m* **de soubassement** basement wall; base wall

mur *m* **de soutènement** retaining wall; breast-high wall

mur *m* **de terasse** retaining wall

mur *m* **de type I ou IV** type I or type IV wall

mur *m* **double** cavity wall; double wall

mur *m* **en agglomérés** block wall

mur *m* **en galets** pebble-stone wall

mur *m* **en meulières** stone wall built with "meulières"

mur *m* **en moellons** wall built from small

stones (moellons); rubble wall
mur *m* **en parpaings** block wall
mur *m* **en pierres maçonnées** mortar-bound stone wall
mur *me* **n pierres sèches** drystone wall; dyke
mur *m* **en retour** flank wall; return wall
mur *m* **extérieur, type (I à IV)** exterior wall, classified type (I to IV)
mur *m* **latéral** side wall
mur *m* **mitoyen** party wall
mur *m* **non porteur** non-load-bearing wall
mur *m* **orbe** blank wall; blind wall
mur *m* **pignon** gable wall
mur *m* **portant**; **mur** *m* **porteur** bearing wall; load-bearing wall
mur *m* **simple** single wall; single thickness wall
murage *f* masonry; walling
muraille *f* high or thick wall
muraille *f* **qui pousse** bulging wall
murer *v* brick (to); lay bricks (to); wall (to); wall up (to)
muret *m*; **murette** *f* low wall

naissance *f* spandrel (of arch); spring (of arch)
nettoyage *m*; **nettoiement** *m* cleaning; cleansing
neuf, neuve *adj* new
▪ **à l'état neuf** = as new
nez *m* nosing (stairs)
nez *m* **de marche** nosing of step (stair-case); nosing plane
nickel *m* nickel
niveau *m* level; stage; storey
niveau *m* **à bulle 1 semelle** spirit level with one base plate
niveau *m* **à bulle (d'air)** spirit level
niveau *m* **de bruit** noise level
niveau *m* **de maçon** mason's level
niveler *v* make level (to); measure with a spirit level (to)
nivellement *m* levelling
norme *f* standard
▪ **NF** = Norme Française
noue *f* valley (roof); valley-gutter; valley-rafter

obstruction *f* blockage; obstruction; stoppage
œuvre *f* work; piece of work; task; undertaking
orifice *m* aperture; opening; orifice
orifice *m* **de ramonage** access aperture for cleaning (eg of soot-box)
orifice *m* **de sortie** outlet
ossature *f* framework; structure
ossature *f* **métallique** metal framework
outil *m* tool
outillage *m* equipment; implements; machinery; tools
ouverture *f* gap; hole; opening
ouvrage *m* building work; work
ouvrier *m* worker; workman
ouvrier *m* **de chantier** labourer
ouvrier *m* **de construction** construction worker

paille *f* straw; fault (in metal); flaw
paille *f* **de fer** steel wool; iron scale
palier *m* landing (of a staircase)
▪ **le même palier** = the same floor
pan *m* face; side
pan *m* **de bois** timber frame; stud wall
pan *m* **de fer** iron frame
panne *f* purlin; side-timber
panne *f* **fillière** purlin
panneau *m* fascia; panel
panneau *m* **composite** composite insulation panel
panneau *m* **de particules** chipboard
panneau *m* **"sandwich"** insulation panel, faced both sides
panneau *m* **simple** single material insulation panel
papier *m* **à tapisser** lining paper (wall)
papier *m* **bituminé** bitumenised paper
papier *m* **d'émeri** emery paper
papier *m* **kraft™** kraft™ paper
papier *m* **peint** wallpaper
papier *m* **peint lavable et lessivable** washable wallpaper
papier *m* **peint vinyl** vinyl wallpaper
papier *m* **sablé** sand paper
papier *m* **verré**; **papier** *m* **de verre** sand paper; glass paper

parcelle *f* parcel (of land)
parcelle *f* **de terre** plot of land
pare-vapeur *m* vapour barrier; vapour barrier membrane
parement *m* face; facing (eg of wall)
parement *m* **d'un mur** face of wall
parement *m* **extérieur** outer facing; exterior dressing
parer *v* dress (to) (stone); trim (to)
paroi *f* interior surface; partition; side; wall
paroi *f* **interne/externe** internal/external wall
paroi *f* **taillée avec fruit** sloped wall; wall cut with a batter
parois *fpl* **de fouille.** walls of excavation
parpaing *m* bond-stone; breeze-block; concrete block with air channels; perpend
parpaing *m* **aggloméré** breeze block
parquet *m* parquet floor; wooden floor
parqueter *v* lay a wooden or parquet floor (to)
passage *m* change; changeover; passage; way
passage *m* **interdit** no entry
patte *f* fastening; clamp; cramp; holdfast
patte *f* **à crochet** pipe-strap
patte *f* **à scellement** cramp; holdfast
patte *f* **d'attache** clip (for conduits); saddle
patte *f* **de liason** wall tie
patte *f* **de liasonnement avec goutte d'eau** wall tie with water drip
patte *f* **de maintien** support bracket
patte *f* **de support** support bracket
patte *f* **métallique** metal wall tie
pavage *m* pavement; paving
pavage *m* **en briques** brick pavement
pavé *adj* **en brique** brick paved
pavillon *m* house; pavilion; villa
peindre *v* paint (to)
peindre *v* **les boiseries** paint the woodwork (to)
peintre *m/f* painter
peintre *m* **en bâtiment** house painter
peintre-décorateur *m* painter and decorator
peinture *f* paint; painting; paintwork
peinture *f* **antirouille** antirust paint
peinture *f* **bitumineuse** bitumastic paint
peinture *f* **crépi** masonry paint
peinture *f* **emulsion** emulsion paint

peinture *f* **laqueé/satineé** gloss/satin-finish paint
peinture *f* **laquée** enamel
peinture *f* **protectrice** protective coating
peinture *f* **vernissante** enamel
pelle *f* shovel; digger; excavator
pelle *f* **mécanique** mechanical shovel/digger
pelleter *v* shovel (to); shovel up (to)
pelleteuse *f* excavator; mechanical shovel
pelote *f* **de cordeau** ball of string
pelouse *f* lawn
pénétration *f* abutment
pente *f* pitch (of roof); slant; slope
▪ **en pente** = sloping
percement *m* boring; drilling; piercing
perlite *f* perlite; pearlite
permis *m* **de construire** building permit; planning permission
permis *m* **de démolir** permit to demolish a building
perron *m* covered porch reached by an outside staircase; front steps (of a house); steps (leading to an entrance)
pièce *f* room (of house); member; part; piece
pièce *f* **de renfort** stiffener
pièce *f* **principale** main room
pièces *fpl* **d'eau** . bathrooms, kitchens, shower rooms etc
pied-de-biche *m* claw hammer; claw-bar; clawed spike-lever
pied-droit *m*; **piédroit** *m* pier (brick-work); pillar (of arch); door or window jamb
pierre *f* stone
pierre *f* **à aiguiser** rag stone; whetstone
pierre *f* **à chaux** limestone
pierre *f* **angulaire** cornerstone
pierre *f* **calcaire** limestone
pierre *f* **de taille** ashlar; building stone; cut stone; freestone
pierre *f* **du pays** local stone
pierre *f* **non-taillée** uncut stone
pierre *f* **ponce** pumice stone
pierre *f* **tendre** soft stone
pieu *m* pile (constr); post; stake
pignon *m* gable; pinion
▪ **à pignon** = gabled
pilier *m* column; pillar
pilot *m* pile (constr)

pilotage *m* pile-driving; piling
piloter *v* drive in piles (to); pile (to)
pilotis *m* piling; pile
pince *f*; **pinces** *fpl* crowbar; pincers; pliers; tongs
pince *f* à décoffrer crowbar, dismantling
pince *f* à levier crowbar
pince-monseigneur *f* crowbar
pinceau *m* paintbrush
pinces *fpl* **plates.** flat-nosed pliers
pioche *f* pick-axe; hammer-pick; pick
pioche *f* ordinaire pick-axe
pioche *f* à défricher mattock
piquet *m* picket; post; stake
piquet *m* de clôture fence post
piscine *f* swimming pool
pistolet *m* à peinture paint spray gun
placage *m* veneer; veneering
placard *m* cupboard
placard *m* à balai broom cupboard
placard *m* de cuisine kitchen cupboard
placer *v* bord à bord place edge to edge (to)
Placoplâtre™ *m* plasterboard; insulating plasterboard
plafond *m* ceiling
plafond *m* à caissons coffered ceiling
plafond *m* diffuseur d'air ventilated ceiling
plafond *m* en lambris boarded ceiling
plafond *m* lambrissé panelled ceiling
plafond *m* lumineux lighted ceiling
plafond *m* suspendu suspended ceiling
plafond *m* voûté vaulted/arched ceiling
plan *m* drawing; plan; blueprint; project; scale drawing; plane (surface)
plan *m* d'ensemble housing development plan
plan *m* d'implantation de la maison sur le terrain siting plan for house
plan *m* de construction building plan
plan *m* de la façade frontage or front elevation plan
plan *m* de la maison house plan
plan *m* de masse solid mass plan; aerial plan of mass
plan *m* de situation du terrain drawing/ plan of situation of site
plan *m* masse see 'plan de masse'
planche *f* board; floorboard; plank; shelf

planche *f* à dessin drawing board
planche *f* d'échafaudage scaffold board
planche *f* voilée warped board
plancher *m* floor; flooring
plancher *m* chauffant heated floor
plancher *m* solide solid floor
planchette *f* small shelf
planchéiage *m* boarding; flooring
planchéier *v* board (to); floor (to)
planelle *m* building block part perforated, part insulated
planelle *m* de rive edge block
planéité *f* flatness; planeness
plaque *f* sheet (of metal); plate
plaque *f* d'arrêt check plate
plaque *f* d'assise bed plate; foundation plate; baseplate
plaque *f* d'égout manhole cover
plaque *f* de cuivre copper plate
plaque *f* de liège cork sheet; cork slab
plaque *f* de marbre marble slab
plaque *f* de polystyrène polstyrene panel
plaque *f* de propreté finger plate
plaque *f* de protection cover plate
plaque *f* de renfort reinforcing plate; stiffening plate
plaque *f* en tôle sheet iron cover
plaque *f* foyère fire base
plaque *f* rigide rigid panel
plaquer *v* veneer (to)
plate-forme *f* platform; roof-plate; wall-plate; footing-block; sole-plate
plateau *m* d'échafaud scaffold board
platoir *m* finishing trowel; laying-on trowel (cement or plaster)
plâtrage *m* plastering
plâtras *m* lump of plaster; plaster debris
plâtre *m* plaster
plâtrer *v* plaster (to); render (to)
plâtrier *m* plasterer
plinthe *f* base-board; skirting; skirting board; plinth
plomb *m* lead (metal); plumb; plumb-bob; plumb-line
plomb (à) perpendicular; plumb
plomb *m* d'œuvre work-lead
plomb *m* de maçon mason's plumb; plumb-bob

plomb *m* **en feuilles** sheet lead
plombage *m* leading; plumbing
plomberie *f* leadwork; plumber's work-shop; plumbing
plombier *m* plumber
plot *m* contact (elect); pin; plug; stud; pad
poêle *f* lead-pot (of plumber); stove
poinçon *m* awl; bradawl; king post
poinçonnage *m*; **poinçonnement** *m* punching; stamping
point *m* dot; place; point
point *m* **d'appui** fulcrum; support; point of support
point *m* **de congélation** freezing point
pointerolle *f* **de maçon** mason's point; mason's punch; broach
polychlorure *m* **de vinyl** polyvinyl chloride
polystyrène *m* **expansé** expanded polystyrene
polyurethane *m* polyurethane
polyéthylène *m* polyethylene
pompe *f* pump
pompe *f* **de circulation** circulating pump
pompe *f* **électrique** electric pump
ponce *f* pumice
pondération *f* **des bruits** noise rating
pont *m* **thermique** heat bridge
porche *m* porch; porchway
porosité *f* porosity
portail *m* double gate; front entrance (archit); portal
portail *m* **métallique** metal double gate
porte *f* door; doorstep; doorway; gate
porte *f* **coulissante/pliante** sliding/folding door
porte *f* **d'entré** entrance; front door
porte *f* **de derrière** back door
porte palière *f* landing door
porte *f* **à claire-voie** open-lattice gate or door; glazed door
porte *f* **à deux battants** double door or gate
porte-fenêtre *f* french window
portée *f* loading; span
portée *f* **d'un plancher** distance between floor supports
porter *v* bear (to); carry (to); support (to)
porter *v* **sur** be supported by/on (to)
porter *v* **à faux** be out of plumb/true (to)

pose *f* **des sols** laying floors/flooring
poser *v* fix (to); lay (to); place (to); set (to)
poser (se) *v* be set (to), etc
poser *v* **des tuyaux** lay pipes (to)
poser *v* **les fondements d'une maison** lay the foundations of a house (to)
poser *v* **un rayon** put up a shelf (to)
poser *v* **une vitre** put in a window pane (to)
poseur *m* **de tuyaux** pipe fitter
poteau *m* pole; post
poteau *m* **d'ancrage** anchor post
poteau *m* **d'huisserie** door post; jamb-post
poteau *m* **d'inertie** inertial post
poteau *m* **de bornage** boundary post
poteau *m* **télégraphique** telegraph pole/post
pourriture *f* **humide** wet rot
pourriture *f* **sèche** dry rot
poussier *m*, **poussière** *f* dust
poutrage *m*; **poutraison** *f* girderage; set of beams
poutre *f* beam; girder
poutre *f* **en béton armé** reinforced concrete beam
poutre *f* **en fer laminé** rolled-iron girder
poutrelle *f* beam or girder (small); joist
poutrelle *f* **en acier marchand** rolled steel joist
poutrelle *f* **en céramique** beam encased in terra cotta blocks (floor beams)
poutrelle *f* **en treillis** metal trellis beam (flooring support); lattice girder
poutrelle *f* **précontrainte** prestressed concrete beam
poutres *fpl* **apparentes** exposed beams
pouvoir *m* **d'adhérence** adhesive power
pouzzolane *f* pozzolana
préciser *v* give precise details (to); make clear (to); specify (to); stipulate (to)
précontraint,-e *adj*, also *m* prestressed (concrete)
■ **béton précontraint** = prestressed concrete
prédalle *f* thin prestressed concrete slab forming base of final cast slab
préfabrication *f* prefabrication
prélinteau *m* lintel; pre-lintel
premier/deuxième étage *m* first/second floor
première *f* **couche** priming coat

prise *f* hold; inlet/intake; power point; setting (of cement, etc); grip; taking (eg measurements)
- **prise rapide/lente** = rapid/slow setting

prise *f* d'air air inlet; air sample

prise *f* d'eau water tap/cock; hydrant

prise *f* de courant (mâle/femelle) electric plug/socket; power point

prise *f* multiple adaptor (elect)

prise *f* pour résoir électrique razor point

procéder *v* par paliers proceed by stages (to)

profondeur *f* depth

projet *m* plan; project; scheme

projeter *v* consider (to); plan (to); project (to)

projeter *v* de faire plan to do (to)

propriétaire *m* landlord; owner; proprietor
- **ancien propriétaire** = former owner

propriété *f* characteristic; estate; ownership; possession; property

propriété *f* fonciére real estate/freehold

protection *f* aux chocs protection against impacts or shocks

protection *f* incendie protection against fire

puisard *m* sump; soakaway

puits *m* shaft; well

puits *m* artésien artesian well

puits *m* perdu cesspool; sink; soakaway

puits *m* profond deep well

purgeur *m* bleed-tap (of radiator); drain-cock; trap

purgeur *m* vertical vertical trap

PVC; polychlorure de vinyl polyvinyl chloride

quadrillage *m* en fil de nylon nylon fibre mesh

quincaillerie *f* hardware; ironmongery

quinconce (en) staggered; zigzag

raboteuse *f* planer; planing machine

rabotin *m* dresser (for stone)

raccord *m* connecting; connection; coupling

raccordement *m* connecting; joining

raccordement *m* au réseau connecting the telephone

raccordement *m* aux égouts connecting to the drains

radier *m* raft; foundation raft; over-site concrete

ragréage *m* cleaning down (eg brickwork); cement mortar used for screeding or rendering

ragréer *v* restore (to); finish off (to); clean down (brickwork) (to); smooth (to)

ragrément *m* cleaning down; finishing off; smoothing

raideur *f* stiffness; steepness (eg of a staircase); tautness (eg of rope)

raidir *v* stiffen (to)

raidisseur *m* brace; stiffener; tensioner; partition wall support; tightener

rail *m* rail

rainurage *m* chasing; grooved surface; grooving

rainure *f* groove; slot; rabbet

rainurer *v* chase (to); groove (to)

rainureuse *f* slot-drilling machine

ramassage *m* d'ordures refuse collection

ramonage *m* cleaning; sweeping a chimney or flue

rampant *m* slope

rampe *f* flight of stairs; rise; slope; stair rail

rampe *m* d'accè access ramp

rampe *f* d'escalier banisters; flight of stairs

rampe *f* de chevrons pitch of roof

rang *m* row

rangée *f* row

ravalement *m* finishing; cleaning; restoration; cutting back (agric); resurfacing; rough-casting; levelling (soil)

ravaleur *m* stone restorer

rebord *m* edge; edge-plate (of lock); rim

rebord *m* de la fenêtre window-ledge; window-sill

rebouchage *m* filling in; refilling

reboucheur *m* filler

recoin *m* nook; recess

recouvrement *m* covering; lap; overlap; over-lapping

récupération *f* de chaleur heat recovery

réduction *f* de bruit noise reduction

refaire *v* surface resurface (to)

refouillement *m* deepening; recess (of a masonry joint)

refouler *v* drive in, down (etc) (to); force in

or out (to) (eg bolt, pin)

regard *m* access port; inspection hole; manhole

règle *f* **de maçon** mason's rule; mason's straight-edge

règlement *m* regulation(s); settlement/ payment (eg of an invoice)

règlement *m* **intérieur** bye-laws; rules and regulations

réglementation *f* control; regulation(s)

réglementation *f* **en vigueur** regulations in force

régler *v* line (to); regulate (to); rule (to); settle (to) (a bill, a problem)

▪ **non réglé** = outstanding, unpaid

rehaussement *m* heightening

rehausser *v* raise (to) (ceiling); build higher (to) (eg wall); heighten (to)

rejointoiement *m* pointing after wall has been built; regrouting; repointing

▪ **jointoiement** = pointing as wall is built

rejointoyer *v* regrout (to); repoint (to)

rémaçonner *v* repair (to) (masonry)

remblai *m* backfill; banking up; embankment; filling up (eg ditch)

remblaiement *m*; **remblayage** *m* filling; back-filling; banking up

remblayer *v* fill (to); fill up (to); embank (to)

remettre *v* **à neuf** refurbish (to); renovate (to)

remplissage *m* filling; filling up

rénovation *f* modernisation; redevelopment; renovation; restoration

rénover *v* modernise (to); renovate (to); restore (to) (a building)

réparation *f* mending; repairing; restoring

réparer *v* mend (to); repair (to)

repeindre *v* repaint (to)

reprendre *v* **en sous-œuvre** underpin (to)

reprise *f* **en sous-œuvre** underpinning

réseau *m* grid; network; system

réseau *m* **communal d'assainissement** communal sewerage system

réseau *m* **d'alimentation** supply system

réseau *m* **d'éclairage** lighting system

réseau *m* **d'égouts** sewerage system

réseau *m* **primaire en boucle** ring-main

(elect)

réservoir *m* reservoir; tank; fishpond

réservoir *m* **d'eau** cistern; water butt; water tank

résidence *f* residence; residential flats

résidence *f* **principale** main home

résidence *f* **secondaire** second home; holiday home

résidu *m* residue

résistance *f* **au feu** fire resistance

résistance *f* **mécanique** mechanical resistance

résistance *f* **à l'écrasement** compressive strength; crushing strength

résistance *f* **à la compression** compressive strength; crushing strength

résistance *f* **à la rupture** breaking strength; ultimate strength

résistance *f* **à la traction** tensile strength

restauration *f* restoration

restaurer *v* restore (to)

▪ **un bâtiment restauré** = a restored building

rétenteur *m* **d'eau** water retainer

retrait *m* shrinkage

rétrécissement *m* contraction; narrowing; shrinkage

revêtement *m* cladding; coating; covering; facing; surface; lining

revêtement *m* **de bitume** bitumen coating

revêtement *m* **d'étanchéité** damp-proof covering

revêtement *m* **de plomb** lead flashing (roof)

revêtement *m* **de sol** floor covering; flooring

revêtement *m* **de zinc** zinc flashing (roof)

revêtement *m* **des tubes** pipe wrapping

revêtement *m* **élastomère** elastomeric covering

revêtement *m* **enduit** lining

revêtement *m* **étanche** water-tight lining

revêtement *m* **imperméable** waterproof coating

revêtement *m* **mural** wall covering

revêtement *m* **mural imitation carrelage** imitation tile wall covering

rez-de-chaussée *m*; **rdc** *abb* ground floor; street level; ground floor flat

rez-de-jardin *m* garden level

riflard *m* **de maçon** wall scraper; roughing

file

rigole *f* channel; foundation trench; trench (small)

risque *m* **d'enfoncement** risk of giving way; risk of sinking (eg foundation)

risque *m* **d'éboulement** risk of caving in; risk of earth-fall

risque *m* **de glissement** risk of earth-fall; risk of slippage

rive *f* bank (river); border; eaves; edge

rive *f* **d'une planche** thickness of a board

rivet *m* rivet

riveter *v* rivet (to)

robinet *m* tap

robinet *m* **à flotteur** ballcock

robinet *m* **d'arrêt** stopcock

robinet *m* **de fermature** stopcock

robinet *m* **mélangeur/mitigeur** mixer tap

robinet *m* **purgeur** drain-cock

robinetterie *f* plumbing; tap trade; taps and fittings

rocaillage *m* pebble-work; pebble facing; pebble working

roche *f* rock; stone

roche *f* **concassée** crushed rock; crushed stone

rondelle *f* washer

rouille *f* rust

rouleau *m* roller

rouleau léger *m* light roller

rouleau *m* **à peinture** paint roller

ruban *m* **d'étanchéité** damp-proof strip

ruban *m* **isolant** insulating tape

rupture *f* **de joint** break in continuity of the joint; discontinuous joint; staggered joint

sablage *m* sandblasting; sanding

sable *adj* sand-coloured

sable *m* sand; gravel (not common); sand-glass

sable *m* **à bâtir** building sand

sable *m* **doux** soft sand

sable *m* **grossier** coarse sand

sableuse *f* sandblaster (machine)

sablière *f* wall plate; sole plate; sand-pit

saignée *f* groove; trench; ditch; saw cut

salle *f* room; hall (of a château)

salle *f* **à manger** dining room

salle *f* **d'eau** shower room

salle *f* **de bain** bathroom

salle *f* **de douches** shower-room; showers

salle *f* **de séjour** living room

salon *m* living room; lounge; sitting room

salpêtre *m* saltpeter

sanitaire *adj* sanitary

sanitaire *m* bathroom installations

sanitaires (les) *mpl* bathroom; bathroom suite; bathroom plumbing

scellement *m* embedding; sealing

sceller *v* embed (to); seal (to)

schéma *m*; **schème** *m* diagram; plan; scheme; sketch

schéma *m* **de câblage** circuit diagram; wiring diagram

scie *f* **à métaux** hacksaw

scie *f* **de coffreur** formworker's saw

scie *f* **pour bêton cellulaire** saw for cellular concrete

scie *f* **pour pierre tendre et plâtre** saw for soft stone and plaster

scorie *f* slag; clinker; furnace clinker

seau *m* bucket; bucketful; pail; pailful

seau *m* **d'incendie** *m* fire-bucket

seau *m* **en toile** canvas bucket

seau *m* **en tôle galvanisée** galvanized iron bucket

séchage *m* drying; seasoning (wood)

sèche *m* **rapidement** rapid drying

séchoir *m* drier; drying shed

second *m* **œuvre** finishing works; completion work

secteur *m* local electricity supply area; sector

séjour *m* dwelling place; living room; lounge; sojourn; stay

séjour *m* **double** living room; through-lounge

semelle *f* base-plate; wall-plate; roof-plate; footing; foundation (load distributing element); sole (of a plane); tread; table (of a girder)

semelle *f* **de répartition** load-spreading plate

semelle *f* **résiliente** resilient base-plate

serrage *m* tightening; screwing tight; grip; holding

serrage *m* **du béton** compaction of concrete

serre *f* glasshouse; greenhouse; conservatory (attached to house)

serre-joint *m* **de maçon** mason's clamp; mason's G-clamp

serrure *f* lock

serrurerie *f* ironwork; lock-work; metal-work; hardware

serrurier *m* locksmith

servitude *f* **de passage** right of way

seuil *m* door sill; doorstep; doorway; sill; threshold

siège *m* seat; seating

siège *m* **de cabinet** WC seat; toilet seat

siphon *m* siphon

smille *f* mason's scappling-hammer

smiller *v* scabble (to); scapple (to)

socle *m* bed-plate; pedestal; plinth; stand

soffite *m* soffit

sol *m* earth; ground; soil; floor; flooring; earth (elect); ground floor

sol *m* **argileux/glaiseux** clay soil

sol *m* **de mosaïque** terrazzo

sol *m* **en béton** concrete floor

solin *m* coating of fill-in material (eg plaster, mortar); fillet-gutter; spacing between joists; glazing fillet (eg of putty); mortar bedding (of ridge tile)

solivage *m* girderage; (secondary) joisting

solive *f* girder; joist; beam

solive *f* **d'enchevêtrure** tail trimmer

solive *f* **de plancher** floor joist

solive *f* **en acier** steel joist

sollicitation *f* stressing

solliciter *v* stress (to)

soubassement *m* subfoundation; substructure; base; basement; dado (wall, window)

souche *f* chimney stack; stack; tree stump

souche *f* **protegée** protected chimney stack; stack covered with raised slab

souillure *f* blister (paint); blemish; stain

source *f* source; spring (water)

source *f* **de lumière** light source

sous-couche *f* undercoat

sous-face *f* underface; underside; soffit

sous-œuvre *m* substruction; underpinning

sous-sol *m* basement; lower ground floor (of shop); subsoil; substratum

sous-toiture *f* covering of the underside of a roof

soutènement *m* support; supporting

souterrain *m*; also *adj* subterranean; underground

spatule *f* spatula

spatule *f* **de maçon** mason's jointer

spécification *f* specification

stockage *m* stocking; storage

stockage *m* **sur le chantier** storage on (building) site

suie *f* soot

superficie *f* surface; surface area

superficie *f* **de plancher hors œuvre nette** overall net floor area

support *m* support

surbaisser *v* lower (to) (eg ceiling); surbase (to) (eg vault)

surcharge *f* overloading

surestimer *v* overestimate (to); overvalue (to)

surestimer *v* **une masison à vendre** over-value a house for sale (to)

surface *f* surface; surface area

surface *f* **d'appui** support surface

surface *f* **de portée** bearing surface

surface *f* **des étages** floor surface (of building)

surface *f* **habitable** habitable surface area of dwelling

surface *f* **hors œuvre nette** basic area of house; habitable floor area (see also 'superficie')

surface *f* **lisse** smooth surface

surface *f* **nue** bare surface; unbroken surface

surface *f* **portante** bearing surface

surprofondeur *f* excess depth

système *f* method; system

système *f* **d'égouts** sewerage system

table *f* sheet (eg of lead); slab; table

table *f* **d'une enclume** face of an anvil

table *f* **d'une poutre** table/tread of a girder

table *f* **à tapisser** wallpaper pasting table

tableau *m* board; vertical side of opening in façade; reveal

tablier *m* flue-shutter

tache *f* spot; stain

tâche *f* job; task

tache *f* blanchâtre white stain (eg from efflorescence)

taille *f* height (person); size; cutting (eg stone)

tailler *v* cut (to) (stone)

tailleur *m* de pierre stonecutter; stone-mason

talochage *m* surface finishing with a float (eg concrete)

taloche *f* darby; float; hawk

taloche *f* à pointes devil float; scratch trowel

taloche *f* plastique plastic float or hawk

talocher *v* float (to); roughcast (to)

talus *m* bank; batter (eg of a wall); slope

tamis *m* sieve

tamis *m* bois sieve with wooden frame

tamis *m* métallique gauze; wire gauze; wire sieve

tamisage *m* sieving; sifting

tamiser *v* sieve (to); sift (to)

tampon *m* de ramonage cleaning plug (of a flue)

tapée *f* outer support for a persienne

tapisser *v* cover (to); line (to); wallpaper (to)

tapisserie *f* wall-paper; wall covering

taquet *m* peg; wedge

tas *m* heap; pile

tasseau *m* bracket; cleat (wood); stake; strip of wood

tassement *m* settlement; settling; squeeze; squeezing (roof); tamping down

tassement *m* du remblais settlement of the earthworks (remblais)

taxe *f* d'habitation community charge; rates

té *m* de dessin T-square

té *m* de raccordement T connection

té *m* double cross; cross connection

té *m* à tubulure oblique oblique T-coupling

téléphone *m* sans fil cordless telephone

tenaille *f* pincers; tongs

terrain *m* building land/site; ground; land; plot (of land); terrain

terrain *m* à bâtir building plot/site

terrain *m* avec/sans viabilité land with/ without services laid on

terrain *m* boisé wooded land

terrain *m* clos enclosed land

terrain *m* constructible land on which technically and legally one can build

terrain *m* viabilisé site with services laid on

terrasse *f* terrace; flat roof

terrasse *f* à pente nulle zero slope terrace (below 1% slope)

terrasse *f* inaccessible inaccessible terrace

terrasse *f* plate flat terrace

terrasse *f* rampante sloping terrace

terrasse-jardin *f* terrace garden

terrassement *m* earthwork(s); embankment; excavation

terre *f* earth; earth (elect); ground; land; soil

terre *f* argileuse clayey soil

terre *f* calcaire chalky soil

terre *f* cuite fired clay; terra cotta

terre *f* sableuse sandy soil

terre-plein *m* earth platform; platform; solid earth; terrace

têtu *m* de maçon mason's stone-hammer

tige *f* rod; shank; stem

tille *f* de couvreur slater's hammer

tirage *m* draught (eg of a fire); drawing; pulling

tirant *m* stay; tie-bar; tie-beam

tirer *v* des plans draw up plans (to)

tirer *v* la chasse flush the toilet (to)

toile *f* à bâche tarpaulin

toile *f* à sac sacking

toile *f* de jute hessian

toile *f* émeri emery cloth

toile *f* goudronnée tarpaulin; roofing felt

toit *m* roof

toit *m* en mansarde mansard-roof

toiture *f* roof; roofing; roof structure

toiture-terrasse *f* roof terrace

tôle *f* plate; sheet; sheet iron

tôle *f* d'acier inoxydable stainless steel sheet

tôle *f* de cuivre sheet copper

tôle *f* galvanisée galvanized iron sheet

tôle *f* ondulée corrugated metal sheet

tôle *f* zinguée galvanized iron sheet

tolérance *f* limit; margin; tolerance

tolérance *f* d'exécution permitted tolerance

tourbe *f* peat

tournevis *m* screwdriver

tout-à-l'égout *m* mains drainage

tracer *v* draw (to); lay out (to); trace (to)

traitement *m* antirouille rustproofing

tranchée *f* cut; surface cut; trench

transformer *v* alter (to); change (to); transform (to)

trappe *f* flap; hatch; trap door

trappe *f* **accès combles** trap door access to attic/loft

trappe *f* **de ramonage** trap-door for cleaning flue

travail *m* **préparatoire** preparatory work; prior work

travailler *v* work (to)

travailleur *m*; **travailleuse** *f* worker

travaux *mpl* **de finition** finishing off

traverse *f* cross-bar; cross-beam; cross-tie; horizontal side piece of door or window; template (beam)

traverser *v* cross (to); pass through (to); traverse (to)

traversée *f* crossing; passage through

travertin *m* sinter, calcareous; travertine

treillis *m* netting; trellis; wire netting; grillage (foundations); mesh

treillis *m* **métallique** wire netting

treillis *m* **soudé** welded trellis (reinforcement)

trémie *f* cavity; hearth cavity; stair cavity

trémie *f* **d'escalier** stair well

trémie *f* **de cheminée** chimney opening

treuil *m* crab; hoist; winch

treuil *m* **électrique** electric hoist

tronçonnage *m*, **tronçonnement** *m* cutting into sections; sawing up

trop-plein *m* overflow; overflow-pipe; waste pipe

trou *m* hole

trou *m* **d'homme** manhole

trou *m* **de regard** inspection hole

trou *m* **de serrure** keyhole

truelle *f* trowel

truelle *f* **dentelée** serrated trowel

truelle ronde *f* trowel, round

trumeau *m* pier; overmantel (fireplace)

tubage *m* casing; introduction of metal liner tube into existing flue; tubing

tube *m* pipe; tube; tubing

tube *m* **d'égout** soil pipe

tube *m* **de chauffage** heating pipe

tubulure *f* side-pipe; tail-pipe (of a cock); tubulure

tuile *f* roof tile; tile

tuile *f* **creuse/romaine/ronde** curved tile

tuile *f* **faîtière** ridge tile

tuile *f* **romaine** Roman tile

turbine *f* **statique** ventilated chimney top

tuyau *m* pipe; piping; tube; hose; conduit; flue

tuyau *m* **d'arrosage** hosepipe

tuyau *m* **d'écoulement** drain

tuyau *m* **d'égout** soil pipe

tuyau *m* **de descente** downpipe

tuyau *m* **de trop-plein** overflow pipe

tuyau *m* **en caoutchouc** rubber tubing

tuyau *m* **en cuivre** copper pipe/piping

tuyau *m* **en plastique** plastic pipe

tuyau *m* **en terre** earthenware pipe

tuyauterie *f* pipes; pipes and fittings; pipework installation; piping; tubing

tuyauterie *f* **des eaux usées** waste water piping/sewer

tuyauteur *m* pipe fitter (see also 'poseur de tuyaux')

type *m* **de joint** type of pointing (eg sloped, curved etc)

urbanisme *m* town planning

valet *m* **d'établi** clamp

vase *f* mud; silt

vasistas *m* fanlight; opening roof-light

vélux™ *m* roof light; velux™

ventilateur *m* fan; ventilator

ventilateur *m* **extracteur** extractor fan

ventilateur *m* **électrique** electric fan

ventilateur *m* **de toit** roof ventilator

ventilation *f* ventilation

ventilation *f* **mécanique contrôlée**; **VMC** *abb* mechanically controlled ventilation

ventouse *f* air-vent; draught-hole (of fire, furnace); underfloor draught pipe of fireplace

véranda *f* veranda

vermiculite *f* vermiculite

vermoulu,-e *adj* worm-eaten

vermoulure *f* woodworm; woodworm traces

■ **vermoulures** *pl* = worm holes

verre *m* **cellulaire** cellular glass

viabilité *f* practicability; availability of

services (eg water, etc) at building site

vice *m* defect; fault; flaw

vice *m* **cache** hidden fault/defect

vice *m* **de construction** construction fault/ defect

vice *m* **de forme** legal flaw or irregularity

vidanger *v* drain off (to) (water, oil); empty (to); empty out (to)

vide *m* empty; empty space; gap; vacuum; void (archit)

vide *m* **d'air** air void

vide *m* **d'une vis** groove of a screw

vide *m* **sanitaire** under-floor space

vider *v* clear (to); drain (to); empty (to)

villa *f* cottage; modern house; villa

virole *f* clip; ferrule; thimble

virole *f* **de penetration** penetration ferrule

virole *f* **pour tubes de chaudière** ferrule for boiler tubes

vitre *f* pane of glass; window pane

vitrerie *f* glass items; glaziery; glazing

vitrier *m* glazier

voie *f* **de dégagement** slip road

voile *f* shell; envelope (defining exterior contour of building)

voile *f* **de béton** thin concrete wall

voile *f* **de verre** glass cloth

voiler *v* buckle (to) (metal); conceal (to); screen (to); veil (to); warp (to) (wood)

voirie *f* highway system; system of roads;

refuse collection; rubbish dump

volet *m* shutter

volige *f* roof board; roof sheathing; scantling (timber)

voussoir *m*; **vousseau** *m* arch-brick; arch-stone; quoin; voussoir

voussure *f* arching; cornice; coving

voutain *m* small arch

voutain *m* **d'une poutrelle** haunch

voûte *f* arch; archway; vault

vrac (en gros) in bulk; in quantity; loose; non-packaged

vrille *f* gimlet

WC *m* water-closet; WC

zinc *m* zinc

zinguer *v* cover with zinc (to)

zone *f* **bâtie** built-up area

zone *f* **d'aménagement différé** future development zone

zone *f* **littorale** coastal zone

zone *f* **à urbaniser en priorité** urban development zone

4. CHARPENTIER ET MENUISIER

abattre *v* knock down (to); demolish (to) (eg a wall); cut down (to); fell (to) (a tree); clinch (to) (nail, rivet)

▪ abattre une arête = to chamfer an edge

about *m* butt; butt-end; extremity of piece of timber

▪ en about = abutting

aboutage *m* **aboutement** *m* abutting; butt-jointing; abutment

abouter *v* butt (to); butt-joint (to)

accoler *v* join side by side (to)

accore *m* prop or shore (usually wood)

adent *m* indent; key; dovetail

adenter *v* indent (to); key (to); dovetail (to)

adhérence *f* adhesion

adhérer *v* adhere (to); stick (to)

adossé, -e *adj* back-to-back

adoucir *v* soften (to); make smoother (to)

adoucir *v* **une courbe** to ease a curve

adoucir *v* **une surface avec de la toile d'émeri** to rub down/to smooth a surface with emery paper

adoucissement *m*; **adoucissage** *m* softening; smoothing-out

aération *f* aeration

aérer *v* air (to); ventilate (to)

affaisement *m* giving way; collapse; sagging; deflection; subsidence

affaissée *f* overloaded piece of timber which is bowed or moved from normal position

affaisser *v* give way (to); sag (to); subside (to)

affiner *v* refine (to); thin (to) (eg board)

affleurement *m*; **affleurage** *m* levelling; making flush

affleurer *v* make flush (to); level (to); be level with (to); be level (to); be flush (to)

■ **désaffleurer** *v* = to be not level (with)

affûtage *m* sharpening; grinding; set of bench-planes used by joiner

affûter *v* sharpen (to); grind (to); set (to) (a saw)

affûteuse *f* grinder; sharpening machine

aggloméré *m*; **agglo** *abb* chipboard; particle board; conglomerate (stone)

aggloméré *m* **bouveté** tongued-and-grooved chipboard

agrafage *m* fastening; hooking; stapling

agrafe *f* clamp; fastener; hook; staple

agrafer *v* clip (to); staple (to)

agrafeuse *f* stapler

aiguille *f* wood or metal piece reinforcing a tie-beam; king-post; thin headless nail; needle

ais *m* board or plank 3 to 6 cm thick

aisselier *m* wooden angle or corner brace

ajustage *m* **lâche/facile** loose/easy fit

ajustement *m*; **ajustage** *m* adjustment; fit; fitting

ajustement *m* **précis** close fit; exact fit

ajustement *m* **serre** close fit; tight fit

alaise *f* widening piece (wood); make-up piece (wood)

alaise *f* **rapportée** lipping; banding; door edging (wood) (see also 'couvre-chant')

aléser *v* ream (to)

alésoir *m* reamer

âme *f* core; material forming inner core (eg of a door)

aménager *v* fit out (to); equip (to); lay out (to); convert (to); plan (to); develop (to)

■ **à aménager** = for conversion

aménager *v* **du bois** to cut up wood (eg a tree)

angle *m* **d'attaque** cutting angle (of a cutting tool)

angle *m* **de coupe** cutting angle

appentis *m* lean-to (building); shed; roof with a single slope; penthouse (roof)

appui *m* bearing; support; rest; sill; buttress

appui *m* **d'escalier** banisters

appui *m* **de fenêtre** window sill

appui *m* **de porte** door sill

appui *m* **des poutres** beam support

appui *m* **des solives** joist support

appuyer *v* support (to); hold up (to); prop up (to)

appuyer *v* **(sur, contre)** lean (to); rest (to)

arasement *m* levelling; making flush; planing (down); cutting to length; shoulder (of tenon)

araser *v* level (to); make level (to); cut off level (to); saw off (end) (to); plane (down) (to); square timber (to)

arbalétrier *m* principal rafter; main rafter; inclined beam of roof trussing carrying the purlins

arbre *m* tree; shaft; axle; spindle

arbre *m* **moteur** driving shaft

architrave *f* architrave (see also 'encadrement')

arête *f* ridge; edge; arris

arête *f* **chanfreinée** bevelled edge; chamfered edge

arête *f* **de coupe** cutting edge (of tool)

arête *f* **tranchante** cutting edge (of tool)

arête *f* **vive** sharp edge; square edge

arêtier *m* hip-rafter; angle-rafter; hip (roof)

armature *f* reinforcement; trussing; bracing; strap; stirrup-strap

armature *f* **à toit** roof truss/trussing

armé,-e *adj* trussed; braced; reinforced

■ **poutre armée** = trussed beam

armoire *f* cupboard; wardrobe

armoire *f* **arasée** built-in cupboard

armoire *f* **à linge** linen cupboard

arrachage *m*; **arrachement** *m* extraction (eg of nails); pulling out

arrache-clou *m* nail-extractor

arracher *v* pull out (to) (eg nails)

arrêt *m* stop; stoppage; stay; arrest; ward (of lock)

arrêt *m* **de chanfrein** chamfer-stop
arrêt *m* **de chassis** window stay
assemblage *m* assembling; assembly; assemblage; joint; jointing;
assemblage *m* **à baguette** assembly of tongued-and-grooved boards with beaded edge
assemblage *m* **à charnière** hinged joint
assemblage *m* **à chevilles** dowel joint
assemblage *m* **à dents de scie** indented joint
assemblage *m* **à double embrèvement** double joggle-joint; double stepped housing
assemblage *m* **à double tenon** double-tenon joint
assemblage *m* **à embrèvement** joggle- joint
assemblage *m* **à embrèvement anglais** bridle joint; notch-and-bridle joint
assemblage *m* **à embrèvement avant** notched and bolted joint
assemblage *m* **à embrèvement à étrier** joggle-joint with stirrup
assemblage *m* **à embrèvement boulonné** bolted joggle-joint
assemblage *m* **à endent** indent joint; cog joint
assemblage *m* **à enfourchement** slot-mortise joint
assemblage *m* **à entaille** notch-joint
assemblage *m* **à/en fausse coupe** bevel joint; diagonal joint
assemblage *m* **à fausse coupe renversée** reversed bevel joint
assemblage *m* **à feuillure** rabbeted joint; rebated joint
assemblage *m* **à feuillure et liteau** rabbeted joint with batten
assemblage *m* **à goujon et douille** dowel joint
assemblage *m* **à languette rapportée** slip-tongue joint; filleted joint
assemblage *m* **à mi-bois** halved joint; half-lap joint; lap joint; overlap joint; step-joint
assemblage *m* **à mi-bois en queue d'aronde** dovetail halved joint
assemblage *m* **à onglet**; **assemblage** *m* **d'onglet**; **assemblage** *m* **en onglet** mitre(d) joint; bevel joint
assemblage *m* **à petits cadres** small frame assembly

assemblage *m* **à queue d'aronde** dovetail joint
assemblage *m* **à queues droites** *m* combed joint; box joint
assemblage *m* **à rainure et languette** tongued-and-grooved joint
assemblage *m* **à tenon et cheville** pinned tenon joint
assemblage *m* **à tenon et joue** tenon and cheek joint
assemblage *m* **à tenon et mortaise** mortise and tenon joint
assemblage *m* **à tenon et mortaise à embrevement** stepped mortise and tenon joint
assemblage *m* **à tenon et mortaise à double embrèvement** double-stepped mortise and tenon joint
assemblage *m* **à tenon renforcé** tenon and tusk joint
assemblage *m* **à tenon simple** single tenon joint
assemblage *m* **à tenon à double epaulement** tenon joint with double shoulder
assemblage *m* **à tenon avec cheville** pinned tenon joint
assemblage *m* **à tourillons** pinned assembly; pegged joint (*eg* with dowels)
assemblage *m* **avec embrèvement** joggle joint
assemblage *m* **à vif** butt joint
assemblage *m* **cloué** nailed assembly; nailed construction
assemblage *m* **d'angle à mi-bois** angled halved joint
assemblage *m* **en about** butting joint
assemblage *m* **fausse languette** loose-tongue joint; slip-tongue joint
assemblage *m* **flotté** mortise and tenon joint between pieces of different thickness
assemblage *m* **par boulons**. bolted joint or assembly
assemblage *m* **par collage** glued joint or assembly
assemblage *m* **par crampon** assembly using spiked or toothed metal plates
assemblage *m* **par éléments métalliques** joint made with metal fixing pieces
assemblage *m* **par goujons** keyed joint;

pinned joint; dowel assembly

assembler *v* assemble (to); join (to); joint (to)

assembler *v* **à plat** join side by side (to) (in one plane)

assembler *v* **à queue d'aronde** dovetail (to)

assembler *v* **bout à bout** butt joint (to)

assembler *v* **en bout** join end to end (to)

Association Française de Normalisation; AFNOR French Standards Association

atelier *m* workshop

auvent *m* small roof (covering entrance, balcony etc); canopy; porch-roof; hood

auvent *m* **en débordement** extending roof or canopy

avant-clou *m* gimlet

avant-toit(s) *m(pl).* eaves; verge (of roof)

baguette *f* bead; beading; reed; moulding

baguette d'angle *f* angle strip (wood); corner moulding

baie *f* bay; opening

baie *f* **de fenêtre** window opening

baie *f* **vitrée** picture window

balancer *v* balance (to); sway (to); swing (to)

balancer *v* **une marche d'escalier** balance or dance a stair step (to)

balcon *m* balcony

balustrade *f* balustrade; handrail

balustre *m* baluster; banister

bardage *m* cladding

bardeau *m* shingle; cladding board

barre *f* bar; batten; ledge; piece of wood; rail; rod

barre *f* **transversale** crosspiece; strut

barreau *m* baluster; banister; bar; rail; rung (of ladder)

bastaing *m* plank (approx 7 x 16.5 cm in section)

bâti *m* frame; framework; framing

bâti *m* **dormant** fixed frame (door/window)

battant *m* **de porte** door/leaf of double doors

battre *v* **une ligne** chalk a line (to); trace a line with a cord (to); (abbreviated as 'à battre' or 'à claquer')

bédane *m* framing-chisel; heading-chisel; mortise-chisel

bédane *m* **double** double mortise-chisel

bédaner *v* mortise (to)

béquille *f* handle; latch-lever

biais *m* slant; skew

▪ **de biais** = slantwise

biais,-e *adj* oblique; skew; skewed

bielle *f* brace (of steel roof truss); connecting rod; strut

biellette *f* link; rod

biellette *m* **de liaison** link

bisaiguë *f* double-sided axe; mortise-axe

biseau *m* bevel; chamfer

▪ **en biseau** = bevelled

biseau *m* **(outil)** side chisel; skew chisel

biseautage *m* bevelling

biseauter *v* bevel (to)

blanchir *v* trim (to) (wood); plane (to); smooth (to) (board)

blindage *m* shoring up; sheeting (with wood or metal) (an excavation); timbering

blinder *v* shore up (to); timber (to)

bloc-baie *m* door or window frame (prefabricated in wood, steel or reinforced concrete)

bloc-porte *m* door unit (prefabricated and usually comprises door, frame and furniture)

bloc-porte *m* **isoplane** door unit with flush door

blocage *m* clamping; locking

blochet *m* tie-beam; tie-brace

bois *m* timber; wood; woodland

bois *m* **avivé** square-sawn unplaned wood

bois *m* **blanc** deal; whitewood

bois *m* **carié** rotten wood

bois *m* **carré** square-sawn timber

bois *m* **compact** close-grained wood

bois *m* **contreplaqué** plywood

bois *m* **d'about (en)** cross grain

bois *m* **de bout** end grain timber

bois *m* **de charpente** building timber

bois *m* **de construction** builder's timber; constructional timber

bois *m* **de fil** wood cut with the grain; side grain timber

bois *m* **de menuiserie** timber

bois *m* **de sciage** sawn timber

bois *m* **déroulé** veneer sheet; peeled veneer

bois *m* **dur** hardwood

bois *m* **déjeté** warped timber

bois *m* **déversé** warped timber
bois *m* **flache** waney-edged timber
bois *m* **lamellé** laminated wood
bois *m* **massif** solid wood
bois *m* **raboté** planed wood
bois *m* **tendre** softwood
bois *m* **vermoulu** worm-eaten wood
bois *m* **verni** varnished wood
bois *m* **vert** green wood; unseasoned wood
bois *m* **vif** green wood; green timber
boisage *m* timbering; timberwork
boiser *v* panel in wood (to)
boiserie *f* panelling; wainscoting; woodwork
boîte *f* box
boîte *f* case (of a lock)
boîte *f* **à coupe** cutting box; mitre cutting box
boîte *f* **à onglet(s)** mitre box
bouchon *m* bung; cork; plug; stopper
bouchon *m* **à vis** screwed plug/cap
bouchonnage *m* plugging a wood fault
boulon *m* bolt; pin
▪ **boulons et écrous** = bolts and nuts
bourrage *m* ramming; tamping
bout *m* end
▪ **bout à bout** = end to end
bout *m* **rejeté** cut end (of timber)
bouton *m* **de porte** door knob
bouvet *m* plough plane
bouvet *m* **à languette** tonguing plane
bouvet *m* **à rainure** grooving plane
bouveter *v* match (boards) by tongue-and-groove (to); match (to); tongue-and-groove (to)
▪ **bouveté** = tongue-and-groove matched
briquet *m* flap-hinge
briser *v* break (to)
▪ **toit brisé** = roof with two different slopes
brisis *m* lower and steeper slope of mansard roof
burin *m*; **burin** *m* **à froid** chisel; cold-chisel; mortise-chisel
burinage *m*; chipping; chiselling

cadre *m* frame; framework; framing
cadre *m* **d'attent** temporary protective support for a door frame
cage *f* **d'escalier** space occupied by a stairway; staircase; stairwell

caisson *m* box; case; casing; caisson; housing for a sliding window, blind etc; sunk panel
calage *m* keying; locking; wedging; blocking; chocking; adjustment
cale *f* choc; packing-piece; wedge; sandpaper block
caler *v* chock (to); pack (to); wedge (to)
calfeutrement *m*; **calfeutrage** *m* draughtproofing; filling; sealing up gaps; stopping up
calfeutrer *v* draughtproof (to); fill (to); stop up (to)
calibrage *m* gauging; grading; measuring
calibre *m* bore; calibre; diameter; gauge; template
calibre *m* caliper(s)
carrelet *m* wood length with square cross-section
carton-cuir *m* leatherboard
Centre Scientifique et Technique du Bâtiment, Paris *m*; **CSTB** *abb*. Scientific and Technical Building Centre, Paris
cerce *f* flexible rule for drawing curves
certificat *m* **de suivi et marquage** certificate of conformity of manufacture to given standards; quality certificate of the manufactured article
chambranle *m* architrave; casing; frame; jamb-lining
champ *m* edge (*eg* of board)
▪ **de champ** = edgeways; edgewise
chanfrein *m* chamfer; bevel
chanfrein *m* **arrêté** stopped chamfer
chanfreiner *v* chamfer (to); bevel (to)
chant *m* edge (eg of a board, door)
chant *m* **plat** flat edge strip; wood edge cover strip
chantignolle *f*; **échantignolle** *f* purlin-cleat
chantournage *m* jig-sawing
chantournement *m* **fermé** closed fretwork
chantourner *v* jig-saw (to)
charnière *f* butt-hinge; hinge
charnon *m* knuckle (of a hinge)
charpente *f* frame(work) (*eg* of house); framing; skeleton
charpente *f* **à croisillons** lattice-bracing
charpente *f* **de chêne** frame of oak
charpente *f* **de comble** roof-frame; roof truss

charpente *f* **en bois** timber frame; carpentry

charpentier *m* carpenter (see also 'menuisier')

chasse *f* set (of the teeth of a saw)

chasse-clou *m* brad-punch; nail-punch; nail-set

chasse-goupille *m* pin-drift; pin-punch

chasse-pointe *m* brad-punch; nail-punch; nail-set

chasser *v* drive (to); shoot (to)

chasser *v* **le pêne d'une serrure** shoot the bolt of a lock (to)

chasser *v* **un clou** drive in a nail (to)

châssis *m* frame (of window); framework; framed roof-light; velux™; glazed frame

châssis *m* **de charpente** open framework (timber); outer frame; supporting frame

châssis *m* **de fenêtre** window frame

châssis *mpl* **fixes.** fixed glazed sections of window

châssis *mpl* **mobiles** mobile glazed sections of a window

châtière *f* air-vent; small covered triangular vent in roof; cat-flap (door)

chevaucher *v* lap over (to); overlap (to); span (to)

chevêtre *m* trimmer beam; trimmer; trimming joist

chevêtre *m* **sous la marche palière** landing trimmer (staircase)

chevêtrier *m* trimming-joist

chevillage *m* dowelling; pegging; plugging

cheville *f* dowel; peg; bolt; pin; plug; spike; wall-plug

cheville *f* **en bois** dowel

cheviller *v* peg (to); pin (to) (joinery)

chevron *m* common rafter; rafter

chevron *m* **arbalétrier** principal rafter

chevron *m* **d'arête** hip rafter

chevron *m* **d'arêtier** hip rafter; angle rafter

chevron *m* **intermédiare** common rafter

chevronnage *m* raftering

chevronner *m* place rafters (to); install rafters (to)

chien-assis *m* lucarne with a backward sloping roof

chignolle *f* hand-drill;

chignolle *f* **électrique** portable electric drill

cimaise *f* cyma; wall rail; picture moulding; picture rail

cimaise *f* **à lambris** framing for panels

cingler *v* trace out a line using string (to) (see also 'battre')

cintre *m* arch; centering; curve

cintrer *v* bend (to); curve (to); make into an arch (to); vault (to)

cisailles *fpl.* shears

ciseau *m* chisel

ciseau *m* **à bois** wood chisel; firmer chisel

ciseau *m* **à chanfrein** bevel-edged chisel

ciseler *v* chisel (to)

ciselure *f* chiseling

claquer *v* snap (to) (to trace a line using string) (see also 'battre')

clavette *f* cotter pin; feather; key; spline

clip *m* clip

clipsage *m* fixing by clips, etc.

cloison *f* division; partition; partition wall

cloison *f* **en bois** wood partition

cloisonnage *m* partitioning

clou *m* nail (see also 'pointe')

clou *m* **à tête plate** flat head nail

clou *m* **de Paris** wire nail

clouage *m*; **clouement** *m* nailing

clouer *v* nail (to)

coefficient *m* **de rétractibilité** coefficient of contraction

coffrage *m* framing; shuttering

coffre *m* **à outils** tool chest; tool box

coffre *m* **de volet roulant** roller shutter housing-box

coin *m* corner; wedge; chock

coin *m* **à fendre le bois** wedge for splitting wood

collage *m* gluing; sticking

colle *f* adhesive; glue; size

colle *f* **contact** contact adhesive

collet *m* collar; flange; narrowest part of a balanced step (staircase); neck (of a chisel)

colombage *m* half-timbered; half-timbering

comble *m* roof; roof space

combles *mpl* loft; roof space; attic; roof timbers

comble *m* **à une/deux pente(s)** roof with one/two slope(s)

comble *m* **brisé** curb roof; mansard roof

comble *m* **d'un bâtiment** roof (of a building)

comble *m* **mansardé** French roof; mansard

roof

comble *m* **sans ferme** untrussed roof

comble *m* **sur ferme** trussed roof

compas *m* calipers; compass; pair of compasses

compas *m* **de sécurité** window security stay

condamnation *f* locking; locking device

confection *f* making; making up

confectionner *v* make (to); make up (to)

console *f* bracket; wall-bracket; support; corbel

contre-cloison *f* wall lining

contre-fer *m* break-iron; frog (of a plane)

contre-fiche *f* strut; spur; brace (of a truss)

contre-jaugeage *m* counter-gauging; marking out mortises and tenons

contre-jauger *v* counter-gauge (to)

contre-latte *f* counter lath

contre-limon *m* wall string

contre-marche *f* riser (of staircase)

contre-parement reverse side (to face)

contre-plinthe *f* quarter round beading; top beading of a skirting board

contreplaqué *m* plywood

contrevent *m* brace or strut; shutter; strut; wind-brace

contreventement *m* wind-bracing; reinforcing piece between king-post and ridge beam

coquille *f* shell; soffit; underpart of spiral stair

corbeau *m* corbel; support piece embedded in wall

cordeaux *m* cord; line; string

corniche *f* cornice; coving

corroyage *m* dressing (wood); trimming

corroyer *v* dress (to) (wood); trim (to); rough plane (to)

coupe *f* cut; cutting; cutting out

couper *v* cut (to); cut off (to)

coupole *f* dome

■ **petite coupole** = cupola; small dome

coursive *f* alley; passage; walkway

couverture *f* roof; roof covering; roofing

couvre-chant *m* door edging strip (wood) (see also 'alaise rapportée')

couvre-joint *m* butt-strip; cover strip; covering piece

coyau *m* furring; eaves board

coyau *m* **d'un comble** furring-piece (of a roof)

crampon *m* clamp; cramp; dog-spike; spike; toothed metal plate

crampon *m* **à deux pointes** staple

crampon *m* **de fermeture** window-fastener; window-catch

crayon *m* **de charpentier** carpenter's pencil

crémaillère *f* (**limon à**) cut or open string (of staircase)

crémone *f* casement or Cremona bolt; espagnolette

■ **fermeture** *f* **à crémone** = espagnolette closure

■ **tige de crémone** = shank of espagnolette bolt

crête *f* comb; crest; ridge (of roof)

creuser *v* dig (to); excavate (to); deepen (to); hollow (out) (to)

croisée *f* window; casement window

croquis *m* sketch

croupe *f* hip; hipped end of roof

d'axe en axe from centre to centre (see also 'entraxe')

dé *m* bearing; bearing-piece; dado or die of a pedestal

débattement *m* clearance; displacement; deflection

débillarder *v* cut diagonally (to); saw into required shape (to); wreath (to)

■ **limon débillardé** = wreathed string (stairs)

débit *m* cutting up; sawing up; flow rate; output; yield

débit *m* **de bois** sawn piece of timber (*eg* plank, beam)

débitage *m* cutting up; sawing; sawing up

débiter *v* cut up (to); saw up (to)

décharge *f* **d'une poutre** brace of a beam (of a timber frame)

découpage *m* cutting; cutting out; cutting up; fretwork

découper *v* cut (to); cut out (to); cut up (to); fretsaw (to)

dédoublage *m* splitting/dividing in two

dédoubler *v* split/divide into two (to)

défaut *m* blemish; defect; flaw; fault

défonçage *m*; **défoncement** *m* recess; recessing

défoncer *v* recess (to)

défonceuse *f* recessing-machine; router

dégagement *m* disengagement; freeing; clearance; headroom

dégauchir *v* straighen (to); surface-plane (to); true (to); true up (to)

dégauchissage *m*; **dégauchissement** *m* surface-planing; truing; truing up

dégauchisseuse *f* surface-planing machine

dégrossir *v* rough hew (to); rough plane (to); trim to size (to)

dégrossissage *m*; **dégrossissement** *m* roughing down; trimming

dégueulement *m* oblique jointing of the hip-rafters with a roof-post

déjeter *v* spring (to); warp (to); buckle (to) (metal)

délarder *v* cut a piece of wood along its length to alter cross-section (to); adjust (to); to pare down (wood); to notch (edge of timber)

déligneuse *f* edge trimming saw

demi-ferme *f* half-truss

demi-rond *m* half-round (moulding, section)

demi-rondin *m* half-round

demi-varlope *f* jack-plane

désaffleurer *v* join wood pieces out of level (to); make unlevel (to)

dévers *m* cant; inclination; slope

dévers,-e *adj* out of plumb; out of true

dévisser *v* unscrew (to)

dimension *f* dimension; measurement; size

dispositif *m* device; framework; system; arrangement

division *f* cutting into two pieces; division

division *f* sur champ cutting (board) edgewise

division *f* sur plat cutting (board) flatwise

dormant *m* frame (of door, window); casing (of door, window)

double *f* équerre T-square

double *f* fenêtre double-glazed window

double *m* métre bois two metre wooden rule

doucine *f* ogee; ogee plane; ogee moulding

douille *f* socket (bulb); bush

dresser *v* dress (to) (wood); trim (to) (timber); align (to); level off (to)

dresser *v* le champ d'une planche shoot the edge of a board (to)

ébéniste *m* cabinet maker

ébénisterie *f* cabinetwork

écartement *m* distance; gap; moving apart; pushing aside; space between; clearance; separation

échafaudage *m*; **échafaud** *m* scaffold; scaffolding; staging

échantignolle *f* see 'chantignole'

échappée *f* headroom (*eg* of a staircase)

écharpe *f* brace (of a timber frame); diagonal tie

échauffement *m* de l'outil heating of the tool

échelle *f* ladder; scale (of drawing etc)

échelle *f* de meunier open staircase

échiffre *m*; **échiffe** *m*; partition-wall of a staircase; wall supporting treads of a staircase; string wall

éclat *m* chipping; splinter

écrou *m* nut

effort *m* effort; force (mechanical); stress

égoïne *f* hand-saw

égout *m* eaves; slope (of roof)

égout *m* du bord du toit eaves

emboîtement *m* boxing; fitting (together); housing

emboîture *m* clamp; joint; socket; rail (eg of door)

embout *m* de tournevis screwdriver bit/tip

embrèvement *m* joggle; notch made in a mortise and tenon joint to reinforce it; skew notch

embrèver *v* joggle (to)

emmarchement *m* groove cut in a string to receive end of stair tread; width of stair tread

empanon *m*; **empannon** *m* small hip-rafter; jack-rafter

empannon *m* de croupe jack rafter

empannon *m* de long pan jack rafter

empannon *m* à noulet valley rafter

empauchement *m* hole in masonry for embedding wooden piece

empêcher *v* avert (to); prevent (to)

encadrement *m* frame; framing

▪ **encadrement de porte** = door frame

enchevêtrer des solives *v* trim joists (to)

enchevêtrure *f* tail trimmer; trimming (joists round opening in floor)

endentement *m* toothed joint (timber)

endenter *v* indent (to); scarf (to) (timbers)

enfourchement *m* slot-mortise; forked mortise and tenon joint; jointing of rafters into a ridge (roof)

enlever *v* remove (to); carry away (to); lift (to)

enrayure *f* framing (of roof); set of beams radiating from a centre

entaillage *m* grooving; notching; slotting

entaille *f* cut; groove; notch; recess cut in door to receive lock

entaille *f* **à affûter les scies** saw clamp

entaille *f* **à mi-bois** halved-joint; lap-joint

entailler *v* groove (to); notch (to); slot (to); cut (to)

entrait *m* tie-beam; collar beam; horizontal roof beam; ceiling joist

entrait *m* **retroussé** collar beam; raised tie-beam

entraxe *m*; **entr'axe** *m* spacing between centres (see also 'd'axe en axe')

entretoise *f* brace; diagonal brace; strut; cross-piece; spacing piece

enture *f* scarf; scarf joint; splice joint; joining two wood pieces end to end

enture *f* **à sifflet multiples** multiple scarf joint

enture *f* **à sifflet simple** oblique scarf; splayed joint

enture *f* **à tenon en croix** tenon cross joint

enture *f* **à tenon mi-bois** halved tenon joint

enture *f* **à trait de Jupiter simple** splayed indent scarf

enture *f* **en paume** lapped scarf

enture *f* **en sifflet** splayed scarf

épaisseur *f* thickness

épure *m* working-drawing; working-plan

équarrir *v* square (to); ream (to); ream out (to)

équarrissage *m*; **équarissement** *m* squaring (timber); squareness; reaming; reaming out; scantling; dimensions

équerre *f* angle iron; set square; square (instrument)

équerre *f* **à 45°** set square of 45°

équerre *f* **à dessin** set-square

équerre *f* **de menuisier** carpenter's square

équerre *f* **en T** T-square

équerre *f* **pour fixation sur béton** bracket for fixing wood to concrete

équerre *f* **renforcée** reinforced right-angled metal bracket

équerre *f* **simple** right-angled metal bracket

escalier *m* staircase; stairs; stairway; steps

escalier *m* **à quartier tournant** quarter turning staircase

escalier *m* **balancé** *m* staircase with balanced steps

escalier *m* **courbe** curved staircase

escalier *m* **de dégagement** private or back staircase

escalier *m* **de meunier** open-tread staircase

escalier *m* **de service** service or back staircase

escalier *m* **droit** straight staircase

escalier *m* **en colimaçon** spiral staicase

escalier *m* **helicoïdal** spiral staircase

escalier *m* **spiral** spiral staircase

escalier *m* **tournant** spiral staircase

escalier *m* **traditionnel** traditional staircase

escargot *m;* **escalier** *m* **en escargot.** spiral stairs

établi *m* bench; workbench

établi *m* **de charpentier** carpenter's bench

établi *m* **roulant pour étaux** movable vice-stand/vice-bench

établissement *m* establishing; setting-up; conventional carpentry signs used to differentiate pieces of wood

étagère *f* shelf; shelf unit

étagère *f* **acier** metal shelves unit

étanchéité *f* waterproofness

étau *m*; **étaux** *mpl.* vice

étau *m* **à chaine** chain vice

étau *m* **à mors parallèles** vice with parallel jaws

étau *m* **à rotule** swivel vice

étayer *v* shore up (to); support (to); prop (to)

étrésillon *m* brace; bridging piece; cross-piece; strut (between joists)

étrier *m* strap; U-bolt; U-strap; joist hanger

exécuter *v* carry out (to); execute (to)

fabrication *f* construction; make; making; manufacture

fabriquer *v* construct (to); make (to); manufacture (to)

façade *f* facade; front; facia; facia (door or drawer) for kitchen unit

fait sur commande *adj* custom-built; custom-made

faîtage *m* ridge; crest (of roof); ridge beam; ridge pole; ridge capping (eg tiles, lead)

faîte *m* ridge

faîtière *f* ridge tile

faîtière *adj* ridge

fausse *f* **coupe renversée** reversed bevel

fausse *f* **crémaillère** cut wall string(er); open wall string(er)

faux *m* **entrait** collar; collar beam; span-piece

faux *m* **limon** wall string; wall stringer

fenêtre *f* window

fenêtre *f* **à bascule**; **fenêtre** *f* **basculante** centre-hung window (horizontal pivot)

fenêtre *f* **à battants** casement window

fenêtre *f* **à coulisses** sash window

fenêtre *f* **à croisillons** lattice window

fenêtre *f* **à guillotine** sash window

fenêtre *f* **à l'anglaise** casement window, outward-opening

fenêtre *f* **à la française** French window; inward-opening casement window

fenêtre *f* **à meneaux** mullioned window

fenêtre *f* **à pivot**; **fenêtre** *f* **pivotante** centre-hung window (vertical pivot)

fenêtre *f* **à soufflet** window pivoted at base, inward opening

fenêtre *f* **à tabatière** skylight

fenêtre *f* **à vitrage simple** single-glazed window

fenêtre *f* **cintrée** arched window; rounded window

fenêtre *f* **coulissante** sliding window

fenêtre *f* **en saillie** bay window; bow window

fenêtre *f* **mansardée** mansard dormer window

fenêtre *f* **ordinaire** casement window; French window

fenêtre *f* **treillagée** lattice window

fer *m* **de rabot** plane-bit; plane-iron

ferme *f* roof truss; roof timbers; truss **ferme**

f **de comble** roof truss

ferme *f* **de croupe** hip-truss

ferme *f* **en acier** steel roof truss

ferme *f* **en écharpes** scissors truss

ferme-imposte *m* fanlight stay; mechanical window opener (remote)

fermette *f* small triangular roof truss for light loads

fermeture *f* catch; closing; fastening; latch; locking; shutter; shutting

ferrage *m* door furniture (hinges, handle, lock etc); fitting door furniture etc

ferrure *f* door or window fittings; hinge (ornamental); ironwork

feuiller *v* rabbet (to); rebate (to)

feuilleret *m* fillister plane

feuillet *m* layer (of wood); thin sheet; thin panel

feuillure *f* rabbet; rebate; fillister; sash fillister

fibre *f* **de bois** wood fibre; wood wool (for packing)

fibre *f* **du bois** grain of wood

fil *m* cutting edge (of a tool); grain (of wood); thread; wire

■ **couper dans le sens contraire du fil** = to cut against the grain

fil *m* **de bois** grain of wood

filière *f* purlin; side-timber

fixation *f* fastening; fixing

flache *adj*; **flacheux,-euse** *adj* waney; waney-edged

foret *m* twist drill; drill; bit

foret *m* **à bois** wood drill

fourniture *f* provision; supply; furnishing; providing; supplying

fourrure *f* cover; cover-piece; cover-plate; filler; packer; wood reinforcing piece; metal plate connecting wood pieces; wooden piece in core of door to receive door furniture

fraisage *m* countersinking; milling; reaming

fraise *f* countersink; countersink-bit; cutter; reamer

fraise à dégrossir *f* roughing cutter; slabbing cutter

fraise *f* **pour rainures** slotting cutter

fraiser *v* countersink (to); mill (to); ream (to)

fraisure *f* countersink

frise *f* frieze; wood strip (often tongued-

and-grooved for panelling); floor board
frise *f* **à baguette** floor board with rounded
beading

gabarit *m* gauge; jig; template; former
galère *f* jack-plane
galet *m* roller; runner
garde *m* **de corps**; **garde-corps** *m* guard
rail; handrail; railing; parapet
gauchir (se) *v* distort (to); warp (to)
gauchissement *m* buckling; warping
gerce *f* split; cleft; crack
giron *m* going (of a step)
gond *m* hinge; hinge pin; hinge bracket and
pin (eg for shutter, gate)
gond *m* **de porte** gate-hook
gond *m* **et penture** hook and hinge; hook and
ride
gonflement *m* inflation; swelling
gonfler *v* inflate (to); swell (to)
gouge *f* gouge (carpenter's); hollow chisel
goujon *m* dowel; stud bolt; joggle; plug
tenon; pin
gousset *m* gusset; gusset plate; shelf bracket
grattoir *m* scraper
grattoir *m* **triangulaire** shave-hook
grenier *m* attic; loft
guillaume *m* rabbet plane; rebate plane
guillaume *m* **d'ébéniste** cabinet maker's
rabbet plane
guillaume *m* **d'établi** bench rabbet plane

habillage *m* covering; trim
hache *f* hatchet; axe
hachette *f* **de charpentier** axe-hammer;
carpenter's hatchet
hauteur *f* height
hauteur *f* **de marche** rise (*ie* vertical height
of step)
herminette *f* adze
huisserie *f* door-frame (with adjoining
timbers); door-framing; frame (door or
window)
huisserie *f* **banchée** door-frame (for incorporation in concrete)
huisserie *f* **traditionelle** door-frame (for
incorporation in masonry)
hydrofuge *m*; also *adj* waterproofing
(treatment); waterproofing solution or paint

ignifuge *adj* fire-resisting; fireproof
ignifugeant *m* fireproofing agent; fire
retardant
ignifuger *v* fireproof (to)
imposte *f* fanlight; impost; transom
(window)
intrados *m* intrados (of arch); soffit
isorel™ *m* hardboard

jalousie *f* **accordéon** folding slatted blind
or shutter; jalousie
jambage *m* jamb; jamb-post; door post;
stone pier; foundation wall;
jambage *m* **d'une baie de porte** jamb-post
of a doorway
jambage *m* **d'une cheminée** jamb of a
fire-place
jambage *m* **de force** strut; prop; brace
jambe *f* **de force** strut (of roof-truss); knee
strut; brace; prop
jet *m* **d'eau**; ou **rejet** *m* **d'eau** door or
window drip; weather board
joint *m* **à adent** cog joint; notch joint
joint *m* **anglais** bridle joint
joint *m* **à vif** butt joint
joint *m* **bout à bout** butt joint
joint *m* **bouveté** matched joint
joint *m* **en bout** butt joint
joint *m* **plat** butt joint; butting joint
jour *m* daylight; opening; gap; clearance;
width of stair well
jour *m* **d'escalier** stair well
jouée *f* reveal (archit); side or cheek of a
lucarne

lambourde *f* backing-strip (as flooring
support); wall-plate; bearing joist; wood strip
(section approx 25 x 75 mm)
lambourdette *f* wood support strip (*eg* for
parquet flooring)
lambris *m* panelling; wainscoting; lining;
floor boards (tongue-and-grooved)
lambris *m* **d'appui** sill-height panelling
lambris *m* **de hauteur** room-height panelling
lambrissage *m* panelling; wainscoting
lambrisser *v* panel (to); wainscot (to); line
(to)

lame *f* blade; floor strip; parquet strip; lath; wooden strip; thin metal strip

lame *f* de couteau cutting knife blade

lame *f* de parquet floorboard; parquet strip

lame *f* de scie saw blade

lamellation *f* lamination

lamelle *f* slat (of persienne); strip; thin sheet

lamellé,-e *adj* laminated

laminé,-e *adj* laminated

languette *f* feather; tongue

languette *f* de bois cleat; strip of wood

languette *f* rapportée loose tongue; slip-tongue

languette *f* venue de bois feather; tongue

lanternau *m* air-vent at roof-ridge level; skylight

laque *f* shellac

laquer *v* lacquer (to); shellac (to)

largeur *f* breadth; width

largeur *f* de giron going (of step)

largeur *f* de marche tread (of step)

lattage *m* lathing

latte *f* batten; lath; slat

latté *m* blockboard

latte *f* de rive edge batten

latter *v* lath (to)

lattis *m* lathing; lathwork

liaisonner *v* bond (to); link (to)

lignage *m* line trace marked with cord or chalk; marking out

ligne *f* de bris break line (*eg* of a mansard roof)

ligne *f* de foulée walking-line (of stairs)

ligne *f* de giron going of the flight (staight stairs); walking-line

lime *f* file

lime *f* demi-ronde half-round file

lime *f* plate à main flat-sided file

lime *f* ronde round file

lime *f* triangulaire triangular file

lime *f* à deux queues two-tang file

limon *m* string; string-board (staircase); stringer

limon *m* à crémaillère cut or open string

limon *m* à l'anglaise cut or open string

limon *m* à la française closed string

limon *m* débillardé wreathed string of staircase

limon *m* droit closed string; housed string

linçoir *m* trimmer; chimney trimmer

linteau *m* lintel; transom

linteau *m* courbe curved lintel

lisse *adj* flush; plain; smooth

lisse *m* hand-rail; smoothness; bearer beam

lisser *v* smooth (to)

liteau *m* batten; bracket (for shelf)

long-pan *m* longest side of roof

longueur *f* length

longueur *f* hors-tout overall length

lucarne *f* dormer window; skylight

lucarne, types de:
  lucarne rampante
  lucarne "chien assis"/retroussée
  lucarne rentrante
  lucarne droite "à chevalet"
  lucarne "à foin"
  lucarne à la capucine
  lucarne flamande
  lucarne bombée

machine *f* à couper d'ongle mitre-cutting machine

madrier *m* beam; plank; deal

maillet *m* mallet

maillet *m* caoutchouc rubber mallet

main *f* courante handrail

maison *f* à colombage half-timbered house

maison *f* à ossature bois wood-framed house

manche *m* handle (of tool); shaft (eg of axe)

mansarde *f* attic

▪ **la chambre est mansardée** = the room has a sloping ceiling

marche *f* step; tread (of stair)

marche *f* balancée balanced step; dancing step (staircase)

marche *f* carrée flier (staircase)

marche *f* cintrée commode step (staircase)

marche *f* courbe commode step (staircase)

marche *f* dansante winder (staircase); dancing step

marche *f* de départ first step (staircase)

marche *f* droite flier (staircase)

marquage *m* de bois marking wood components for identification

marteau *m* hammer

marteau *m* **arrache-clou** claw hammer
marteau-piqueur *m* jack-hammer;
pneumatic drill or hammer
marteau *m* **américain avec arrache-clous**
adze-eye hammer
marteau *m* **à dent** claw hammer
marteau *m* **à panne** peen hammer
mastic *m* cement; putty
massette *f* small club or lump hammer
mèche *f* drill; drill bit
mèche *f* **à trois pointes** centre-bit
mèche *f* **anglaise** centre-bit
mèche *f* **bois à spirale** twist-drill; wood drill
mèche *f* **hélicoidale** twist-drill
meneau *m* mullion (vertical); transom
(horizontal)
menuiserie *f* carpentry; joinery; piece of
joinery/carpentry; joiner's workshop
menuiseries *fpl* **aluminium** aluminium
frames/framework
menuiseries *fpl* **PVC** PVC frames/frame-
work
menuisier *m* carpenter; joiner
menuisier *m* **d'art** cabinet-maker
mètre *m* metre; metre rule
mètre *m* **carré** square metre
milieu *m* centre; medium; middle
moisage *m* bracing
moise *f* binding-piece; brace
moiser *v* brace (to)
montage *m* assembling; fitting; mounting;
setting up
montant *m* jamb; post; prop; riser (of
staircase); stile (of door frame etc); strut;
upright
montant *m* **de battement** shutting stile (of
door frame etc)
montant *m* **de rive** hanging stile (of door
frame etc)
montée *f* **de l'escalier** vertical height (base to
top) of a staircase
mortaisage *m* mortising
mortaise *f* mortise
mortaiser *v* mortise (to)
mortaiseuse *f* mortising-machine; slotting
machine
mortaiseuse *f* **à chaine** chain mortising
machine
mortaiseuse *f* **à meche** drill mortising

machine; square chisel mortiser
moulure *f* moulding; trunking (elect)
moulurière *f* moulding machine (wood
working)
mur *m* **d'échiffre** supporting wall of a
staircase
mur de refend *m* cross-wall

nez *m* nose
nez *m* **de marche** nosing of step; nosing-
plane
niveau *m* level
niveau *m* **de maçon** mason's level
niveau *m* **à bulle (d'air)** spirit level
niveler *v* level (to); make even (to); measure
with a spirit level (to)
nœud *m* knot (wood, cord); knuckle (of a
hinge)
noue *f* valley rafter; valley (roof);
valley-gutter (*eg* curved tiles, lead sheet)
noue *f* **charpente** valley-rafter
noue *f* **métallique** valley flashing
noulet *m* small valley-rafter
noyau *m* core; centre; newel (of spiral
staircase)

oculus *m* opening in a door for a glazing
panel; oculus; bull's-eye window
œil-de-bœuf *m* bull's-eye window;
oeil-de-boeuf; round window
onglet *m* mitre; mitred angle
oriel *m* oriel window
ossature *f* framework; structure
ossature *f* **métallique** metal framework
outeau *m* small triangular lucarne acting as
roof-light
outil *m* tool
outil *m* **pour arasage** shaver
outillage *m* equipment; implements;
machinery; tools
ouverture *f* opening
ouverture *f* **de porte** door opening; doorway
ouvrage *m* building work; work
ouvrant *m* door flap; door leaf; opening
section of a window

palier *m* landing (of a staircase)
■ **le même palier** = the same floor
palissade *f* boarding; fencing
pan *m* face; frame; pane; side (eg of nut)
pan *m* **de bois** timber frame/framing; wood partition; stud wall
pan *m* **de couverture** roof frame
pan *m* **de fer** iron frame
panne *f* purlin; side-timber; pane; peen (of a hammer)
panne *f* **bombée** ball peen (of a hammer)
panne *f* **faîtière** ridge board; ridge-beam
panne *f* **filière** purlin
panneau *m* panel
panneau *m* **de copeaux** chipboard
panneau *m* **de fibre** fibre board; hardboard
panneau *m* **de fibres dures** fibre board; hardboard
panneau *m* **de particules** chipboard
panneau *m* **de particules surfacé mélaminé** chipboard with melamine surface
panneau *m* **de porte** door panel
panneau *m* **décor** decorative panel; faced panel
panneau *m* **isolant** insulating board
panneau *m* **latté** blockboard
panneau *m* **mélaminé** chipboard faced with melamine
panneautage *m* panelling
papier *m* **abrasif** abrasive paper; sandpaper
papier *m* **de verre** glass-paper; sandpaper
papier *m* **d'émeri** emery paper
parclose *f* glazing bead; glazing fillet; cover strip; beading
parement *m* face; facing
paroi *f* interior surface; side; wall; covering panel
parquet *m* parquet floor; wooden floor; wood panel flooring; floorboards
parqueter *v* lay a wooden or parquet floor (to)
passage *m* passage; passageway
passe-plat(s) *m* service-hatch
patte *f* cramp; clamp; fastening; clip
patte *f* **à scellement** cramp; holdfast; fixing cleat
paumelle *f* door hinge; hinge; split hinge
paumelle *f* **double** H-hinge; lift-off hinge
penture *f* strap (of strap hinge)

perçage *m* boring; drilling
percement drilling; boring (with a drill)
percer *v* bore (to); ; drill (to); pierce (to)
perceuse *f* drilling machine; power drill
petit bois *m* wooden glazing bar; wood beading; wood strip
pièce *f* **d'appui** window ledge; window sill
pied *m* **à coulisse** callipers (vernier)
pieu *m* pile (constr); post; stake
pignon *m* gable; pinion
■ **à pignon** = gabled
pistolet *m* **de scellement** stud driver; stud gun
piquage *m* marking out of assembled carpentry
piquet *m* picket; post; stake; peg
piquet *m* **de clôture** fence post
pivot *m* pin; pivot
placage *m* veneer; veneering
placard *m* cupboard; wardrobe
placard *m* **à balai** broom cupboard
placard *m* **de cuisine** kitchen cupboard
plafond *m* ceiling
plafonnage *m* ceiling; ceiling material; ceiling work
plan *m* **d'épure** diagram; working drawing
plan *m* **d'exécution** working drawing
planche *f* board; floorboard; plank; shelf
planche *f* **à dessin** drawing board
planche *f* **à dresser** shooting-board
planche *f* **d'échafaudage** scaffold board
planche *f* **lorraine** lorraine board (wide wooden board, at least 3 m long)
planche *f* **voilée** warped board
plancher *m* floor; flooring
plancher *m* **incombustible** fireproof floor
plancher *m* **ordinaire** single floor
plancher *m* **simple** single floor
plancher *m* **sur poutre pan de bois** framed floor
plancher *m* **sur poutre(s)** double floor
planchette *f* small board; small shelf
planchéiage *m* boarding; flooring; planking
planchéier *m* board (to); floor (to)
planer *v* plane (to); smooth (to)
plaque *f* **de propreté** finger plate
plaquer *v* veneer (to)
plateau *m* board; scaffold board or platform
plateau *m* **mélaminé** board with melamine

surface

plinthe *f* base-board; skirting; skirting board

plomb *m* lead (metal); plumb; plumb-bob; plumbline

poignée *f* handle (*eg* of a tool)

poignée *f* **de porte** door handle

poinçon *m* punch; drift; bradawl; crown-post (roof timbers); king-rod (of iron/steel roof-truss); king-post; roof-post; truss-post

pointe *f* nail; brad; point; panel pin; tack

pointe *f* **à tracer** scriber

pointe *f* **tête homme** finishing nail

pointe *f* **tête plate** flat-head nail

pointe *f* **torsadée** twist nail

pointeau *m* centre-punch; prick-punch; punch

ponçage *m* sand-papering; sanding down; pumicing; rubbing down

ponce *f* pumice; pumice-stone

poncer *v* rub down (to); sand down (to); sandpaper (to)

ponceuse *f* sander; sanding machine

ponceuse *f* **à bande** belt sander

ponceuse *f* **à disque** disk sander

ponceuse *f* **à parquet** floor sander

ponceuse *f* **à ruban abrasif** belt sander

ponceuse *f* **orbitale** orbital sander

ponceuse *f* **vibrante** orbital sander

portail *m* double gate; front door; front entrance; portal

portail *m* **en bois** wooden gate(s)

porte *f* door; doorstep; doorway; gate

porte à *f* **claire-voie** open-lattice gate; barred gate; glazed door

porte *f* **à deux battants** double door or gate; folding door with two leaves

porte *f* **à deux vantaux** double door

porte *f* **à revêtment ignifuge** fireproof door

porte *f* **accordéon** folding door

porte *f* **anti-feu** fire-resistant door

porte *f* **automatique** self-closing door

porte *f* **battante** swing door

porte *f* **coulissante** sliding door

porte *f* **d'entrée** entrance; front door

porte *f* **de derrière** back door

porte *f* **de garage basculante** up-and-over garage door; swing-up garage door

porte *f* **demi-plein** part solid, part panelled door

porte *f* **extensible** folding door; folding partition

porte *f* **glissante** sliding door

porte *f* **ignifugée** fireproofed door

porte *f* **palière** landing door

porte *f* **pivotante** pivoted door or double doors

porte *f* **pleine** solid door

porte *f* **pliante** folding door

porte *f* **sur barres** batten door; ledge door

porte *f* **sur châssis** framed door

porte *f* **va-et-vient** swing door

porte *f* **vitrée** glass panelled door; glazed door

porte-fenêtre *f* french window

porte-foret *m* hand-drill

porteé *f* span; range; reach

pose *f* laying; fixing; setting

poser *v* fix (to); place (to); put up (to); fit (to)

poteau *m* post; newel post; column; pole

poteau *m* **cornier** corner post

poteau *m* **d'ancrage** anchor post

poteau *m* **d'angle** corner post

poteau *m* **d'huisserie** door post; jamb-post

poteau *m* **d'inertie** inertial post

poteau *m* **de bornage** boundary post

poteau *m* **télégraphique** telegraph pole/ post

potelet *m* small post; strut

pourrir *v* decay (to); rot (to)

pourrissement *m* decay; deterioration

pourriture *f* **du bois** timber rot; wood decay

pourriture *f* **humide** wet rot

pourriture *f* **sèche** dry rot

poutre *f* beam; joist; girder; baulk

poutre *f* **apparente** exposed beam

poutre *f* **armée** trussed beam

poutre *f* **en béton armé** reinforced concrete beam

poutre *f* **maîtresse** main beam; main support beam

poutre *f* **principale** main beam; principal beam

poutre *f* **sous-bandée** trussed beam (under-braced)

poutrelle *f* small beam; small girder; joist

précadre *m* sub-frame in opening (eg to take door or window)

presse *f* press

presse *f* **d'angle** angle clamp; angle cramp

presse *f* à coller screw-clamp; gluing clamp
presse *f* à vis G-cramp; screw-clamp
procéder *v* par paliers proceed by stages (to)

queue *f* shank (of a drill); tang (of a file)
queue-de-vache *f* eaves; eaves overhang; skirt roof; rafter end
queue-d'aronde *f* dovetail
queue-d'aronde *f* cachée secret dovetail

rabot *m* plane
rabot *m* à dégrossir jack plane
rabot *m* d'établi bench plane; jointer
rabot *m* rainuré bench plane with grooved base (used for resinous woods)
rabotage *m* planing
rabotement *m* planing
raboter *v* plane (to)
raboteuse *f* planer; planing machine
raccord *m* connecting piece; connection; coupling piece (metal)
raccord *m* en Z Z-shaped metal connector
raccord *m* Gerber™ metal connector for Gerber™ beam system
raclage *m* scraping
racler *v* scrape (to)
racloir *m* scraper
racloir *m* de menuisier joiner's scraper
ragréer *v* restore (to); finish off (to); clean down (brickwork) (to); smooth (to)
ragrément *m* cleaning down; finishing off; smoothing
raidir *v* render rigid (to); stiffen (to)
rail *m* rail
rainure *f* groove; slot; rabbet
rallonge *f* extension-piece; lengthening-piece
rallongement *m* lengthening
rallonger *v* lengthen (to)
rampant *m* slope (of a roof or staircase)
rampe *f* banisters; flight (of stairs); handrail; rise; slope
râpe *f* rasp
rapporter *v* add (to); join on (to); put in (to)
rattrapage *m* de jeu taking up play
rebord *m* edge; edge-plate (of lock); rim
rebord *m* de la fenêtre window-ledge;

window sill
reboucheur *m* filler
recaler *v* level (to); relevel (to); reset (to); smooth (to)
recouper *v* recut (to)
refendre *v* cleave (to); rip (to); split (to)
refente *f* cleaving; ripping; splitting
réglage *m* adjustment; regulation; setting
règle *f* rule; ruler; straight-edge
relier *v* connect (to); couple (to)
remplissage *m* filler; filling
rénette *f* (de charpentier) combined saw-set and marking knife
renforcer *v* reinforce (to); strengthen (to); truss (to) (a beam)
renforcé,-e *adj* braced; reinforced; strengthened
repérage *m* marking; marking out; lining up
repère *m* identifier; indicator; mark; marker
repérer *v* line up (to); locate (to); mark out (to)
replanir *v* plane (to) (eg floor)
replanissage *m*; replanissement *m* planing; cleaning off (flooring)
reporter *v* transfer (to)
repos *m* notch or cut used to lock a skewed beam; repose; rest; resting; bearing (of a beam); intermediate landing (of stairs)
repos *m* d'escalier intermediate landing (of stairs)
réseau *m* en nid d'abeille honeycomb network
resserrer *v* draw tighter (to); tighten (to); tighten up (to); contract (to)
resserrer (se) *v* narrow (to); shrink (to)
restaurer *v* restore (to)
retrait *m* shrinkage
retroussé,-e *adj* hitched up; raised up
■ entrait retroussé = raised tie-beam
riflard *m* jack-plane
rive *f* edge; lip; lower edge of timber frame of roof
rive *f* d'une planche thickness (of a board)
rond *m* round wooden rod
rondelle *f* washer
rondin *m* bar of timber; round timber
rosace *f* ceiling rose

sablière *f* roof beam at base of slope; wall

plate

sablière *f* **basse** groundsill; sill

sablière *f* **de comble** roof-plate; pole-plate; wall-plate

sablière *f* **haute** head-plate; plate

saillie *f* jutting out; ledge; projection

■ **en saillie** = projecting; overhanging

saillie *f* **d'une vis** depth of thread of a screw

saillie *f* **de rive** roof edge projection

sauteuse *f*; **scie** *f* **sauteuse** jig saw

scellement *m* **au pistolet** fixing by stud gun

sceller *v* bed (to); embed (to); fasten (to); fix (to); fix to (to); seal (to)

sciage *m* sawing

sciage *m* **par 'trait bas'** sawing wood flatways with the grain

sciage *m* **par 'trait haut'** sawing wood edgeways

scie *f* saw

scie *f* **à araser** tenon saw; dovetail saw

scie *f* **à bois** wood saw

scie *f* **à chainette** chainsaw

scie *f* **à chantourner** fretsaw; jig-saw

scie *f* **à chevilles** peg saw; dowel saw

scie *f* **à dos** back-saw; carcass-saw; tenon-saw

scie *f* **à débiter** cutting out saw; dado saw; felling saw

scie *f* **à découper** fretsaw

scie *f* **à guichet** keyhole saw; lock-saw

scie *f* **à métaux** hacksaw

scie *f* **à moulure** mitre saw; beading saw

scie *f* **à placage** veneer-saw

scie *f* **à refendre** rip-saw; cleaving saw

scie *f* **à ruban** band-saw

scie *f* **à tenon** tenon saw

scie *f* **à tronçonner** cross-cut saw; chain saw

scie *f* **allemande** rip-saw

scie *f* **circulaire** circular saw

scie *f* **de travers** cross-cut saw

scie *f* **égoïne** hand-saw

scie *f* **électrique** power saw

scie *f* **mécanique** power saw; sawmill

scie *f* **sans fin** bandsaw; endless saw

scie *f* **sauteuse** jig-saw (powered)

sculpteur *m* **sur bois** wood carver; wood worker

sécher *v* dry (to)

semelle *f* footing-block; roof-plate; sole of

plane; tread; table (of a girder); wall-plate; footing

serrage *m* clamping; closing up; gripping; tightening

serre-joint *m* clamp; G-clamp; G-cramp; joiner's clamp

serrure *f* lock

seuil *m* doorstep; doorway; sill of door; threshold

sifflet *m* **simple** splayed joint

socle *m* plinth at base of door jamb; base; stand; pedestal

soffite *f* soffit (archit)

solin *m* coating of fill-in material (*eg* plaster, mortar); fillet-gutter; glazing fillet; space between joists, tiles etc

solivage *m* joisting; girderage

solive *f* joist; beam; girder

solive *f* **de plancher** floor joist

solive *f* **d'enchêvetrure** tail trimmer

solive *f* **en acier** steel joist

sommier *m* lower crossbar (of grille, etc); springer (of arch); transom (of window, door); lintel (door)

sous-face *f* soffit; underside; lower face

spécification *f* specification

stockage *m* storage

stratifié *m*; also *adj* laminate

structure *f* structure

structurel,-elle *adj* structural

support *m* bearer; pedestal; stand; support

table *f* table; tread (of a girder)

tableau *m* vertical cheek of an opening; reveal (of door, window)

tablette *f* small board; shelf

tablette *f* **de cheminée** mantelpiece; mantelshelf

taillage *m* cutting

talon *m* heel; talon; nib (of a beam, tile)

tapée *f* wooden piece on outer side of window for attachment of shutter

taper *v* hit (to); knock (to)

■ **taper sur un clou** = to hit a nail

taquet *m* cleat

tarière *f* auger

tasseau *m* square-edge length of wood; batten; bracket

tenaille(s) *f* pincers; nippers; tongs

tenaille *f* **de menuisier** carpenter's/joiner's pincers

tennonage *m* tenoning

tenon *m* tenon

tenon *m* **avec renfort carré** haunched tenon

tenon *m* **bâtard** barefaced tenon

tenon *m* **invisible** stub-tenon

tenon *m* **renforcé** tusk tenon

tenon *m* **simple** mortice-and-tenon joint

tennoner *v* tenon (to); make a tenon (to)

tenonneuse *f* tenon cutting machine

terrasson *m* almost flat roof; upper part of a mansard roof

têtière *f* edge-plate (of a lock); selvedge

tige *f* rod; shank; stem

tige *f* **creuse** hollow rod

tige *f* **de crémone** shank of Cremona or espagnolette bolt

tige *f* **de fer** iron rod

tige *f* **de rallonge** extension piece

tirant *m* stay; stretcher; stringer; tie-beam; tie-rod; truss-rod; collar beam

tire *m*; **tire-fond** *m* spike; screw-spike; coach screw; coach bolt

tiroir *m* drawer

toile *f* **d'émeri** emery cloth

toit *m* roof

▪ **avant-toit** = eaves

toit *m* **en mansarde** mansard-roof

toit *m* **en pente** sloping roof; gable roof

toit *m* **en terrasse** terraced roof; flat roof

toit *m* **plat** flat roof

toupie *f* spindle moulding machine; router

toupillage *m* making wood mouldings; wood profiling

tour *m* **à bois** wood-turning lathe

tourelle *f* turret

tourillon *m* dowel; pin; treenail; trunnion; pivot; swivel pin (of iron gate)

tourne-à-gauche *m* wrench; hand wrench; saw setting tool

tourner *v* turn (to); revolve (to); rotate (to)

tournevis *m* screwdriver

tournevis *m* **à cliquet** ratchet screwdriver

tournevis *m* **cruciforme** Phillips™ screwdriver

tournevis *m* **pour vis Phillips™** screwdriver (type Phillips™)

traçage *m* drawing; laying out; tracing

tracer *v* draw (to); lay out (to); plot (to) (eg a curve); set out (to); trace (to)

traceret *m* marking awl; scriber; tracing awl

trait *m* cutting-line; line; streak; stroke

trait *m* **bas** low line (see also 'sciage')

trait *m* **carré** trace obtained by raising a perpendicular on a straight line

trait *m* **de scie** kerf; sawcut; sawing line

trait *m* **haut** high line (see also 'sciage')

traitement *m* **anti-parasite** anti-parasite treatment

traitement *m* **de préservation du bois** wood preservation treatment

traitement *m* **fongicide** *m* fungicide treatment

trappe *f* flap; hatch; trap door

trappe *f* **accès combles** trap door access to attic/loft

travers *m* across; crosswise

▪ **scier/couper en travers** = io saw; to cut across

traverse *f* cross-bar; cross-beam; cross-piece; rail (of door frame or window sash); strut; transom; traverse

travée *f* bay; span; spacing between joists

▪ **travée de comble** = roof span

trémie *f* opening in a floor or roof to receive a staircase, chimney etc; stair well

trémie *f* **de cheminée** chimney opening

trenail *m* treenail; wood plug

trépan *m* bit; chisel; rock drill bit

tronçonnage *m* cutting into sections; cut-ting up

tronçonner *v* cut into sections (to); cut off (to); cut up (to)

tronçonneuse *f* chainsaw

trou *m* hole; air vent; pit

trou *m* **de serrure** keyhole

trou *m* **de vers** worm hole

trou *m* **de visite** manhole

troussequin *m*; **trusquin** *m* marking gauge; scriber; mortise gauge; drawing compass used by joiners; beam compass

vaisselier *m* dresser

valet *m* carpenter's clamp

vantail *m*; **vantaux** *mpl.* leaf (of a door/window)

71

varlopage *m* trying; trying up
varlope *f* jointing plane; trying plane
varloper *v* try (to); try up (to)
vélux™ *m* roof window; velux™
véranda *f* veranda
vérin *m* screw-jack
vérin *m* **pneumatique** pneumatic jack
vermoulu,-e *adj* worm-eaten
vermoulure *f* woodworm; woodworm traces
■ **vermoulures** *pl.* = worm holes
vernir *v* lacquer (to); varnish (to)
vernissage *m* lacquering; varnishing
verrou *m* bolt
verrou *m* **de fermeture** locking bolt
versant *m* side; slope
versant *m* **d'un comble** side of a roof
vide *m* empty; empty space; gap; vacuum; void (archit)
vide *m* **d'une vis** groove of a screw
vide-sanitaire *m* underfloor space
vilebrequin *m* brace; brace and bit
vilebrequin *m* **à cliquet** rachet-brace
vilebrequin *m* **de menuisier** carpenter's brace and bit
vis *f* screw
vis *f* **à bois** wood screw
vis *f* **à fente** slot-head screw
vis *f* **à jour** open-newel stair; open-well stair
vis *f* **à tête fraisée** slot-head countersunk screw
vis *f* **à tête ronde** round-headed screw
vis *f* **en tête cruciforme** cross-head screw

(type Phillips™)
vis *f* **pozidriv**™ cross-head screw (type pozidriv™)
vissage *m* screwing; screwing on/down

visser *v* screw (to); screw on (to); screw down (to)
visser *v* **à fond** screw home (to)
visserie *f* factory manufacturing screws/ bolts etc; nuts and bolts; screws, nails, hooks etc
vitrerie *f* glass; glazing
■ **une porte avec vitrerie** = door with glazing
voiler *v* warp (to) (wood); buckle (to) (metal)
volée *f* **d'escalier** flight (of stairs)
volée *f* **droite** straight flight (of stairs)
volet *m* shutter
volet *m* **d'aération** louvre; air damper
volet *m* **persienne** louvre shutter
volet *m* **plein barres et écharpes** barred and braced shutter
volet *m* **roulant** roll-down shutter; roller shutter
volige *f* roof board; batten; lath
volige *f* **chanlattée** eaves-board; eaves-lath
voligeage *m* roof boarding; battening; lathing
voliger *v* batten (to); lath (to)
vrille *f* gimlet

wastringue *f* spokeshave

5. BOIS ET PLACAGES

acacia *m* acacia; false acacia; locust tree
acajou *m* mahogany
acajou (en). made of mahogany
auine *m* alder

bois *m* wood; timber
bois *m* **blanc** whitewood; deal
bois *m* **contreplaqué** faced wood sheet

bois *m* **d'ébène** ebony wood
bois *m* **de menuiserie** timber
bois *m* **de rose** rosewood
bois *m* **de sapin** deal
bois *m* **déroulé** peeled veneer
bois *m* **des îles** exotic wood
bois *m* **exotique** exotic wood
bois *m* **rond** unhewn/uncut timber
bois *m* **vert** green wood; unseasoned wood

bouleau *m* birch
bouleau *m* **blanc** silver birch
buis *m* box tree; boxwood

cèdre *m* cedar
charme *m* hornbeam
châtaignier *m* chestnut; sweet chestnut
chêne *m* oak
chêne *m* **blanc** white oak
chêne *m* **campagne** country oak
chêne *m* **fumé** fumed oak
chêne-liége *m* cork-oak
chêne *m* **massif** solid oak
chêne *m* **moyen** medium oak
chêne *m* **rouge d'Amérique** red American oak
chêne *m* **vert** holm oak
contreplaqué *m* plywood
cyprès *m* cypress

ébène *f*; **ébénier** *m* ebony
épicéa *m* spruce
épicéa *m* **de Sitka** Sitka spruce
érable *m* maple
érable *m* **champêtre** common maple; field maple
érable *m* **plane** plane-tree maple
érable *m* **sycomore** sycamore maple; plane-tree maple
framiré *m* black afara; indigbo
frêne *m* ash

hêtre *m* beech; beechwood

if *m* yew
iroko *m* iroko

madrier *m* deal
marronier *m* chestnut; horse chestnut
marronier *m* **d'Inde** horse chestnut
mélèze *m* larch
méranti *m* meranti
merisier *m* cherry wood

niangon *m* niangon
noyer *m* walnut
noyer *m* **d'Europe** European walnut

okoumé *m* gaboon (mahogany)
orme *m* elm

palissandre *m* rosewood
peuplier *m* poplar
pin *m* pine
pin *m* **de montagne** mountain pine
pin *m* **de Panama** Panama pine
pin *m* **des Landes** pine (from Landes region); maritime pine
pin *m* **d'Oregon** Oregon pine
pin *m* **laricio de Corse** Corsican pine
pin *m* **maritime** maritime pine
pin *m* **parasol/pignon** maritime/umbrella pine
pin *m* **sylvestre** scotch fir; scots pine
pitchpin *m* pitch pine
placage *m* veneer
platane *m* plane tree

ramin *m* ramin
robinier *m* false acacia; locust tree

sapelli *m* sapele
sapin *m* fir; deal
sapin *m* **d'altitude** fir (grown at high altitude)
sapin *m* **de douglas** douglas fir
sapin *m* **du Nord** northern pine
saule *m* willow
saule *m* **pleurer** weeping willow
séquoia *m* sequoia; redwood
sipo *m* sipo; sipo mahogany
sycomore *m* sycamore

teck *m* teak
thuya *m* western red cedar; thuja
tilleul *m* lime; lime tree

6. COUVREUR

about *m* **d'arêtier** end hip tile
about *m* **faîtière** end ridge tile
accrochable *adj* hangable; hookable
accrocher *v* hook (to); hook on (to); attach (to)
acier *m* **galvanisé** galvanized steel
agrafage *m* fastening (up); hooking (up); stapling
agrafe *f* fastener; hook; staple
agrafer *v*. fasten (up) (to); hook (up) (to); staple (to); seam (to) (sheet metal)
agrafeuse *f* stapler
agrès *mpl* equipment; hoisting tackle
air *m* air
aluminium *m* aluminium
amiante-ciment *m* asbestos cement
appentis *m* lean-to; penthouse (roof); single slope roof
arbalétrier *m* principal rafter
ardoise *f* slate (roof); slate tile
ardoise *f* **d'Espagne** Spanish slate
ardoise *f* **de rive** edge slate
ardoise *f* **en amiante-ciment** asbestos-cement slate
ardoise *f* **naturelle d'Espagne** Spanish slate
ardoise *f* **taillé en biseau** bevelled slate
ardoiser *v* slate (to)
ardoises *fpl* **d'échantillon** sized slates
ardoises *fpl* **en bardeli** row of slates protecting outermost rafter
ardoisé,-e *adj* slate-grey
arêtier *m* angle-rafter; hip; hip-rafter; hip covering; hip tile
arêtier *m* **cornier** corner hip tile
arêtier *m* **fermé** hip tile (angled)
arêtier *m* **ondulé** undulated hip tile
arêtière *f* hip tile
armature *f* **à toit** roof truss/trussing
armature *f* **en tissus de jute** hessian reinforcement
auge *f* mixing tray (eg for mortar); trough
avant-toit *m* eaves; projecting roof

bâchage *m* covering over; sheeting
bande *f* band; strip; metal roofing strip
bande *f* **d'egout** gutter band
bardeau *m* shingle; wooden tile

bardeau *m* **bitumé** bitumised shingle
bardeli *m* row of slates protecting edge rafter
bardeli *m* **décoré** row of trimmed slates protecting edge rafter
basculement *m* tilted row of edge tiles
bavette *f* flashing (metal sheet)
bavette *f* **zinc** zinc flashing
billes *fpl* **de polystyrène** polystyrene granules
biseau (en) bevelled
bois *m* timber; wood
bord *m* edge
boudin *m* strip; curved metal cover piece; beading
brique *f* **de couvert** cover tile; terra cotta shingle
brisis *m* lower slope of mansard roof

caisson *m* air-ventilation enclosure below eaves
cale *f* block; packing piece; wedge
cale *f* **d'onde** block for corrugated sheet
calfeutrement *m* **en ciment** filling of cement; cement or mortar fillet
carton *m* **bitumé** roofing paper; roofing felt
chanlatte *f*; **chanlate** *f* eaves-board; eaves-lath; eaves-batten
chape *f* coating (mortar, cement); screed
chape *f* **bitumineuse** bituminous coating
chapeau *m* **de gendarme** small roof vent
chaperon *m* flashing; coping (archit)
chatière *f* air-vent; roof ventilator; ventilation tile
chaume *m* thatch
chaumière *f* thatched cottage
chéneau *m* gutter (roof)
chéneau *m* **à l'anglaise** parapet gutter
chéneau *m* **en zinc** zinc gutter
chéneau *m* **encaissé** parallel gutter; trough gutter
chevauchement *m* lap (of tiles); overlap
cheville *f* **en bois** wooden peg
chevron *m* rafter
chevron *m* **arêtier**; **chevron** *m* **d'arêtier** angle-rafter; hip; hip-rafter
chevron *m* **d'arête** hip rafter
chevron *m* **de long pan** common rafter (of

hip roof)
chevron *m* **de rive** edge rafter
chevron *m* **intermédiaire** common rafter
chevron *m* **principal** principal rafter
chevronnage *m* raftering
chignole *f* hand-drill; portable electric drill
chlorure *m* **de polyvinyl**; **PVC** *abb*
polyvinyl chloride; PVC
chute *f* drop; pitch; slope; downfall
chute *f* **de comble** pitch of roof
chute *f* **en fonte** cast iron downpipe
clou *m* nail
clou *m* **à ardoise** slate nail
clou *m* **à latter** lath nail
clou *m* **tête large** felt nail
clou *m* **de cuivre** copper nail
clou *m* **de cuivre rouge** copper nail
clou *m* **de Paris** French nail; wire nail
clou *m* **de plomb** lead nail
clou *m* **galva tête plate** flat-headed galvanized nail
clou *m* **galvanisé** galvanized nail
comble *m* roof timbers; roof space
■ les combles = the attic; the loft
comble *m* **à autant de versants que de côtés**
pavilion roof; pyramidal roof
comble *m* **à croupe et deux longs pans**
hipped ridge roof
comble *m* **à deux long pans** double-pitched
roof; ridge roof; span roof
comble *m* **à deux long pans avec croupes**
hip and ridge roof; hipped ridge roof
comble *m* **à deux long pans sans fermes**
couple roof
comble *m* **à deux pentes** double-pitched
roof; ridge roof; span roof
comble *m* **à deux pentes asymétriques**
double-pitch roof with asymmetric sides
comble *m* **à deux rampes** double-pitched
roof; ridge roof; span roof
comble *m* **à deux versants** double-pitched
roof; ridge roof; span roof
comble *m* **à deux égouts** double-pitched
roof; ridge roof; span roof
comble *m* **à la française** curb roof; French
roof; mansard roof
comble *m* **à la mansarde** curb roof; mansard
roof
comble *m* **à plusieurs pentes** multiple-

pitched roof
comble *m* **à un versant** single-pitch roof
comble *m* **à une pente** single-pitch roof
comble *m* **à une seule pente** single-pitch
roof
comble *m* **aménagé** converted roof space;
attic which has been lined
comble *m* **avec avant-toit** umbrella roof
comble *m* **brisé** curb roof; French roof;
mansard roof
comble *m* **d'un bâtiment** roof (of building)
comble *m* **en croupe** hip roof; hipped roof
comble *m* **en dent de scie** saw-tooth roof;
shed roof; square-to roof
comble *m* **en dôme** dome roof
comble *m* **en mansarde** curb roof; mansard
roof
comble *m* **en pavillon** pavilion roof;
pyramidal roof
comble *m* **mansardé** French roof; mansard
roof
comble *m* **non aménagé** unconverted roof
space; attic without lining
comble *m* **pyramidal** pavilion roof;
pyramidal roof
comble *m* **retroussé** collar-beam roof;
collar-tie roof
comble *m* **sans ferme** untrussed roof
comble *m* **sur fermes** trussed roof
comble *m* **sur pignon(s)** gable roof
comble-shed *m* shed roof; saw-tooth roof;
square-to roof
compas *m* calipers; compass; pair of
compasses
complément *m* **étanche à l'eau** waterproof
under-roof sheeting (eg polyethylene or felt)
contre-latte *f* counter lath
cordage *m* cordage; rope
corde *f* cord; line; rope
corde *f* **à nœuds** knotted rope
corde *f* **en aloès** aloe rope
corde *f* **en chanvre** hemp rope
cordeau *m* line; string
couche *f* **d'isolant** insulation layer
couper *v* cut (to)
coupole *f* cupola; dome
couverte en ardoises roofed with slates
couverture *f* cover; roof; roofing
couverture *f* **à agrafure simple** roof sheets

joined by single seams/welts (eg zinc sheet)

couverture *f* à claire-voie open tiling with reduced lateral overlap

couverture *f* à double agrafure roof sheets joined by double-lock seams/welts (eg zinc sheet)

couverture *f* à pureau développé tiling with enlarged area of uncovered tile

couverture *f* à recouvrement roof sheeting with lap joins

couverture *f* béton concrete roofing

couverture *f* de chaume thatched roofing

couverture *f* en ardoises "brouillées" roofing with slates of variable width

couverture *f* en bardeli form of slate tiling

couverture *f* en modèles carrés square tiles hung with one diagonal horizontal

couverture *f* en tuiles tiled roofing

couverture *f* en verre glass roof

couverture *f* étanche à l'air air tight roofing

couverture *f* métallique sheet metal roofing

couvre-joint *m* butt-strip; cover strip; covering piece

couvreur *m* roofer; slater; tiler

couvrir *v* de chaume thatch (to)

couvrir *v* un toit d'ardoises slate a roof (to)

crapaudine *f* grating; screen (of vent pipe)

crête *f* comb; crest; ridge (of roof)

crochet *m* hook; slate hook; tile hook

crochet *m* à agrafe clip-on hook

crochet *m* à pointe hook with pointed end; nail-on hook

crochet *m* à tige ondulée slate-hook with undulated shank

crochet *m* d'échelle ladder hook (holding top of ladder)

crochet *m* de gouttière gutter bracket; gutter clip

crochet *m* de sécurité safety hook (roof)

crochet *m* en acier inoxydable; stainless steel hook

crochet *m* en cuivre copper hook

crochet *m* en S S hook

crochet *m* inox stainless steel hook

crochet *m* inoxydable uncorrodable hook

croupe *f* hip

cuivre *m* copper

cuvette *f* hopper-head (of downpipe)

débitage *m* cutting up; sawing up; splitting up

débiter *v* cut up (to); saw up (to); split up (to)

déblayage *m* des gravats clearance of debris/rubble

débord *m* border; edge; overflow; side

débordement *m* extending out; jutting out; overflowing; overhang

déborder *v* jut out (to); overflow (to); overhang (to)

décintroir *m* cutting-hammer

découpage *m* cutting; cutting up

découper *v* cut (to); cut up (to)

défense *f* security rope; thick rope

degâts tempête *mpl* storm damage

demi-ferme *f* half-truss

demi-latte *f* half-lath

demi-longueur *f* half-length

demi-ardoise *f*; demie *f* half-slate

démolition *f* de couverture removal of roofing material

démontage *m* taking down; taking to pieces

dôme *m* dome

doublis *m* double row of tiles/slates forming eaves

dressage *m* dressing (a stone); erecting (scaffolding); straightening (eg rod, bar)

dresser *v* dress (to) (eg wood); make out (to) (eg estimate, report); trim (to) (timber)

eau *f* de fonte thaw water

eaux *fpl* pluviales rain-water

échafaud *m* scaffold; scaffolding; staging

échafaud(age) *m* volant hanging scaffold; travelling cradle

échafaudage *m* erecting scaffolding; scaffolding

échafauder *v* erect a scaffold (to); scaffold (to)

échantillonnage *m* gauging; process of marking rafters for lathing; sampling

échelle *f* courante standard ladder

échelle *f* de couvreur roof ladder

échelle *f* plate cat ladder; roof ladder

écran *m* barrier; screen

écran *m* en polyéthylène polyethylene sheet (waterproof) barrier écran *m* non tendu loose (waterproof) barrier; unstretched barrier

écran *m* rigide rigid (waterproof) barrier

écran *m* souple flexible (waterproof) barrier

écran *m* tendu *m* stretched (waterproof) barrier

écran *m* étanche waterproof barrier

égout *m* eaves; slope (of roof)

égout *m* du bord du toit eaves

embarrure *f* pointing of a ridge (mortar, plaster)

emboîtement *m* fitting; interlocking

empêcher *v* prevent (to); stop (to)

enclume *f* anvil; slater's anvil; dressing iron

endroit *m* face-up side (eg of slate); right side

enduit *m* étanche sealant

engravure *f* sheet of roofing lead; lead coping; flashing; slot to receive edge of flashing

envers *m* face-down side (eg of slate); reverse side; wrong side (opp. 'endroit')

épaufrure *f* chip; spalling; splinter

épaulement *m* shoulder

essente *f* roofing shingle

essette *f*; assette *f* slater's hammer

étanche *adj* waterproof; watertight

étanchéité *f* airtightness; waterproofness; watertightness

évacuation *f* des eaux du toit roof drainage

façonnage *m*; façonnement *m* forming; shaping

faîtage *m* ridge-beam; ridge-pole; ridge tiles; ridge tiling; ridge-capping; ridge-lead

faîtage *m*; faîte *m* crest (of roof); ridge;

faîtage *m* terre cuite terra cotta ridge tiling

faîtage *m* à emboîtement interlocking ridge tiling

faîtière *f* ridge tile; skylight

faîtière *f* à bourrelet spigot-and-socket type ridge tile

faîtière *f* angulaire angled ridge tile

faîtière *f* losangée lozenge-shape ridge tile

fendeur *m*; fendeuse *f* splitter (of slates)

fendre *v* cleave (to); split (to)

fente *f* crack; fissure; split

ferme *f* truss

feuille *f* de zinc zinc sheet

feutrage *m* felting

feutre *m* felt; felting

feutre *m* bitumé bitumised roofing felt

feutre-toiture *m* roofing felt

fibrociment *m* fibrocement

filet *m* fillet

film *m* bitumeux bitumised roofing sheet; roofing felt

film *m* plastique plastic sheeting

film *m* sous toiture under-roof sheeting

fonte *f* cast iron

format *m* format; size

forme *f* d'une comble roof shape

gabarit *m* pattern; template; jig; gauge

galvaniser *v* coat with zinc (to); galvanise (to)

gouttière *f* gutter

gouttière *f* à l'anglaise English gutter (depth progressively increases)

gouttière *f* de Laval Laval gutter (angled sheet metal with acute angle profile)

gouttière *f* en dessus parapet gutter

gouttière *f* havraise/nantaise triangular section roof gutter (lying at base of roof)

gouttière *f* pendante eaves gutter; bracket supported gutter

grand moule *m* tiles per square metre (12 to 15)

gravats *m* rubble

grenier *m* attic; loft

grue *f* crane

habillage *m* assembly; lagging; sealing

hacher *v* chop (to); cut (to)

hachette *f* hatchet

hourder *v* deaden (to); deafen (to); pug (to); rough-wall (to)

imbrex *m*; imbrices *mpl* imbrex (imbrices *pl*) (Roman curved over-tile)

imbrication *f* overlapping

isolant *m* laine de roche rock wool insulant/ insulator

isolant *m* laine de verre glass wool

insulant/insulator
isolant *m* **minéral** mineral insulant/insulator
isolation *f* insulation
isolation *f* **sous rampant** insulation under the
slope of roof
isolation *f* **thermique** thermal insulation
isolement *m* insulation; isolation

jambière *f* leg strap
joint *m* **mousse** foam rubber joint/gasket

laine *f* **de roche** rock wool; mineral wool
laine *f* **de verre** glass wool
lambourde *f* backing strip; wall plate
larmier *m* drip
latte *m* lath
latter *v* lath (to)
lattis *m* lathing; lathwork
lauze *f* slate (variable in shape); roofing
stone
lé *m* length; strip
lé *m* **de feutre bitumé** strip of bitumised felt
levage *m* hoisting; lifting
levage *m* **à la grue** lifting by crane
levage *m* **à la poulie** lifting by block and
pulley
liège *m* **expansé** expanded cork
lignage *m* lining up; marking the line
ligner *v* line (to); mark the line (to)
lignolet *m* ridge course; topmost two rows of
slates next to ridge
lignolet *m* **decoré** *m* ridge course with
pointed slates
lignolet *m* **simple** ridge course of ordinary
slates
lisse *f* handrail; rail; wood strip
liteau *m* batten
liteau *m* **de rive** edge batten
liteau *m* **recloué** renailed batten
liteau *m* **sapin traité** treated deal batten
liteaunage *m* battening

machine *f* **à tailler** tile-cutting machine
maison *f* **à toit de chaume** thatched cottage
(see also 'chaumière')
mansarde *f* attic; mansard roof

manutention *f* handling
marteau *m* hammer
matériaux *mpl* **de couverture** roofing
materials
mentonnet *m* nib; lug; ear; flange
modèles *mpl* **d'ardoise** types of slate (by size
and weight)

viz:	ordinaire	ordinary or standard
	anglais	English
	carré	square
	historique	historic (H1 and H2)

montée *f* **sur le toit** raising to the roof
moule *m* format; matrix; mould; number of
tiles per square metre (see 'grand moule',
'petit moule')

nervure *f* rib
nervuré *adj* ribbed; finned
nettoyage *m* cleaning
nettoyer *v* clean (to)
noquet *m* flashing; valley flashing; soaker
noquet *m* **biais** oblique-cut soaker/flashing
noquet *m* **droit** straight-cut soaker/flashing
noquet *m* **zinc** zinc soaker/flashing
noue *f* valley (roof); valley tile; valley-
gutter; valley-lead; valley-rafter; soaker
noue *f* **préfabriquée en terre cuite** terra
cotta valley tile
noulet *m* valley (roof)

oreille *f* ear; lug; wing
orifice *m* **grillagé** inlet with grille; grilled
opening
outeau *m* small covered vent in roof
outeau *m* **plat** flat-top vent in roof
outeau *m* **triangulaire** triangular-shaped air
vent in roof
outillage *m* equipment; tools
outils *mpl* **du couvreur** slater's/roofer's tools

pan *m* face; side; pane
panne *f* purlin; side-timber
panne *f* **faîtière** ridge beam; ridge pole
panneau *m* **de mousse de polystyrene** foam
polystyrene panel
panneton *m* wiring lug on underside of tile

pannetonnage *m* fixing tiles by wiring to underlying batten

pare-vapeur *m* vapour barrier

parement *m* **en mortier** mortared edge of tiled roof

patte *f* **à tasseau** tingle; cleat

pénétration *f* penetration; method of sealing along intersections (tiled roof)

pente *f* pitch (of roof); slant; slope

▪ **en pente** = sloping

perçage *m* boring; drilling

petit moule *m* tiles per square metre (21 to 23)

pierre *f* **plate** flat stone (for roofs) (see also lauze)

pignon *m* gable

plafond *m* ceiling

plafonnage *m* ceiling work; ceiling; boarded ceiling

plâtrier *m* plasterer

plaque *f* **asphaltée** asphalted sheet (usually corrugated)

plaque *f* **ciment** cement sheet (usually corrugated)

plaque *f* **ondulée** corrugated sheet

plaque *f* **polycarbonate** polycarbonate sheet (usually corrugated)

plaque *f* **polyester** polyester sheet (usually corrugated)

plaque *f* **PVC** PVC sheet (usually corrugated)

plaquette *f* small plate or board; washer

plâtre *m* plaster

plomb *m* **d'œuvre** work-lead

plomb *m* **en feuille** lead sheet

plombage *m* leading; plumbing

pointe *f* brad; nail; point

pointe *f* **galvanisée** galvanized nail

polyuréthane *m* **expansé** expanded polyurethane

poulie *f* pulley; pulley-block

pureau *m* bare; margin; uncovered or visible part of tile or slate

quernage *m* slate splitting

querner *v* split (slate) (to)

queue *f* **de vache** eaves; eaves overhang ; skirt roof

raccord *m* **de couverture** repair the tiling; making roofing complete

rampant *m* slope (eg of a roof)

rampe *f* rise; slope

rampe *f* **de chevrons** pitch of roof; roof-pitch

rang *m*; **rangée** *f* row

rapport *m* proportion; ratio; report

rebord *m* edge; flange; rim

recouper *v* recut (to)

recouvrement *m* covered part of tile or slate; lap; overlap

refente *f* **d'ardoises** splitting slates

règle *f* **en bois** wooden rule

règle *f* **souple** flexible rule

remaniable *adj* alterable

remaniage *m*; **remaniement** *m* alteration; altering; redoing; repairing; rebattening

remaniage *m* **de couverture** repairing the roofing/tiling

remaniage *m* **de toiture** repairing the roof

remanier *v* alter (to); redo (to); repair (to)

remplir *v* fill (to); fill up (to)

remplir *v* **de nouveau** refill (to)

remplissage *m* filling; filling up

remplissage *m* **mortier entre chevrons** mortar filling between rafters

réparation *f* repair; repairing

réparation *f* **de toiture** repair of roof/roofing

réparer *v* repair (to)

reposer *v* **des ardoises** relay slates (to)

revêtement *m* coating; covering; facing

riflard *m* paring-chisel; plastering trowel

rive *f* edge; roof-edge; border

rive *f* **d'une planche** thickness of a board

rive *f* **de débord** side edge

rive *f* **de pénétration** intersection edge (of roof with a wall)

rive *f* **de tête** top or upper edge (of roof)

rive *f* **de tête biaise** skewed top edge (of roof)

rive *f* **droite** verge; right-angled edge

rive *f* **en arêtier** hip; hip edge

rive *f* **exposée** exposed edge (of roof)

rive *f* **laterale droite** verge

rondelle *f* **étanche** watertight washer

rondissage *m* trimming of slates

rondisseur *m* slate trimmer (person)

rondisseuse *f* slate trimming machine
rouille *f* rust
ruellée *f* mortar flashing between roof and wall; verge pointing (roof)

sablière *f* **de comble** pole plate; roof plate; wall plate
sceller *v* seal (to); embed (to)
sciage *m* sawn timber; sawing
scie *f* **égoïne** handsaw
sellette *f* small cradle
shingle *m* American shingle; shingle (manufactured)
solin *m* fillet; gutter-fillet; flashing between roof and wall
solin-ciment *m* cement fillet
soudage *m*; **soudure** *f* soldering; welding
soulever *v* lift (to); raise (to)
sous-face *f* underface
sous-faîte *m* under ridge-board
sous-toiture *f* under roof covering or cladding
stockage *m* storage
superficie *f* surface area; surface
support *m* prop; support
support *m* **de couverture** roofing support
surface *f* surface; surface area

tablier *m* belt with pocket for carrying tools
talon *m* heel; spur; talon
taquet *m* block; cleat; stop
tasseau *m* cleat; strip of wood; batten
tegula *f* tegula (Roman flat under-tile)
tendre *v* stretch (to); tauten (to); tighten (to)
terrasson *m* flat or slightly inclined section of roof; upper slope of Mansard roof
terre *f* **cuite** terra cotta; fired clay
tige *f* rod; shank; stem
tige *f* **du crochet** shank of (slate) hook
tige *f* **filetée** threaded rod
tille *f* **de couvreur** slater's hammer
tire-clou(s) *m* nail-puller; nail-draw
tire-fond *m* coach screw; screw-spike
toit *m* roof
toit *m* **en mansard** curb roof; mansard roof
toiture *f* roof; roofing
toiture-terrasse *f* flat roof; roof terrace

tôle *f* sheet
tôle *f* **de cuivre** copper sheet
tôle *f* **galvanisée ondulée** galvanized corrugated sheet iron
tôle *f* **laminée** rolled steel sheet
tôle *f* **ondulée** corrugated iron
tôle *f* **plombée** sheet iron coated with lead
tôle *f* **zinguée** galvanized iron sheet
tourelle *f* small tower; turret
trancher *m* cut (to); cut off (to); cut up (to)
travaux *mpl* **de couverture** roofing work
truelle *f* trowel
truelle *f* **berthelet mixte** toothed trowel
truelle *f* **bretellée** toothed trowel
tuile *f* tile; roof tile
tuile *f* **à douille et chapeau** tile with socket and cowl vent
tuile *f* **à emboîtement** interlocking tile; single-lap tile
tuile *f* **à glissement** interlocking tile with lateral ribs only
tuile *f* **à rebord** flange tile
tuile *f* **arêtière** hip tile
tuile *f* **canal** arched tile; curved tile; Spanish tile; mission tile
tuile *f* **coffine** tile which is convex across width
tuile *f* **cornière** corner tile
tuile *f* **creuse** curved tile
tuile *f* **de courant** channel tile; under-tile; waterway tile
tuile *f* **de couvert** cover tile; roll-tile
tuile *f* **de dessous** under tile
tuile *f* **de dessus** cover-tile; over-tile
tuile *f* **de rive** angle tile; edge tile
tuile *f* **de ventilation** ventilation tile
tuile *f* **en béton mécanique** concrete tile (interlocking)
tuile *f* **en dos d'âne** saddle tile
tuile *f* **en S** pantile
tuile *f* **en terre cuite** fired-clay tile; terra cotta tile
tuile *f* **en terre cuite mécanique** terra cotta tile (interlocking)
tuile *f* **en verre** glass tile
tuile *f* **faîtière** ridge tile
tuile *f* **gambardière** tile which is concave across the width
tuile *f* **gauche** tile which is half curved

tuile *f* **mécanique** interlocking tile
tuile *f* **panne** combined channel and roll tile
tuile *f* **plate** flat tile; plain tile
tuile *f* **plate écaille** plain tile with rounded
   end
tuile *f* **romaine** curved tile; Roman tile;
   interlocking Spanish tile
tuile *f* **ronde** curved tile; Spanish tile
tuile *f* **tranchée** cut tile
tuileau *m* broken tile; part tile; piece of tile
tuileaux *mpl* **hourdés au mortier** part tiles
   rough-set in mortar
tuiles *fpl* **imbriquées** overlapping tiles
tuilier *m* tiler
tuyau *m* **de descente** downpipe; stackpipe

ventilation *f* ventilation
verniculite *f* granules of foamed glass
verre *m* **expansé** foam glass; cellular glass
verre *m* **moussé** cellular glass; foam glass
versant *m* slope (of roof)
volige *f* batten; lath; roof board
volige *f* **chanlattée** eaves board; eaves lath
voligeage *m* battening; lathing; roof boarding
voliger *v* batten (to); lath (to); roof board (to)

zinc *m* zinc
zinguer *v* cover a roof with zinc (to)
zinguerie *f* zinc work

7. QUINCAILLIER

agrafe *f* 1 hook; clamp; cramp; staple
   2 casement-fastener
agrafe *f* **à T** T clamp
alliage *m* alloy
ancre *f* anchor
ancre *f* **de maintien** fixing anchor
ancre *f* **en forme d'un S** S-shaped anchor;
   S-plate
anneau *m* **brisé** split ring
appareillage *m* fittings; equipment
arbre *m* shaft; axle; spindle
armature *f* fastening; strap
arrêt *m* stop; catch
attache *f* fastener; fastening; tie; clip
attache *f* **de fixation** fixing clip

bague *f* ring
bande *f* **de recouvrement** covering plate;
   cover strip
barre *f* **de securité pour porte de garage**
   security bar for garage door
béquille *f* handle
boîte *f* **aux lettres** letter box
bouchon *m* stopper; plug

bouchon *m* **à vis** screwed cap; screwed plug
boulon *m* bolt
boulon *m* **à clavette** cotter bolt
boulon *m* **à croc; boulon** *m* **à crochet** hook
   bolt
boulon *m* **à écrou** screw bolt
boulon *m* **à tête carrée** square-headed bolt
boulon *m* **à tête fraisée** countersunk-headed
   bolt
boulon *m* **à tête ronde fendue** slotted
   round-headed bolt
boulon *m* **d'ancrage** anchor bolt
boulon *m* **d'assemblage** assembling bolt
boulon *m* **de fixation** holding-down bolt
boulon *m* **de fondation** foundation bolt
boulon *m* **de retenue** retaining bolt
boulon *m* **poêliers** stove bolt
boulon *m* **tête hexagonal** hexagonal-headed
   bolt
boulon *m* **tête ronde collet carré** round-
   headed bolt with square collar
boulonnerie *f* nuts and bolts
bouton *m* knob; button
bouton *m* **à olive** oval knob
bouton *m* **de porte** door knob

bouton *m* **de sonnerie** bell push
bouton *m* **moleté** milled knob
bretelle *f* brace; strap; suspender
bridage *m* clamping; fastening together
bride *f* collar; flange; cramp; clamp
bride *f* **à capote** G-clamp; clamp
bride *f* **filetée** threaded flange
broche *f* spike; spike-nail
brosse *f* **en fil de fer** wire brush
brosse *f* **métallique** wire brush

cache-entrée *m* keyhole guard
cadenas *m* padlock
cadenas *m* **à combinaisons** combination padlock
charnière *f* hinge; butt-hinge
charnière *f* **à ressort** spring hinge
charnon *m* knuckle (of a hinge)
cheville *f* bolt; plug; wallplug; spike; pin; dowel; peg
cheville *f* **à expansion pour parois creuses** expanding plug for hollow walls
cheville *f* **pour matériaux creux** plug for hollow materials
cheville *f* **pour matériaux friables** plug for brittle materials
cheville *f* **pour matériaux pleins** plug for solid materials
chevillette *f* pin; peg
chute *f* downfall pipe
clou *m* nail
clou *m* **à deux pointes** staple; wire staple
clou *m* **à latter** lath nail
clou *m* **à parquet** flooring nail
clou *m* **à patte** holdfast; wall holdfast
clou *m* **à river** rivet
clou *m* **à tête plate** flat-headed nail
clou *m* **barbelé** barbed-wire nail
clou *m* **de Paris** French nail; wire nail
clou *m* **decoupé** cut nail
clou *m* **en zinc** zinc nail
clou *m* **fondu** cast nail
clou *m* **sans tête** brad
clou *m* **tapissier** upholstery pin; upholstery nail
coin *m* corner; wedge; key
collier *m* collar
collier *m* **à ressort** spring clip

collier *m* **d'attache** pipe clip
collier *m* **de fixation** fixing collar; clamp
compas *m* stay
compas *m* **à frein reglable** stay with adjustable stop
compas *m* **genouillère** jointed stay
condamnation *f* locking; locking device
conduit *m* staple
console *f* bracket
console *f* **métallique** metal bracket
console *f* **murale** wall bracket
coquille *f* bush; bearing
cornière *f* angle-piece; angle-iron; L-iron
corps *m* body; substance; head (of a hammer)
coulisse *f* slide; slider; runner
coulisse *f* **de tiroir** drawer runner
coulisseau *m* slide-block; small slide
coulisseau *m* **à frein réglable** sliding stay with adjustable stop
couvre-joint *m* joint cover; covering strip; butt strip
crampillon *m* staple
crampon *m* staple; cramp; cramp-iron; spike; dognail
crampon *m* **à deux pointes** staple
crémaillère *f* shutter retaining hook
crémone *f* espagnolette bolt; French window locking bolt; Cremona bolt
crochet *m* **à tableau** picture hook
crochet *m* **d'armoire** cupboard hook
cuvette *f* **pour vis** screw cup
cylindre *m* cylinder; cylinder lock

écrou *m* nut
écrou *m* **à chapeau** box nut
écrou *m* **à entailles** slotted nut
écrou *m* **à oreilles** wing nut
écrou *m* **à rainures** slotted nut
écrou *m* **à six pans** hexagonal nut
écrou *m* **borgne** blank nut; blind nut
écrou *m* **carré** square nut
écrou *m* **de blocage** locking nut
écrou *m* **frein** locking nut; lock nut
écrou *m* **indesserrable** irremovable nut; lock nut
écrou *m* **ordinaire** standard nut
entonnoir *m* funnel

équerre *f* angle-iron; T-iron; L-iron; square; set square
équerre *f* d'angle angle-plate; corner-plate
équerre *f* inégale d'assemblage L-plate joining-bracket with unequal plates
équerre *f* pour fixation sur béton bracket for fixing wood to concrete
équerre *f* renforcée reinforced right-angled metal bracket
équerre *f* simple right-angled metal bracket
équipement *m* fittings; fitments
espagnolette *f* espagnolette bolt
esse *f* hook; S-shaped pipe connector
étagère *f* shelf; set of shelves

fer *m* bit; iron
fer *m* cornière angle iron; L iron
fer *m* d'angle angle iron; L iron
fermeture *f* fastening; fastener; lock
ferrage *m* door furniture (hinges, handle, lock etc)
ferronnerie *f* ironwork; ironware
ferrure *f* mountings; iron fittings
ferrure *f* de volets shutter mountings
feuillard *m* strip (eg of iron, steel); strap
fiche *f* plug; peg; pin; cabinet hinge
fiche *f* à bouton hinge with knobbed pin
filière *f* wire gauge

gâche *f* plasterer's trowel; striking plate (lock); strike (plate); lock-staple
galet *m* runner; roller
garniture *f* fittings; fitments
gond *m* hook
gond *m* de porte gate-hook
gond *m* and *f* et penture hook and hinge (eg of gate, shutter); hook and ride
grille *f* de défense protective grill
grille *f* de sécurité security grill; security grating
goupille *m* pin; cotter pin
goupille *f* fendue split pin

joue *f* cheek; flange

laine *m* d'acier steel wool
lame *f* cutter; blade; sheet; thin sheet
lame *f* de scie à métaux hacksaw blade
loquet *m* latch
loquet *m* à bouton lift-latch
loquet *m* à poucier thumb-latch
loquet *m* de porte gate latch
loqueteau *m* catch (e.g. for window, door)
loqueteau *m* magnétique magnetic catch
loqueteau *m* mécanique mechanical catch

métallerie *f* metalwork; metal items; metal grilles etc

œillet *m* eyelet

pas *m* pitch; thread (of screw)
patin *m* furniture shoe
patte *f* holdfast; cramp
patte *f* à crochet pipe-strap
patte *f* à scellement cramp; holdfast
patte *f* d'attache saddle; clip (for conduits)
patte *f* de liason wall tie
patte *f* de maintien support bracket
patte *f* de support support bracket
patte *f* métallique metal wall tie
paumelle *f* hinge; split hinge; door hinge
paumelle *f* double H-hinge
penture *f* hinge ride; strap hinge (eg of gate, shutter)
penture *f* à T T hinge
penture *f* anglaise English hinge; T hinge
pièce *f* de renfort stiffener
piquet *m* post; stake
piquet *m* de clôture fence post
piton *m* screw-eye
piton *m* à anneau screw-eye
piton *m* à crochet screw hook
piton *m* à vis screw-eye
piton *m* plastifié blanc screw-eye, white plastic covered
pitonnerie *f* hooks and eyes
pivot *m* pin; pivot
plaque *f* d'arrêt check plate
plaque *f* de propreté finger plate
plaque *f* de protection cover plate

plaque *f* **de renfort** stiffening plate; reinforcing plate
plaque *f* **en tôle** sheet iron cover
plot *m* stud; contact (elect); pin
poignée *f* handle
poignée *f* **de porte** door handle
pointe *f* nail; brad
pointe *f* **à éclats** lost head nail
pointe *f* **à placage** veneer pin; panel pin
pointe *f* **à tête large** clout nail
pointe *f* **cuivre rouge** copper nail
pointe *f* **d'isolation** insulation nail
pointe *f* **de mouleur** moulder's nail
pointe *f* **de Paris** French nail; wire nail
pointe *f* **de vitrier** glazing brad
pointe *f* **galva** galvanized nail
pointe *f* **galvanisée** galvanized nail
pointe *f* **pour plaque de plâtre** nail for plasterboard
pointe *f* **striée tête fraisée maçonnerie** ridged masonry nail with countersunk head
pointe *f* **tête homme** finishing nail
pointe *f* **tête plate** flat-headed nail
pointe *f* **tête ronde** roundheaded nail
pointe *f* **torsadée** twist nail
pompe *f* pump
poteau *m* post
presse *f* **d'angle** angle clamp; angle cramp
presse *f* **de mécanicien** G-clamp; C-clamp
profilé *m* **en T** T-iron
punaise *f* drawing pin

quincaillerie *f* ironmongery; hardware; ironmonger's (shop)
quincaillerie *f* **de condamnation** locking hardware (eg bolts, locks)
quincaillier,-ière *m,f* ironmonger; hardware dealer

raccord *m* connection; connecting piece; coupling; union
raccord *m* **en Z** Z-shaped metal connector
raccord *m* **Gerber™** metal connector for Gerber™ beam system
rebord *m* edge-plate (of lock)
renfort *m* **de paumelle** hinge reinforcement
ressort *m* spring

ressort *m* **à boudin** spiral spring
rivet *m* rivet
rivet *m* **à tête ronde** round-headed rivet
robinet *m* tap
robinet *m* **purgeur** drain-cock
robinet *m* **à flotteur** ballcock
robinetterie *f* taps and fittings; plumbing; tap trade
rondelle *f* washer
rondelle *f* **à denture** serrated washer
rondelle *f* **carrossier** large washer; coach washer
rondelle *f* **d'étanchéité** washer; seal
rondelle *f* **Grower** split ring washer; spring washer
rondelle *f* **obturatrice** blind washer; blank washer; blank flange
rondelle *f* **plate** flat washer
rouleau *m* roller
roulette *f* castor; roller
roulette *f* **d'arpenteur** surveyor's tape

semence *f* tack
semence *f* **fraisée** countersunk tack
semence *f* **tapissier** upholstery tack; carpet tack
semence *f* **tapissier cuivre** copper carpet tack
serre-joint *m* joiner's clamp; G-clamp; G-cramp
serre-joint *m* **de maçon** mason's clamp; mason's G-clamp
serrure *f* lock
serrure *f* **à encastrer** mortise lock; flush lock
serrure *f* **à larder** mortise lock
serrure *f* **à mortaiser** mortise lock
serrure *f* **à pêne dormant** dead lock
serrure *f* **à ressort** latch lock; spring lock
serrure *f* **de coffre** box/chest lock
serrure *f* **de crémone** lock for espagnolette bolt; Cremona lock
serrure *f* **en applique** rim lock; surface lock
serrure *f* **encloisonnée** rim lock
serrure *f* **entaillée** flush lock; mortise lock
soupape *f* valve
soupape *f* **de bidet** bidet valve
support *m* support; bracket
support *m* **de tuyau** pipe support

tamis *m* sieve; gauze; screen
tamis *m* **à mailles** mesh screen
tamis *m* **en toile métallique** wire mesh
screen
tamis *m* **métallique** wire mesh; wire gauze
tasseau *m* bracket; stake
têtière *f* edge-plate (of a lock); selvedge
tige *f* rod; stem; shank
tige *f* **filetée** threaded rod
tire *m*; **tire-fond** *m* spike; screw-spike;
coach screw
tube *m* **fileté** threaded pipe
type *m* **special** special design

valet *m* **d'établi** bench clamp; bench holdfast
valve *f* valve
vanne *f* valve; shutter; gate
verrou *m* bolt; bolt (of lock)
verrou *m* **à coquille** barrel-bolt
verrou *m* **à ressort** spring-bolt; latch bolt
verrou *m* **de fermeture** locking bolt
verrou *m* **de porte** door bolt
verrou *m* **haute securité** door latch, high-
security
virole *f* ferrule; thimble; clip
vis *f* screw
vis *f* **à bois** wood screw
vis *f* **à bois à tête carrée** square-headed wood
screw
vis *f* **à bois en fer à tête plate** countersunk
iron wood screw
vis *f* **à bois en laiton à tête ronde** round-
headed brass wood screw
vis *f* **à deux filets** double-threaded screw
vis *f* **à métaux** metal screw, (for metals)
vis *f* **à oreilles** wing screw; butterfly screw
vis *f* **à pointeau sans tête** pointed grub screw
vis *f* **à quatre pans** square-headed screw

vis *f* **à tête cylindrique** cylindrical-head
screw
vis *f* **à tête à six pans** hexagon-headed screw
vis *f* **à tête carrée** square-headed screw
vis *f* **à tête fraisée** countersunk-head screw
vis *f* **à tête fraisée bombée** countersunk
and round headed screw
vis *f* **à tête fraisée fendue** slotted countersunk-head screw
vis *f* **à tête plate** flat-headed screw
vis *f* **à tête ronde** round-headed screw
vis *f* **à tôle** metal sheet screw
vis *f* **ailée** winged screw; butterfly screw
vis *f* **autoforeuse** self-drilling screw
vis autotaraudeuse *f* self-tapping screw
vis *f* **d'arrêt** clamp(ing) screw
vis *f* **de blocage** clamp(ing) screw
vis *f* **de fixation** fixing screw; securing screw
vis *f* **de mise à terre** earthing screw
vis *f* **de penture** strap-hinge screw
vis *f* **de reglage** adjusting screw
vis *f* **de sécurité** security screw (smooth
head)
vis *f* **de serrage** clamping screw
vis *f* **double filet** screw, threaded both ends;
double threaded screw
vis *f* **indesserable** irremovable screw
vis *f* **pour plaques de plâtre** screw for
plasterboard
vis *f* **sans tête** grub screw
vis *f* **tête trompette** trumpet-headed screw
visserie *f* screws etc; nails etc; hooks etc;
nuts and bolts

zingué époxy noir *adj* zinc plated and coated
with black epoxy paint
zingué jaune *adj* bichromated (anti-
corrosion)

8. MÉTAUX

acier *m* à haute résistance high-tensile steel
acier *m* à outils tool steel
acier *m* adouci annealed steel
acier *m* au carbone carbon steel
acier *m* au chrome chrome steel
acier *m* au chrome-vanadium chrome-vanadium steel
acier *m* au nickel nickel steel
acier *m* cémenté case-hardened steel
acier *m* chromé chrome steel
acier *m* coulé cast steel
acier *m* de construction structural steel
acier *m* de haute tension high-tensile steel
acier *m* doux mild steel
acier *m* dur hard steel
acier *m* fondu cast steel
acier *m* galvanisé galvanized steel
acier *m* inoxydable stainless steel
acier *m* marchand rolled steel
acier *m* moulé cast steel
acier *m* noir black steel
acier *m* pour la construction structural steel
acier *m* trempé hardened steel
acier *m* zingué zinc-plated steel
aciérer *v* steel (to); case-harden (to)
alliage *m* alloy; alloying
aluminium *m* aluminium
anodiser *v* anodise (to)
antimoine *m* antimony
argent *m* silver
argenter *v* silver (to); silver-plate (to)

bichromaté,-e *adj* bichromate-treated
bronze *m* bronze
bronze *m* à canon gun-metal
bronze *m* au manganèse manganese- bronze; manganese-copper
bronze *m* au zinc zinc-bronze
bronze *m* d'aluminium aluminium-bronze
bronze *m* industriel gun-metal
bronze *m* phosphoreux phosphor-bronze
bronze *m* pour robinetterie cock-brass; tap-metal
bronzer *v* bronze (to)

cémenter *v* case harden (to)

chromage *m* chromium plating
chrome *m* chromium
chromé,-e *adj* chrome; chromium plated
chromer *v* chromium plate (to)
cobalt *m* cobalt
cuivre *m* copper
cuivre *m* jaune brass
cuivre *m* recuit annealed copper
cuivre *m* écroui cold-rolled copper
cuivrer *v* copper (to)

étain *m* tin; tin solder
étain *m* à braser tin solder

fer *m* iron
fer *m* affiné malleable iron
fer *m* battu hammered iron
fer *m* de construction structural iron
fer *m* de fonte cast iron
fer *m* de masse scrap iron
fer *m* doux soft iron
fer *m* ductile malleable iron
fer *m* dur hard iron
fer *m* en lame(s) sheet iron
fer *m* forgé wrought iron
fer *m* galvanisé galvanized iron
fer *m* laminé rolled iron
fer *m* noir black iron
fer-blanc *m* tin-plate
ferblanterie *f* tin-plate working; tinware
ferro-alliage *m* ferro-alloy
feuillard *m* d'acier strip-steel
feuillard *m* de fer strip-iron
feuille *f* sheet
feuille *f* d'aluminium aluminium foil
feuille *f* d'or gold leaf; gold foil
feuille *f* d'étain tin-foil
feuille *f* de plomb lead sheet
fil *m* wire; thread
fonte *f* cast iron; pig iron
fonte *f* brute pig iron
fonte *f* de fer cast iron
fonte *f* chromée ferrochromium
fonte *f* d'acier cast steel
fonte *f* malléable malleable cast iron
fonte *f* mazée plate metal

inox *m*; also *adj* stainless steel
inoxydable *adj* stainless; non-oxidizable
inoxydable *m* stainless steel

laine *f* **d'acier** steel wool
laiton *m* brass
laiton *m* **chromé** chrome-plated brass
laiton *m* **d'aluminium** aluminium brass
laiton *m* **fondu** cast brass
laitonnage *m* brassing
laitonner *v* brass (to)

magnésium *m* magnesium
manganèse *m* manganese
mercure *m* mercury
métal *m* metal
métal *m* **à canon** gun metal
métal *m* **anglais** Britannia metal
métal *m* **tendre** soft metal
métaux *mpl* **ferreux.** ferrous metals
molybdène *m* molybdenum

nickel *m* nickel
nickelage *m* nickel-plating
nickeler *v* nickel-plate (to)

or *m* gold
osmium *m* osmium

platine *m* platinum
plomb *m* lead
plomb *m* **d'œuvre** work-lead
plomb *m* **en feuilles** sheet lead
plombage *m* leading; plumbing

revêtement *m* **de plomb** lead flashing (roof)
revêtement *m* **de zinc** zinc flashing (roof)

titane *m* titanium
tôle *f* **de cuivre** copper sheet
tôle *f* **galvanisée ondulée** galvanized corrugated sheet
tôle *f* **laminée** rolled steel sheet
tôle *f* **zinguée** galvanized iron sheet
tube *m* **en laiton** brass tubing
tungstène *m* tungsten
tuyau *m* **d'acier** steel pipe
tuyau *m* **en cuivre** copper pipe

vanadium *m* vanadium

zinc *m* zinc
zincage *m* galvanizing; zincing
zingué,-e *adj* galvanized; covered with zinc
zinguer *v* cover with zinc (to); galvanize (to)
zinguerie *f* zinc work

9. PLOMBIER

abattant *m* **de W.C** toilet seat and cover
ABS (plastique) ABS (plastic) (acrylonitrile-butadiene-styrene)
absorbeur *m* collector plate (solar)
acier *m* **doux** mild steel
acier *m* **galvanisé** galvanized steel
acier *m* **noir** black steel
admission *f* inlet; intake
adoucir *v* soften (to) (water)
adoucissement *m* **de l'eau** water softening
adoucisseur *m* **d'eau** water softener

adoucisseur *m* **domestique** domestic water softener
agrandir *v* enlarge (to)
alésage *m* **de tuyau** bore of pipe (internal diameter)
aligner *v* align (to)
alimentation *f* supply
alimentation *f* **de chaudière** boiler feed
alimentation *f* **en eau** water supply
aluminium *m* aluminium
amiante *m* asbsestos

amiante *m* **ciment** asbsestos cement
analyse *f* **bactériologique** bacteriological analysis
analyse *f* **chimique** chemical analysis
angle *m* angle; angle-piece
anneau *f* **de joint** gasket ring
anneau *m* **en caoutchouc** rubber ring
antenne *f* communication pipe; link/branch pipe with main
antibélier *m* anti-knocking device
antivibratile *adj* antivibration
appareil *m* appliance; instrument; device
appareil *m* **à battre les collets** flange-forming tool
appareil *m* **à emboîture universel** socket-forming universal tool
appareil *m* **de chasse d'eau** flushing device
appareil *m* **de mesure** measuring instrument
appareil *m* **ménager** domestic appliance
appareil *m* **sanitaire** bathroom appliance
applique *f* elbow connector, with wall bracket
approvisionnement *m* **d'eau** water supply
arrêt *m* stopcock; stoppage (see also 'robinet d'arrêt')
arrêt *m* **double-mâle** stopcock, double-male union
arrêt *m* **femelle** stopcock, female union
arrêt *m* **mâle** stopcock, male union
assainissement *m* draining; drainage; sewage disposal; cleansing; sanitation
assainissement *m* **d'habitation** house drainage
asséchement *m* draining; emptying; drying out
assemblage *m* joining; assembling; joint
assemblage *m* **à clin** lap(ped) joint
assemblage *m* **mécanique** mechanical joining (eg screw-joint)
assemblage *m* **par collage** jointing by gluing
assembler *v* assemble (to); join (to); joint (to)

bac *m* sink; tray; trough; vat
■ **évier avec deux bacs** = double sink unit
bac *m* **de douche** shower tray
bac *m* **à gâcher** mixing tray (eg for mortar)
bac *m* **à graisse** grease trap

bac *m* **à laver** deep sink
bac *m* **dégraisseur** grease trap
bague *f* ring
bague *f* **fendue** split ring
baguette *f* **de brasure** brazing-solder stick
baguette *f* **de nettoyage** cleaning rod
baguette *f* **de soudage** solder stick; bar of solder
baignoire *f* bath
baignoire *f* **d'angle** angled bath; corner bath
baignoire *f* **sabot** hip-bath
bain *m* bath
ballon *m* tank; water cylinder
ballon *m* **d'eau chaude** hot-water tank
ballon *m* **de stockage** storage hot water cylinder; storage cylinder
ballon *m* **solaire** water cylinder of solar heated system
bande *f* strip; band; belt
bande *f* **adhesive** adhesive strip (of insulating material)
bassin *m* bowl; basin
bassin *m* **de bidet** bidet basin
bâton *m* **de soudure** stick of solder
batte *f*; **batte-plate** *f* dresser; lead dresser; beater; bat; mallet
batte *f* **à bourre** tamping bar; tamping rod; tamper
batte *f* **à dresser** dresser; lead dresser; beater
batterie *f* **de serpentins** coil of pipe
battre *v* hammer (to); beat (to)
battre *v* **les collets** form flanges (to)
bidet *m* bidet
bidet *m* **fixé** fixed bidet
bidet *m* **pivotant** pivoted bidet
bloc *m* block; mass; lump; unit
bloc *m* **antivibratile** antivibration support
bloc-cuisine *m* kitchen unit
bloc-douche *m* shower unit
bloc-évier *m* sink unit
boisseau *m* dome (of tap)
bonde *f* plug; bung; plughole; outlet
bonde *f* **de douche** shower plug
bouche *f* **d'égout** drain; bottom outlet; gulley
bouche *f* **d'évacuation de bagnoire** bath drain
bouchon *m* stopper; plug; bung; airlock (in pipe)
bouchon *m* **à vis** screwed plug; screwed cap

bouchon *m* de caoutchouc rubber plug
bouchon *m* de vidange drain plug
bouchon *m* de visite access plug
bouclier *m* thermique heat shield
boue *f*; les boues *fpl*. sludge; mud
bourrelet *m* de brasure brazed flange
boursault *m*; bourseau *m* dresser; lead
dresser; beater; bat
bout *m* de tube end of tube/pipe
bouteille *f* de gaz gas bottle; gas cylinder
branchement *m* connection; connecting-up;
branching; branch-pipe; junction; tapping;
plugging-in; installation
branchement *m* de sortie outlet branch
brasage *m*; brasement *m* brazing; hard-
soldering
brasage *m* capillaire capillary brazing;
capillary soldering
brasage *m* fort hard brazing; hard
soldering
brasage *m* tendre soft brazing; soldering
brasage *m* à la louche wiped solder joint
braser *v* solder (to); braze (to)
braser *v* à l'étain soft-solder (to)
brasure *f* 1 brazing; hard-soldering;
2 brazing-solder; hard solder
brasure *f* au cuivre copper brazing solder
brasure *f* dure hard brazing-solder
brasure *f* tendre soft brazing-solder
broche *f* drift
broche *f* conique taper drift
broyeur *m* crusher; macerator
bruit *m* noise; sound
brûleur *m* burner; burner head (of blow
lamp)
brûleur *m* plombier plumber's burner (large
flame)
brûleur *m* à pointe fine et flamme dard
burner giving fine pointed flame
bulle *f* d'air airlock (in pipe); air bubble
burin *m* chisel; cold chisel
buse *f* nozzle
butane *m* butane

cabine *f* de douche shower cabinet
cabinet *f* de douche shower; shower closet
cabinets *mpl* toilet; WC
cadran *m* dial

calfait *m* caulking chisel; caulking iron
calfatage *m* caulking
■calfatage de plomb = lead caulking
calfater *v* caulk (to)
calorie *f* calorie
calorifuge *m*; also *adj* heat insulator;
non-conductor (of heat)
calorifugeage *m* lagging; insulation
calorifuger *v* lag (to); insulate (to) (against
heat loss)
calorifère *m* d'eau chaude hot water heater
canalisation *f* piping; system of pipes;
pipework; pipeline; canalisation; channel;
pipe duct
■ les canalisations = piping; pipework
canalisation *f* aérienne overhead pipe
system
canalisation *f* apparente visible pipe system;
surface mounted pipe system
canalisation *f* cachée hidden/concealed pipe
system
canalisation *f* de gaz gas pipe line
canalisation *f* des eaux de pluie rain-water
drainage
canalisation *f* dissimulée concealed piping;
ducted piping
canalisation *f* encastrée embedded piping;
below surface pipework
canalisation *f* engravée chased pipework
canalisation *f* enrobée encased pipework
(eg within concrete)
canalisations *fpl* enterrées buried piping;
underground pipes
caniveau *m* street drain; duct (for services)
caoutchouc *m* rubber
caoutchouc *m* vulcanisé vulcanised rubber
capot *m* cowl; cover
capteur *m* solaire solar captor; solar
collector
carneau *m* flue
carneau *m* de chaudière boiler flue
chalumeau *m* blowlamp; blow-torch
chanfrein *m* chamfer; bevelled edge
chanfreiner *v*; chanfreindre *v* chamfer (to)
chapeau *m* d'évent vent hood
chapeau *m* de gendarme pipe coupling with
bend
chapeau *m* de presse-étoupe packing gland
chapeau *m* de ventilation ventilator cowl;

vent cap

chasse *f* **d'eau** flushing cistern of WC; WC flushing box

■ **tirer la chasse** = flush the toilet

château *m* **d'eau** water tower

chaudière *f* boiler

chaudière *f* **cylindrique** cylindrical boiler

chaudière *f* **mixte** combination boiler

chaudière *f* **à eau chaude** hot water boiler

chauffage *m* **des locaux** room heating

chauffe-bain *m* geyser.

chauffe-eau *m* water-heater

chauffe-eau *m* **électrique** electric water heater

chauffe-eau *m* **à élément chauffant** immersion heater

chauffer *v* heat (to)

choc *m* **de l'eau** water hammer

chromage *m* chromium plating

chrome *m* chromium

chromer *v* chromium plate (to)

■ **chromé** = chromium plated

chute *f* down-pipe

chute *f* **d'eau** head of water; waterfall

chute *f* **unique** common vertical outlet drain

chute *f* **WC** vertical outlet pipe from WC

cintrage *m* bending

cintrage *m* **des tubes** pipe bending

cintrer *v* bend (to); curve (to)

cintreuse *f* **de tube** pipe bending machine

cisailles *fpl* shears

cisailles *fpl* **à métaux** metal shears

cisailles *fpl* **à tôles** sheet metal shears

citerne *f* tank; water tank; rain-water tank; cistern

clapet *m* valve; clapper valve; tap washer

clapet *m* **anti-retour** check valve; non-return valve

clapet *m* **d'admission** inlet valve

clapet *m* **d'aspiration** suction valve

clapet *m* **d'obturation** cut-off valve

clapet *m* **de décharge** dump valve; discharge valve; relief valve

clapet *m* **de non-retour** check valve; non-return valve

clapet *m* **de retenue** check valve; non-return valve

clapet *m* **de trop-plein** overflow valve

clapet *m* **sphérique** ball valve

clé *m*; **clef** *f* key; spanner

clé *f* **à chaine** chain pipe wrench

clé *f* **à douille** box spanner or wrench; ring spanner or wrench

clé *f* **à molette** adjustable spanner

clé *f* **anglaise** monkey wrench

clé *f* **crémaillère** crescent adjustable spanner or wrench

clé *f* **de lavabo** spanner for wash basins

clé *f* **serre-tubes** pipe wrench

clé **f** **serre-tubes à chaine** chain wrench

clé *f* **serre-tubes type stillson** pipe wrench; stillson pipe wrench

clé *f* **stillson** stillson pipe wrench

clip *m* clip

coefficient *m* **de dilatation** expansion coefficient

collage *m* gluing

■ **par collage** = by gluing

colle *f* glue; adhesive

colle *m* **au néoprène** neoprene adhesive

collecteur *m* drain; sewer; receiver (tank); collector

■ **grand collecteur** = main sewer

collecteur *m* **EU, EP** waste and storm water drain

collecteur *m* **principal** main sewer

collecteur *m* **à l'égout** main drain (sewage); main sewer

coller *v* glue (to)

collerette *f* flange (of a tube)

collet *m* collar; flange

collet *m* **battu** formed flange; beaten flange (eg on metal pipe)

collet *m* **repoussé** flared collar or flange

collier *m* collar

collier *m* **serré** fixed collar

colmatage *m* sealing off; plugging; filling in

colmater *v* seal off (to); plug (to)

colonne *f* pedestal (hand basin)

colonne *f* **montante** riser pipe; rising main

compas *m* compass; drawing calipers

compteur *m* meter; counter

compteur *m* **à eau**; **compteur** *m* **d'eau** water meter

compteur *m* **de vitesse** flow velocity meter

compteur *m* **de volume** volume meter

compteur *m* **volumétrique** volume meter

condensation *f* condensation

condensation *f* **par surface** surface condensation
conduit *m* flue; pipe; conduit
conduit *m* **coudé** elbow connection
conduit *m* **de cheminée** flue
conduit *m* **de fumée** flue; smoke-pipe
conduit *m* **de trop-plein** overflow pipe
conduit *m* **en grés** earthenware drain pipe
conduite *f* duct; conduit; pipe
conduite *f* **de raccordement** service pipe; connecting conduit
conduite *f* **de retour** return pipe
conduite *f* **des eaux pluviales** storm drain
conduite *f* **montante** riser pipe
confort *m* comfort
▪ **zone de confort** = comfort zone
congélation *f* freezing
▪ **point de congélation** = freezing point
consommation *f* **d'eau** water consumption
consommation *f* **d'eau journalière** daily water consumption
contre-courant *m* counterflow
contrebride *f* mating flange
convection *f* convection
corroder *v* corrode to
▪ **corrodé** = corroded
corrosion *f* corrosion
corrosion *f* **par l'influence du sol** soil corrosion
coude *m* elbow; bend; knee
▪ **coude à 30°** = 30 degree elbow
coude *m* **compensateur** expansion bend
coude *m* **de renvoi** S-bend; double bend
coude *m* **de tube** pipe bend
coude *m* **en U** return bend; U-bend
coude *m* **union cuivre-fer** copper-iron end union
couler *v* run (to); flow (to); leak (to); cast (to) (metal)
coup *m* **de bélier** water-hammer; water-hammering
coupe *f* **tube cuivre** copper pipe cutter
coupe *m* **tube** pipe cutter
coupe *f* **tubes avec pince** pipe cutter and pipe wrench combined
coupe-tuyaux *m* **à chaine** chain pipe cutter
couvercle *m* cover; lid
couvercle *m* **de trou d'homme** manhole cover

crapaudine *f* grating; downpipe grating; strainer; screen (of a vent pipe)
crochet *m* hook; pipe-hook; gutter clip
cuisinière *f* **à gaz** gas cooker
cuivre *m* copper
cuivre *m* **écroui** cold-rolled copper
cuivre *m* **jaune** brass
cuivre *m* **recuit** annealed copper
culotte *f* Y-branch; breeches pipe
cuve *f* bowl (of sink unit); cistern; tank
cuvette *f* wash-basin; bowl
cuvette *f* **de WC** WC basin
cuvette *f* **rotule** ball-socket
cylindre *m* cylinder

dauphin *m* **coudé** shoe; rainwater shoe
débit *m* **journalier** daily flow
débordement *m* overflow
déboucheur *m* **flexible** pipe blockage remover, flexible rod
déboucheur *m* **à air comprimé** pipe blockage remover, compressed air operated
déboucheur *m* **à pression d'eau** pipe/trap blockage remover, water-pressure operated
débrancher *v* disconnect (to)
décaper *v* clean (to); scour (to); pickle (to); flux (to)
décharge *f* discharge; outlet
décharge *f* **des eaux usées** waste water outlet/discharge; disposal of waste water
décolloïdeur *m* filter bed; filter unit (attached to septic tank)
découper *v* cut off (to); clip (to)
dégeler *v* defrost (to)
déglacer *v* defrost (to); de-ice (to)
degré *m* **de dureté** degree of hardness
déioniser *v* deionise (to)
demi-collier *m* pipe collar support, demountable half-collar type
déminéralisation *f* demineralisation
déminéraliser *v* demineralise to
démontable *adj* demountable
départ *m* outlet
déperdition *f* loss; waste; wastage; leakage
déplacer *v* move (to); shift (to); displace (to)
dépôt *m* deposit; sediment
désamorçage *m* draining or dewatering (of a pump)

descente *f* downpipe; rain-water downpipe; fall; slope; incline

désinfection *f* disinfection

détartrage *m* descaling

détartrer *v* descale (to)

détartreur *m* **de chaudière** boiler chemical descaler

détendeur *m* pressure reducing valve; relief valve

diamètre *m* diameter

dilatation *f* expansion

dilatation *f* **thermique** thermal expansion

dilater *v* expand (to)

disque *m* **ceramique** ceramic disk

douche *f* shower; soaking

douille *f* bush; socket (bulb)

drain *m* drain

dureté *f* hardness

dureté *f* **de l'eau** hardness of water

dureté *f* **résiduelle** residual hardness

dureté *f* **temporaire** temporary hardness

eau *f* water

eau *f* **buvable/potable** drinking water

eau *f* **chaude** hot water

eau *f* **de distribution** tap water

eau *f* **de ville** tap water; town water

eau *f* **douce** fresh water; soft water

eau *f* **dure** hard water

eau *f* **fraîche** fresh water

eau *f* **froide** cold water

eau *f* **stagnante** stagnant water

eaux *fpl* **d'égout brutes** raw sewage

eaux *fpl* **mortes** stagnant water

eaux *fpl* **ménagères** household waste water

eaux *fpl* **nocives** noxious waste water; noxious effluent

eaux *fpl* **pluviales**; **EP** *abb.* rain water; storm water

eaux *fpl* **résiduaires** sewage

eaux *fpl* **souterraines** subsoil water; underground water

eaux *fpl* **superficielles** surface water

eaux *fpl* **usées**; **EU** *abb* waste water; domestic waste water; sullage

eaux *fpl* **vannes**; **EV** *abb* foul water; sewage; soil (as opposed to sullage)

échanger *v* exchange (to)

échangeur *m* **de chaleur** heat exhanger

écoulement *m* drainage; drain; flow; outflow

écoulement *m* **naturel** natural drainage

écrou *m* nut

écrou *m* **de blocage** locking nut

écrou *m* **à six pans** hexagonal nut

écrêteur *m* gas pressure regulator or limiter

égout *m* drain; sewer

égout *m* **collecteur** main sewer

égout *m* **pluvial** storm drain

égoutter *v* drain (to); drip (to)

égouttoir *m* draining board (sink unit)

électrode *f* electrode

électrode *f* **de soudure** welding electrode

élévation *f* **de temperature** rise in temperature

embout *m* **femelle** socket end

emboîter *v* house (to); fit into (to); joint (to)

emboîter *v* **des tuyaux** socket pipes (to); fit pipes into each other (to)

embranchement *m* branch; branch pipe; branching

emplacement *m* site; location; position

encroûtement *m* scale deposit

énergie *f* **solaire** solar energy

engorgement *m* stoppage; obstruction

entartrage *m* scale formation

entraîner *v* drive (to); cause (to)

entraîneur *m* driving device

entrée *f* inlet

enveloppe *f* jacket; casing; cover; lagging

enveloppe *f* **de cylindre** cylinder-jacket

épandage *m* spreading

épuration *m* purification; cleansing; filtration

épurer *v* purify (to); filter (to)

ergot *m* **de butée** stop pin

esse *f* S-shaped; S-hook

essuyer *v* wipe (to); dry (to)

étain *m* tin; tin solder

étain *m* **à braser** tin solder

étanchéité *f* waterproofness; waterproofing

état *m* state

■ **en état de marche** = in working order

étau *m* vice; pipe vice

étiquette *f* label

être *v* **à l'abri du gel** be protected from frost (to)

étrier *m* **de suspension des tubes** pipe

hanger

évacuation *f* drain; outlet; discharge

évacuation *f* des eaux d'égouts sewage disposal

évacuation *f* des eaux usées waste water drainage

évasement *m* bellmouth; widening at the mouth; flaring

évaser *v* bellmouth (to); widen at the mouth (to); flare (to)

évaseur *m* socket forming tool

évent *m* vent; air vent

évier *m* sink; kitchen sink

évier *m* simple/double bac single/double sink

évier *m* à un bac/deux bacs single/double sink

expansion *f* expansion

façonnage *m*; **façonnement** *m* shaping; forming

façonnage *m* de brides flanging

façonnage *m* direct direct bonding (of tubes)

fer *m* iron

fer *m* à souder soldering iron

fer *m* à souder électrique electric soldering iron

fer *m* galvanisé galvanized iron

fil *m* d'amiante asbsestos thread; asbestos string

fil *m* de soudure solder wire

filet *m* à droite right-hand thread

filet *m* à gauche left-hand thread

filetage *m* threading; screw-cutting

filetage *m* de tubes pipe threading

fileter *v* thread (to); cut a thread on (to)

filière *f* threading die; pipe threader

filtre *m* à gravier sand and gravel filter; sand filter (for septic tank system)

filtre *m* à permutite™ permutite™/zeolite filter; water softener filter; ion-exchange filter

filtre *m* à sable sand filter

filtre *m* épurateur purification filter

fixation *f* fixing; fixation

flexible *adj* flexible

flux *m* flux

flux *m* décapant cleaning flux; flux

(soldering)

fonte *f* cast iron

formation *f* d'incrustation scale formation

fosse *f* d'aisances cess pool

fosse *f* septique septic tank

fosse *f* septique toutes eaux septic tank, all domestic wastes

fossé *m* d'écoulement drainage ditch

fourreau *m* sleeve; cylinder

fraise *f* countersink bit; milling-cutter; cutter

fuite *f* leak

fuite *f* de tuyau leaking pipe

gâche *f* support bracket; pipe bracket; pipe hook; pipe clip; staple

galvaniser *v* galvanize (to)

▪ **galvanisé** = galvanized

garnir *v* lag (to); jacket (to)

garnir *v* un cylindre lag/jacket a cylinder (to)

garniture *f* d'amiante asbestos packing

gaz *m* gas

gaz *m* butane/propane butane/propane gas

gaz *m* comprimé compressed gas

Gaz *m* de France; **G.D.F** *abb* French Gas Board

gaz *m* de ville mains gas; town gas

gaz *m* en bouteille bottled gas

gaz *m* naturel natural gas

gazoduc *m* gas pipe line

gaînage *m* sleeving; continuous protective sheathing containing pipe(s)

génie *m* sanitaire sanitary engineering

gouttière *f* gutter; drainpipe

humide *adj* damp

humidité *f* damp; dampness; humidity; moisture

imperméable *adj* impermeable

incrustations *f* scale (boiler)

indicateur *m* gauge

ingénieur *m* sanitaire sanitary engineer

inhibiteur *m* inhibitor

inhibiteur *m* de corrosion corrosion inhibitor

inox *m*; also *adj* stainless steel

inoxydable *adj* stainless; non-oxidizable

inoxydable *m* stainless steel
installation *f* sanitaire bathroom plumbing; sanitary installation
installer *v* install (to)
intensité *f* de bruit de fond background noise level
inverseur *m* changeover device
isolation *f* insulation
isolement *m* insulation
isoler *v* insulate (to)

jambonneau *m* hopper; rainwater head/ hopper
jauge *f* gauge
joint *m* joint; seal; gasket
joint *m* à bride flange-joint
joint *m* à emboîtement spigot-joint; spigot-and-socket joint
joint *m* à rotule ball-joint
joint *m* abouté butt joint
joint *m* bourré rammed joint; packed joint
joint *m* brasé brazed joint; soldered joint
joint *m* collé glued joint
joint *m* coulé lead joint
joint *m* d'étanchéité gasket; seal
joint *m* de cuir leather seal
joint *m* de dilatation expansion joint
joint *m* de fibre fibre seal; fibre washer
joint *m* de plomb lead joint; leaded joint; soldered joint
joint *m* défectueux defective joint
joint *m* en biseau chamfered joint
joint *m* en caoutchouc rubber gasket
joint *m* libre free joint; loose joint
joint *m* néoprène neoprene socket; neoprene joint
joint *m* par recouvrement overlapping joint
joint *m* soudé welded joint; soldered joint
joint *m* torique O ring
jonction *f* joining; coupling; junction

label *m* label
laine *f* d'acier steel wool
laine *f* de roche rock wool
laine *f* de verre glass wool
laiton *m* brass

laiton *m* fondu cast brass
lame *f* de scie à métaux hacksaw blade
lampe *f* à souder blow-lamp; soldering lamp
lavabo *m* wash basin
lavabo *m* d'angle corner wash basin
lavabo *m* double double wash basin
lavabo *m* sur colonne pedestal wash basin
lave-linge *m* washing machine
lave-main *m* hand basin
lave-main *m* d'angle corner hand basin
lave-vaisselle *m* dishwasher
liège *m* cork
lime *f* file
limer *v* file (to)
lissoir *m* à tuyau pipe-slick; pipe-smoother
louche *f* ladle
lut *m* jointing paste; luting

machine *f* à cintrer pipe bending mchine
machine *f* à fileter les tubes pipe threading machine
maillet *m* mallet
maillet *m* caoutchouc rubber mallet
maintien *m* maintaining; preservation
malfaçon *f* fault; defect (due to poor workmanship)
manchette *f* socket with spigot tail
manchon *m* coupling; socket; sleeve pipe; bush
manchon *m* buté butt coupling
manchon *m* coulissant slide coupling
manchon *m* de raccordement connecting socket
manchon *m* de tuyau; manchon *m* pour tuyaux pipe socket; pipe coupling
manchon *m* en fonte cast iron sleeve
manchon *m* réduit reducer coupling
manchon *m* vissé screwed socket (for hose)
mandrin *m* drift; driftpin; chuck; expander (plumber's)
manette *f* de commande control tap; control handle
marbre *m* marble
marteau *m* d'ajusteur fitter's hammer
marteau *m* à garnir pin hammer; dressing hammer; dinging hammer
massette *f* club hammer; lump hammer

mastic *m* putty; filler; mastic
mastic *m* pour joints jointing compound
matières *fpl* colmatantes clogging material
mélangeur *f* mixer tap
■ mélangeur inverseur = changeover mixer; bath/shower mixer
mélangeur *m* à disques céramiques mixer tap with ceramic discs
metal *m* d'apport de brasage filler metal for welding/soldering; soft solder
métal *m* tendre soft metal
méthode *f* method
micro-station *f* d'épuration microbiological purification unit (for domestic sewage)
mitigeur *m* mixer tap
mode *m* opératoire operating conditions
moignon *m* gutter outlet
moleté,-e *adj* knurled; milled
monobloc *adj* in one piece; combined unit; packaged unit; cast in one piece
montage *m* américain compression coupling with ring seal
montage *m* bicône compression coupling with olive

naissance *f* gutter outlet; water leg
nappe *f* phréatique ground water table
néoprène *m* neoprene
nettoiement *m*; nettoyage *m* cleaning; cleansing; clearing; clearing out
nettoyer *v* clean (to)
niveau *m* à bulle spirit level
niveau *m* d'intensité sonore loudness level; sound intensity level
niveau *m* de bruit noise level
niveau *m* de l'eau water level
niveau *m* de la nappe phréatique ground water level
niveau *m* sonore sound level
nœud *m* joint; soldered joint; knot; node
nœud *m* d'empattement T-joint; oblique joint (brased)
nœud *m* de jonction butt-joint
nœud *m* de soudure wipe-joint; wiped joint
nœud *m* de tamponnage plug; seal; end-of-pipe seal

obstruction *f* stoppage; obstruction
obturateur *m* stopper; plug; cut-off; blank flange; blind washer
obturation *f* shutting off; cutting off; stopping up (a conduit)
olive *f* olive
orifice *m* opening; aperture; orifice
orifice *m* de sortie outlet
outil *m* tool

pare-flamme(s) *m* flame guard; flame shield
pâte *f* décapante soldering flux
patte *f* de support support bracket
pellicule *f* film; coating
perméable *adj* permeable
perte *f* de chaleur heat loss
pH-mètre *m* pH-meter
pied-de-biche *m* T-coupling; T-piece; crowbar
pied *m* de chute base of down-pipe
pince *f* à cintrer pipe-bender
pince-étau *f* locking wrench; lever-jaw wrench
pipette *f* drip pipe
piquage *m* branch connection (in existing pipe)
pistolet *m* à souder électrique electric soldering pistol
plaque *f* d'amiante asbestos sheet
plaque *f* d'égout manhole cover; drain cover plate
plaque *f* de liège cork slab
pliage *m* folding; bending
plomb *m* lead; plumbline; plumb-bob
plombage *m* leading; plumbing; sealing with lead
plomber *v* plumb (to); lead (to)
plomberie *f* plumbing; leadwork; plumber's workshop
plombier *m* plumber
poche *f* d'air air pocket
poêle *f* de plombier lead-pot; melting pot
point *f* de dérivation branch-off point
pointe *f* à tracer scriber
polychlorure *m* de vinyle; PVC *abb* polyvinyl chloride; PVC
polyéthylène *m* polyethylene

polypropylène *m* polypropylene
pompe *f* de circulation circulating pump
pompe *f* électrique electric pump
pompe *f* à chaleur heat pump
pondération *f* des bruits noise rating
porte-lame *m* de scie à métaux hacksaw
blade holder
poseur *m* de tuyaux pipe fitter
positionneur *m* de tubes pipe positioning
clamp
poste *f* de soudage à l'arc arc welder
unit
préfiltre *m* prefilter
pression *f* pressure
prise *f* d'eau hydrant; water cock/tap
propane *m* propane
protection *f* protection
protection *f* antirouille rust protection
protection *f* contre déperdition de chaleur
protection against heat loss
protection *f* contre le gel protection against
freezing
puisard *m* water-sump; drain-hole; drainage
well; drain
puissance *f* power
puits *m* well; pit; shaft
puits *m* artésian artesian well
puits *m* d'infiltration soakaway
puits *m* filtrant; puits *m* de filtrage filter
pit; filtering pit
puits *m* perdu cesspool; soakaway; sink
puits *m* profond deep well
purgeur *m* trap; drain-cock; bleed-tap (of
radiator)
purification *f* purification
PVC *abb* polychlorure *m* de vinyle PVC;
polyvinylchloride

qualité *f* de l'eau water quality
queue *f* de cochon auger-gimlet

raccord *m* connecting piece; coupling;
union; joint
raccord *m* à collet battu compression
coupling, flat-collar type
raccord *m* à collet repoussé compression
coupling, taper-joint type

raccord *m* à compression compression
coupling
raccord *m* à emboîtement spigot-and-socket
joint
raccord *m* américain compression coupling
with ring seal
raccord *m* bicône compression coupling with
olive
raccord *m* courbe double S-bend; double
bend
raccord *m* de branchement branch piece;
branch connector
raccord *m* en té double crossbranch
raccord *m* flexible flexible connection
raccord *m* moulé moulded coupling; cast
coupling
raccord *m* olive compression joint, olive
type
raccord *m* par brides flange joint
raccord *m* type bague BAG coupling;
compression coupling with plastic ring or
sleeve
raccord *m* union coupling; pipe union
raccordement *m* connecting; joining; connection
raccordement *m* aux égouts connecting to
the drains
raccorderie *f* de chaudière boiler fittings
radiateur *m* radiator; heating appliance
rainure *f* cut; groove; slot
râpe *f* rasp
ravoirage *m* form of embedding below floor
piping (eg gravel/cement)
rayon *m* de cintrage; rayon *m* de courbure
bending radius
réducteur *m* de pression pressure reducer;
pressure regulating valve
réduction *f* reduction piece; reducer
coupling
réduction *f* de bruit noise reduction
regard *m* man-hole; inspection hole;
peephole; access port
regard *m* de visite inspection/access door;
inspection cover
regard *m* en béton préfabriqué prefabricated concrete inspection chamber
regard *m* siphoïde siphon-type inspection
box
règlement *m* regulation(s)

réglementation *f* regulations; control
régler *v* regulate (to); adjust (to); control (to); settle (to)
régulateur *m* regulator; controller
régulateur *m* **de gaz** gas governer
régulateur *m* **à deux positions** two-position regulator
relevage *m* lifting; raising (eg by pumping)
relever *v* lift (to); raise (to) (eg by pumping)
réseau *m* network; system; grid
réseau *m* **communal d'assainissement** communal network of drainage
réseau *m* **d'alimentation** supply system
réseau *m* **d'égouts** sewerage system
réservoir *m* reservoir; WC cistern; tank
réservoir *m* **d'eau** water tank; cistern; water butt
réservoir *m* **de chasse bas** low-level flushing cistern
réservoir *m* **de chasse haute** high level flushing cistern
ressort *m* **à cintrer** pipe bending spring
robinet *m* tap; bibcock
robinet *m* **d'arrêt** stopcock
robinet *m* **d'essai** test cock
robinet *m* **d'écoulement** outlet cock
robinet *m* **de fermeture** stopcock
robinet *m* **de gaz** gas cock/tap
robinet *m* **de prise d'eau** water cock; water valve
robinet *m* **de purge** drain cock
robinet *m* **de radiateur** radiator tap
robinet *m* **de réglage** water regulating valve
robinet *m* **mélangeur/mitigeur** mixer tap
robinet *m* **principal** main cock
robinet *m* **purgeur** drain cock
robinet *m* **à boisseau** cock
robinet *m* **à flotteur sphérique** ball valve; ball cock
robinet *m* **à trois voies** three-way cock
robinetterie *f* taps and fittings; tap trade; plumbing
robinetterie *f* **de douche** shower fittings
rodoir *m* lapping tool
rodoir *m* **de robinet** lapping tool for taps
rodoir *m* **en plomb** lead lap
rondelle *f* washer

rondelle *f* **caoutchouc** rubber washer
rondelle *f* **d'échanchéité** washer; seal
rondelle *f* **de cuir** leather washer
rondelle *f* **obturatrice** blind washer; blind flange
rouille *f* rust

salle *f* **de la bain** bathroom
salle *f* **de douches** shower; shower-room
sanitaire *adj* sanitary
sanitaire *m* bathroom installations
▪ **les sanitaires** = bathroom; bathroom suite; bathroom plumbing
scie *f* **à métaux** metal saw; hack-saw
scie *f* **midget** small metal saw
scie *f* **égoïne** hand-saw
seau *m* pail; bucket; pailful; bucketful
section *f* **de tuyau** run of pipe
sédiment *m* deposit; sediment
sens *m* **de circulation** direction of circulation
séparateur *m* separator
séparateur *m* **à graisse** grease separator; grease trap
serpentin *m* coil
serpentin *m* **de dilatation** expansion coil
serre-câbles *m* cable clamp
serre-tubes *m* pipe wrench
serrer *v* tighten (to); screw up (to) (a nut)
service *m* **des eaux** water supply (company)
siège *m* seat
siège *m* **à la turque** squatting closet (WC)
siège *m* **de cabinet** toilet seat
siphon *m* trap; U-bend; siphon
siphon *m* **de bidet** bidet trap
siphon *m* **en S** S-trap
siphon *m* **renversé** dip-pipe
soudage *m* soldering; welding
soudage *m* **autogène** gas welding; autogenous welding
souder *v* solder (to); weld (to)
soudeur *m* welder; solderer
soudure *f* soldering; welding; solder
soudure *f* **à l'arc** arc welding
soudure *f* **à nœud** wipe-joint; wiped joint
soudure *f* **à recouvrement** lap-weld; lap-welding

soudure *f* **autodécapante** solder with a flux core

soudure *f* **avec âme décapante** solder with a flux core

soudure *f* **bout à bout** butt weld

soudure *f* **étain** tin solder; soft solder

soupape *f* valve

soupape *f* **à flotteur** float valve; ball valve

soupape *m* **à trois voies** three-way valve

soupape *f* **d'admission** inlet valve

soupape *f* **d'arrêt** stop valve

soupape *f* **d'expansion** expansion valve; relief valve

soupape *m* **de bidet** bidet valve

soupape *f* **de contrôle thermostatique** thermostatic control valve

soupape *f* **de détente** expansion valve

soupape *f* **de sûreté** safety valve

soupape *f* **de trop-plein** balancing valve; overflow valve; relief valve

soupape *f* **directionnelle** changeover valve

station *f* **de pompage** pumping station; waterworks

station *f* **hydraulique** waterworks

système *m* **d'écoulement des eaux** drainage system

système *m* **d'égouts** sewerage system

système *m* **de chauffage** heating system

système *m* **de drainage** drainage system

système *m* **du tout à l'égout** sewage system

système *m* **séparatif d'assainissement** separate sewage system

tampon *m* stopper; plug

tampon *m* **de réduction** reducing plug

tampon *f* **de visite** access plug; cleaning aperture plug

tampon *m* **obturateur** sealing plug

tamponner *v* plug (to); stop (to)

tartre *m* **des chaudières** scale (boiler)

té *m* tee; T-piece

té *m* **double** cross

té *m* **hermétique** cleaning opening (at base of downpipe)

té *m* **réduit** T-piece, with end or branch reduced

té *m* **égal** T-piece, with ends and branch equal

température *f* **ambiante** room temperature; ambient temperature

tertre *m* **d'infiltration** filtration mound; filtration bank (for septic tank drainage)

thermorégulateur *m* temperature regulator

thermostat *m* **à immersion** immersion thermostat

toile *f* cloth

toile *f* **émeri** emery cloth

torche *f* **à braser** brazing torch

toupie *f* plumber's turn-pin; plumber's tool for bellmouthing end of pipe

toupie *f* **articulée** jointed turn-pin (plumber's)

tout-à-l'égout *m* mains drainage; main sewer

traçage *m* laying out; setting out; tracing; drawing

tracé *m* layout; drawn outline; sketch

tracé *m* **des tuyauteries** layout of the pipes

traitement *m* treatment

tranchée *f* trench

trépidation *f* tremor; vibration

trop-plein *m* overflow; waste pipe; overflow pipe

trou *m* **d'homme** manhole

trou *m* **de regard** inspection hole/port

tube *m* tube; tubing; pipe

tube *m* **d'égout** soil pipe

tube *m* **d'épandage** spreader pipe (septic tank)

tube *m* **de descente** downpipe; soil pipe

tube *m* **de dérivation** by-pass pipe

tube *m* **de purge** drip pipe

tube *m* **de rallonge** extension pipe; make-up piece (pipe)

tube *m* **en couronne** coiled piping

tube *m* **fileté** threaded pipe

tube *m* **flexible** hose pipe; flexible pipe

tube *m* **polyéthylène** polyethylene tubing

tube *m* **sans soudure** seamless tube/pipe

tube taraudé *m* threaded pipe

tuyau *m* pipe; piping; tube; hose; conduit; flue

tuyau *m* **à trois voies** three-way fitting

tuyau *m* **d'alimentation** feed pipe; supply

pipe
tuyau *m* **d'arrosage** hosepipe
tuyau *m* **de circulation** circulation pipe
tuyau *m* **d'écoulement** drainpipe; drainage
pipe
tuyau *m* **de descente** downpipe
tuyau *m* **de drainage** drainpipe
tuyau *m* **de drainage souterrain** subsurface
drainpipe
tuyau *m* **d'égout** soil pipe
tuyau *m* **d'entrée** inlet pipe
tuyau *m* **de prise d'eau** stand pipe
tuyau *m* **de raccordement** connecting pipe
tuyau *m* **de trop-plein** overflow pipe
tuyau *m* **d'évent** vent pipe
tuyau *m* **en caoutchouc** rubber tubing;
rubber hose
tuyau *m* **en cuivre** copper piping
tuyau *m* **en fonte** cast iron pipe
tuyau *m* **en plastique** plastic pipe
tuyau *m* **en terre** earthenware pipe
tuyau *m* **galvanisé** galvanized pipe
tuyau *m* **préfabriqué** prefabricated pipework
tuyauterie *f* piping; pipes; tubing; pipes and
fittings; pipework installation
tuyauterie *f* **des eaux usées** waste water
piping/pipework
tuyauterie *f* **enterrée** buried pipework
tuyauteur *m.* pipe fitter

union *f* union; junction

valeur *f* **du pH** pH value
valve *f* valve; trap
valve *f* **d'égout** drain trap
valve *f* **de radiateur** radiator regulating
valve
vanne *f* valve; shut-off; gate
vanne *f* **d'arrêt de l'eau** water shut-off valve
vanne *f* **de sûreté** relief valve

vanne *f* **régulatrice** water regulating valve
vase *m* **d'expansion** expansion tank/vessel
vasque *f* basin; washbasin
ventilation *f* ventilation; venting; vent pipe
ventilation *f* **mécanique controlée** ; **V.M.C.,
VMC** *abb.* mechanically controlled
ventilation
ventilation *f* **primaire/secondaire** primary/
secondary venting (of drains)
vibratile *adj* vibration; vibratile
vibration *f* vibration
vibrer *v* vibrate (to)
vidage *m* discharge; emptying
vidage *m* **automatique** automatic
(lever-type) waste discharge
vidage *m* **à bouchon.** plug and chain waste
discharge
vidage *m* **à chainette** plug and chain waste
discharge
vidange *f* emptying; discharge
vidanger *v* empty (to); empty out (to); drain
off (to)
vide *m* empty; gap
vider *v* empty (to); clear (to); drain (to)
vidoir *m.* sink; mouth of chute
vis *f* **à tête crantée** screw with notched head
vitesse *f* **d'écoulement** velocity of flow
vitesse *f* **de décharge** velocity of outflow

wastringue *f* spokeshave
WC; **W.C.** *m* water-closet; WC; lavatory
WC *m* **à action siphonique** siphonic flush
WC
WC *m* **à chasse direct** direct flush WC
WC *m* **compact** pump operated WC

zéolite *m* zeolite
zinc *m* zinc

10. VITRIER

baie *f* opening; window
baie *f* **de fenêtre.** window opening
baie *f* **de porte** door opening
baie *f* **vitrée** bay window; picture window

calage *m* blocking; wedging; inserting distance or packing pieces
cale *f* distance piece; glazing block; packing piece; shim; wedge
cale *f* **d'assise** base packing piece; seating piece
cale *f* **en bois** wood packing piece
cale *f* **en caoutchouc** rubber packing piece
cale *f* **latéral** side packing piece
cale *f* **périphérique** edge packing piece
carreau *m* **de verre** pane of glass
châssis *m* glazed frame
châssis *mpl* **fixes** fixed glazed sections of window
châssis *mpl* **mobiles** mobile glazed sections of a window
cheville *f* plug of metal or wood used to retain glass in metal frame
claire-voie *f*; **claires-voies** *fpl* skylight
cloison *f* **vitrée** glass partition; glazed partition
contre-feuillure *f* inner side of rebate; cheek
contre-mastic *m* counter putty; inner layer of glazing putty
contre-masticage *m* counter putty; counter puttying
coupe-verre *m* glass cutter (tool)
coupe-verre *m* **à molette** wheel glass cutter
couper *v* cut (to); cut off (to)
couteau *m* **à démastiquer** hacking knife
couteau *m* **à mastiquer** putty knife; stopping knife
couteau *m* **de vitrier** glazier's knife; putty knife
couvre-joint *m* butt-strip; cover-strip; covering piece

découper *v* cut (to); cut off (to)
double fenêtre *f* double-glazed window
double vitrage *m* double glazing

fenêtre *f* window
fenêtre *f* **à bascule**; **fenêtre** *f* **basculante** centre-hung (horizontal pivot) window
fenêtre *f* **à battants** casement window
fenêtre *f* **à coulisses** sash window
fenêtre *f* **à croisillons** lattice window
fenêtre *f* **à guillotine** sash window
fenêtre *f* **à l'anglaise** outward-opening casement window
fenêtre *f* **à la française** inward-opening casement window; French window
fenêtre *f* **à meneaux** mullioned window
fenêtre *f* **à pivot**; **fenêtre** *f* **pivotante** centre-hung (vertical pivot) window
fenêtre *f* **à soufflet** inward opening (pivoted at base) window
fenêtre *f* **à tabatière** skylight
fenêtre *f* **à vitrage simple** single-glazed window
fenêtre *f* **cintrée** arched window
fenêtre *f* **coulissante** sliding window
fenêtre *f* **en saillie** bay window; bow window
fenêtre *f* **mansardée** dormer window
fenêtre *f* **ordinaire** casement window; French window
fenêtre *f* **treillisée** lattice window
fer *m* **à vitrage** glazing bar
fer *m* **en T** glazing T-bar
feuille *f* **de verre** sheet of glass
feuillure *f* filister; rebate; rabbet
feuillure *f* **drainée** drained glazing rebate
flanc *m* **de feuillure** side of rebate
foret *m* **pour le verre** glass drill

glace *f* plate glass; sheet of (plate) glass
gratte *f* **vitres** window scraper

imposte *f* fanlight; transom (window)
imposte, *f* **traverse d'** transom
imposte *f* **en éventail** semi-circular fanlight

jardin *m* **d'hiver** conservatory
joue *f* cheek

losange *m* **de vitrier** small metal lozenge

used as glazing sprig
lucarne *f* dormer window; skylight

marteau *m* **de vitrier** glazier's hammer
mastic *m* filler; mastic; putty
mastic *m* **à l'huile de lin** linseed oil based
putty
mastic *m* **auto marine** mastic for glazing
aquaria, etc
mastic *m* **colle verre** glass adhesive mastic
mastic *m* **de bourrage** filling putty; filler
mastic *m* **de fer** iron putty
mastic *m* **de vitrier** putty; glazier's putty
mastic *m* **obturateur** stopping putty
mastic *m* **silicone** silicone putty/mastic
masticage *m* filling; puttying
mastiquer *v* putty (to); stop up with putty
(to); cement (to)

nettoyant *m* **vitre** glass cleaner; window
cleaner

parclose *f* glazing bead; glazing fillet
parclose *f* **en applique** mounted glazing bead
paroi *f* **vitrée** glass wall
petit bois glazing bar (wood)
petit fer glazing bar (metal)
plaque *f* **de verre** sheet of glass
pointe *f* **vitrier** glazier's point; glazing brad;
glazing sprig
porte *f* **vitrée** glass panelled door; glazed
door
poser *v* **une vitre** put in a window pane (to)
serre *f* conservatory; glasshouse; greenhouse
solin *m* glazing fillet (*eg* of putty)
survitrage *m* secondary glazing

tailloir *m* glazier's knife for cutting lead
té *m* **à vitrage** glazing T-bar
toit *m* **vitré** glass roof
translucide *adj* translucent

transparent,-e *adj* transparent
triangle *m* **de vitrier** small metal triangle
used as glazing sprig

vasistas *m* fanlight; opening roof-light
vélux™ *m* roof light; velux™
verre *m* glass
verre *m* **à glaces** plate glass
verre *m* **argenté** silvered glass
verre *m* **armé** reinforced glass; wire glass
verre *m* **à vitre** window glass
verre *m* **cannelé** corrugated glass
verre *m* **clair** clear glass
verre *m* **coloré** stained glass
verre *m* **coulé** cast glass
verre *m* **de couleur** coloured glass; stained
glass
verre *m* **dépoli** frosted glass
verre *m* **de sécurité** safety glass
verre *m* **durci** toughened glass
verre *m* **étiré** drawn glass,
verre *m* **feuilleté** laminated glass
verre *m* **fumé** smoked glass
verre *m* **incassable** unbreakable glass
varre *m* **plat** sheet glass
verre *m* **strié** reeded glass; corrugated glass
verre *m* **synthétique** synthetic glass;
transparent plastic sheet
verre *m* **trempé** toughened glass
verrerie *f* glass industry; glass trade
verrière *f* glass roof; glass wall; window (eg
of a church)
vitrage *m* glass door; glass partition;
glazing; windows (pl)
vitrage *m* **sans mastic** dry (puttyless)
glazing; patent glazing
vitrail *m* stained glass window,
vitre *f* pane of glass; window pane
vitré,-e *adj* furnished with glass; glass;
glazed
vitrer *v* glaze (to); put glass in (to); put
windows in (to)
vitrerie *f* glass; glass items; glazing
vitrier *m* glazier

11. ÉLECTRICIEN

absorbeur *m* solar panel; collector plate

accessoire *m* accessory; fitting

accessoires *mpl* **électriques** electrical accessories

accessoires *mpl* **pour câbles** cable fittings

accouplement *m* coupling; connection

accouplement *m* **en quantité** multiple connection; multiple circuit

accoupler *v* connect (to); couple (to); group (to)

accu *m* accumulator; storage battery; storage device

accu *m* **rechargeable** rechargeable battery

accumulateur *m* accumulator; storage battery

accumulateur *m* **au plomb** lead accumulator

actif,-ive *adj* active; live

adaptateur *m* adaptor

alimentation *f* supply; supply system

alimentation *f* **en électricité** electricity supply

alimentation *f* **en énergie** power supply

alimenter *v* supply (to)

allumage *m* switching on lighting

allumage *m* **simple** switch and light point; switch and socket

allumer *v* light up (to); switch on (to)

alternateur *m* alternator

alternatif,-ive *adj* alternating

ambiance *f* ambiance; surroundings

âme *f* core

âme *f* **câblée** twisted strand wire core

âme *f* **en cuivre** copper core

âme *f* **massive** solid wire core

amont (en); amont (à l') up; above; up-stream

▪ les points en amont d'une installation = points of an installation nearest the electricity supply

amovible *adj* removable

ampèrage *m* amperage

ampère *m* ampere

ampèremètre *m* ammeter

ampoule *f* bulb; light bulb

ampoule *f* **en 60 W** light bulb, 60W

antenne *f* aerial; antenna; single principal supply line

antiparasitage *m* fitting a suppressor to; interference suppression

antiparasite *adj* anti-interference

antiparasite *m* suppressor

antiparasiter *v* fit a suppressor to (to)

appareil *m* appliance; device

appareil *m* **amovible** removable appliance

appareil *m* **de chauffage** heater

appareil *m* **de commande** control device (*eg* switch)

appareil *m* **de cuisson** cooking appliance

appareil *m* **de mesure** gauge; measuring device

appareillage *m* fittings; fixing; equipment; bonding; electrical installation

appareillage *m* **électrique** electrical fittings; electrical equipment

apparent,-e *adj* surface-mounted; visible

applique *f* wall light/lamp

applique *f* **électrique** wall lamp; spot light; ceiling light; strip-light

appliques *f* **de sdb (salle de bain)** bathroom lighting

attache *f* clip; fastener; tie; strap

attestation CONSUEL *f*; **certificat CONSUEL** affirmation that electrical installation meets the CONSUEL regulations and safety requirements

au fur et à mesure as one proceeds

autonome *adj* independent; free-standing

autonomie *f* operational duration of battery-powered device

autotransformateur *m* autotransformer

auxiliaire *m* auxiliary; auxiliary control

aval (en); aval (à l') down; below; down-stream

▪ les points en aval d'une installation = points of an installation furthest from the electricity supply

baladeuse *f* inspection lamp; hanging lamp

balisage *m* marker lights; beacons

barre *f* bar; rod; solid metal strip conductor

barre *f* **collectrice** busbar

barre *f* **de pontage enclipsable** clip-in bridging strip

barre *f* **omnibus** busbar

barrette *f* wire connector with screws; small bar or strip

barrette *f* **de 12 dominos** strip of 12 (wire) connector blocks
barrette *f* **de connexion** connector strip
barrette *f* **de coupure** power breaker strip
barrette *f* **de mesure** see 'barrette de terre'
barrette *f* **de raccordement** connecting strip
barrette *f* **de terre** removable connector between earth and earth wire (to permit resistance of earth to be measured)
bas voltage *m* low voltage
basse tension *f* low tension; low voltage (between 50v and 1000v)
batterie *f* battery; set of (eg equipment)
bipolaire *adj* two-pole; double pole; bipolar; two-pin
blindage *m* screening (elect)
blinder *v* screen (to) (elect)
bloc *m* **de prise de courant** multiple socket block
bloc *m* **multiprise** multiple socket block
bobine *f* coil; roll; reel; spool; drum
bobine *f* **d'induction** induction coil
bobine *f* **de câble** cable drum
bobine *f* **inductrice** induction coil
bobine *f* **primaire/secondaire** primary/secondary coil
boîte *f* **à fusibles** fuse box
boîte *f* **d'encastrement** wall insert (switch) box
boîte *f* **de branchement** branch box; connection box
boîte *f* **de connexion** branch box; junction box; distribution box; connection box
boîte *f* **de dérivation** junction box
boîte *f* **de distribution** branch box; connection box
boîte *f* **de jonction** junction-box
boîte *f* **de raccordement** cable distribution box
boîtier *m* case; housing; housing for electrical fitment (*eg* switch)
boîtier *m* **de dérivation** junction box
borne *f* terminal; two-wire connector
borne *f* **de câble** cable socket
borne *f* **de réserve** spare terminal
borne *f* **de terre** earth terminal
bornier *m* multiple wire connector
bouton *m* switch
bouton *m* **poussoir** push button

branchement *m* connection; tapping; plugging-in; junction; connecting-up; branching; tap (wire, conductor); installation; branch (wire, conductor)
branchement *m* **d'abonné** consumer connection
branchement *m* **sur le secteur** connection to local electricity supply; connection to the mains (elect)
brancher *v* connect up (to); link up (to); plug in (to)
brin *m* strand
brins torsadés *mpl* twisted strands (of wire)
broche *f* pin (eg of plug)
brucelles *fpl* tweezers
bruits *mpl* **parasites** interference (radio, TV)
burin *m* chisel; cold chisel
buse *f* sleeving; duct

câblage *m* wiring
câblage *m* **de circuit** circuit wiring
câblage *m* **permanent** permanent wiring
câblage *m* **électrique intérieur** house wiring
câble *m* cable; heavy-duty flex
câble *m* **de distribution** mains cable
câble *m* **de mise à la terre** earthing cable/wire
câble *m* **électrique** electric cable
câble *m* **enterré** buried cable
câble *m* **gaine PVC** cable with PVC sheath
câble *m* **multifilaire** cable, multi-wire
câble *m* **métallique** wire rope; stranded wire; wire cable
câble *m* **rigide** rigid cable
câble *m* **souple** flexible cable
cache-fils *m* terminal cover
cale *f* **à poncer** sanding block; pumice block
canalisation *f* cables; cabling; conduit (wiring/cable); canalisation
candela *f* candela
capot *m* cover; lid
cartouche *f* **fusible** cartridge fuse
catégorie *f* category; class
catégorie *f* **d'installation** installation category
cavalier *m* staple; cable staple
cavalier *m* **de repérage** marker staple
certificat *m* **de conformité** certificate of

conformity (that electrical installation conforms to regulations and required standards) (see also 'attestation CONSUEL')

charge *f* charge; electric charge

chargeur *m* battery charger

cheville *f* plug; peg; wall-plug; pin; bolt

cheville *f* **autobloquante** auto-locking plug

choc *m* **électrique** electric shock

cintrer *v* bend (to); curve (to)

circuit *m* circuit

■ mettre en circuit = to connect up

circuit *m* **chauff-eau** hot water heater circuit

circuit *m* **fermé** closed circuit

circuit *m* **électrique** electric circuit

cisaille *f*; **cisailles** *fpl* shears; wire-cutter

ciseau *m* chisel

ciseaux *mpl* **d'électricien** electrician's scissors

ciseler *v* chisel (to); chase (to)

classe *f* class

classe *f* **d'isolation** class of insulation (0 to 3)

clé *f*, **clef** *f* spanner; key

clé *f* **à fourche**; **clef** *f* **à fourche** open-end spanner

clé *f* **fermée**; **clef** *f* **fermée** ring spanner

clipser *v* clip (to)

coffret *m* box; housing

coffret *m* **de comptage** meter box (holding meter on exterior wall of house); meter cupboard

coffret *m* **de coupe-circuit** cut out box

coffret *m* **de distribution** distribution box

coffret *m* **de répartition** distribution box

coffret *m* **d'interrupteur** switch box

collage *m* gluing; sticking

collier *m* collar

collier *m* **de fixation** fixing collar (for electric cable)

collier *m* **de serrage** holding/fixing collar

commande *f* control; controls; controlling

commande *f* **de circuit** circuit control; circuit operation

commutateur *m* commutator; two-way switch; changeover switch; selector switch

commutateur *m* **bipolaire** double-pole switch

commutateur *m* **conjoncteur** circuit closer

commutateur *m* **disjoncteur** circuit breaker

commutateur *m* **va-et-vient** two-way switch

compas *m* compass

compas *m* **à pointe sèche** dividers

comptage *m* metering; counting

compteur *m* meter; counter

compteur *m* **bleu** EDF meter for power requirements up to 9 kW

compteur *m* **électrique** electricity supply meter

condensateur *m* condenser; capacitor

conducteur *m* conductor; lead; wire

conducteur *m* **actif** live conductor

conducteur *m* **de terre** earth conductor

conducteur *m* **neutre** neutral conductor

conducteur *m* **phase** live conductor

conducteur *m* **unique** single conductor

conduction *f* conduction

conduit *m* conduit; pipe; cable duct

conduit (nature) *m* conduit type codes

A résistant aux agents chimiques: chemically resistant

B blindé: screened

C cintrable: bendable

D déformable: deformable

E étanche: waterproof

I isolant: insulating

M métallique (sans isolement): metal (non-insulated)

O ordinaire: standard

P non-propagateur de la flamme: non-propagator of flame

R rigide: rigid

S souple: flexible

T transversalement élastique: transversely elastic

conduit *m* **cintrable** bendable conduit

conduit *m* **rigide** rigid conduit

conduit *m* **souple** flexible conduit

conduite *f* channel; conduit; duct

conduite *f* **de câbles** cable channel

connecter *v* connect (to)

connecteur *m* connector; cable connector

connecteur *m* **de circuit** circuit connection

connexion *f* connection

consommation *f* **de courant** current consumption

CONSUEL abb; **Comité National pour la Securité des Usagers de l'Électricité** French National Committee for the Safety of Electricity Users (see also 'attestation

CONSUEL')
contact *m* contact; connection
contacteur *m* contactor; remote-control switching device
continu,-e *adj* continuous
convecteur *m* convector; electric convector heater
convecteur *m* mural wall mounted convector heater; unit heater
cordon *m* cord; lead
cordon *m* prolongateur extension lead
cordon *m* souple flexible lead
cosse *f* eyelet; connector
cosse *f* électrique terminal connecter (spade, fork or ring type)
couleur *f* colour
couleur *f* des conducteurs wire colour
Neutre: bleu = Neutral: blue
Phase: rouge, marron, noir = Live: red, brown, black
Terre: vert/jaune = Earth: green/yellow
coupe-câble *m* cable cutter
coupe-circuit *m* cut-out; circuit breaker; fuse-holder with fuse; fuse
coupe-circuit *m* à fusible fused circuit-breaker
coupe-fil *m* wire cutter
couper *v* cut (to); cut-off (to); switch off (to)
couper *v* le courant cut off the power (to)
couplage *m* connection; connecting; grouping; coupling; conduit coupling
couplage *m* en étoile star-connection; Y-connection
couplage *m* en parallèle; couplage *m* en quantité parallel connection; multiple connection
couplage *m* en série; couplage *m* en cascade series connection; cascade connection
couplage *m* fermé close coupling; closed connection
coupler *v* connect (to)
coupler *v* en paralléle connect in parallel (to)
coupler *v* en série connect in series (to)
coupler *v* mal connect wrongly (to)
coupure *f* cut; cutting; power cut; disconnection
coupure *f* de courant/d'électricité power cut
courant *m* current; power

courant *m* alternatif alternating current (a.c.)
courant *m* alternatif diphasé à quatre conducteurs two-phase, four-wire alternating current
courant *m* basse tension *m* low voltage current
courant *m* continu direct current (d.c.)
courant *m* de crête peak current
courant *m* de regime normal current
courant *m* de secteur power supply; mains current
courant *m* direct (c.d.) direct current (d.c.)
courant *m* inducteur inductive current
courant induit *m* induced current
courant *m* monophasé single-phase current
courant *m* nominal nominal current
courant *m* triphasé three-phase current
courant *m* triphasé, montage *m* en triangle three-phase current, mesh/delta/triangle connected
courant *m* triphasé, montage *m* en étoile three-phase current, star connected
court-circuit *m* short-circuit
court-circuiter *v* short-circuit (to)
couteau *m* électricien electrician's knife
couvercle *m* cover; lid; top
cuisinière *f* cooker
cuisinière *f* électrique electric cooker
cuivre *m* copper
culot *m* cap (of electric light bulb)
culot *m* à baïonnette bayonet cap
culot *m* à vis screwed cap
culot *m* taraudé screwed cap
cumulus *m* électrique hot water cylinder with immersion heater

déchargeur *m* lightning protector; lightning-arrester (see also 'parafoudre')
déclanchement *m*; déclenchement *m* disengagement; tripping; release; triggering off
déclencher *v* release (to); disengage (to); trip (to)
déclencher *v* un circuit break a circuit (to)
déclencheur *m*; déclancheur *m* trip
déconnecter *v* disconnect (to)
défaillance *f* failure; break-down; fault
délestage *m* power cut; load-shedding

délester *v* cut off power from (to)

délesteur *m* power economiser; power rationer; load shedder

démarrer *v* switch on (to) (electrical appliance); start up (to); start (to)

dépense *f* consumption (*eg* of electricity)

déphasage *m* dephasing

dérivation *f* shunt; junction; shunting; branching; tapping (of current)

dériver *v* divert (to); shunt (to)

différentiel *m* differential device; differential circuit breaker

disjoncteur *m* circuit breaker; trip-switch

disjoncteur *m* **de perte à la terre** earth leakage circuit breaker

disjoncteur *m* **différentiel** differential circuit-breaker; current-sensitive circuit-breaker

disjoncteur *m* **divisionnaire** section circuit-breaker

dispositif *m* device; arrangement

dispositif *m* **anti-parasite** suppressor

domino *m* **bipolaire** two-way connecting block

douille *f* electric light socket; bulb holder

douille *f* **à baïonnette** bayonet bulb socket

douille *f* **à vis** screw bulb socket

dynamo *f* dynamo; generator

éclairage *m* illumination; lighting

éclairage *m* **automatique** automatic lighting; sensor operated lighting

éclairage *m* **autonome** battery-operated lighting; portable torch/lantern light

éclairage *m* **d'ambiance** indirect lighting

éclairage *m* **des tableaux** picture lighting

éclairage *m* **direct** direct lighting

éclairage *m* **indirect** indirect lighting

éclairage *m* **par appliques** wall lighting

éclairage *m* **ponctuel** limited lighting; selective lighting; spot lighting

éclipse *f* eclipse; safety guard in electric socket

écoulement *m* flow; flowing; leakage; outflow

écoulement *m* **d'électricité** flow of electricity

EDF; Électricité de France French electricity supply company

électricien *m* electrician

électricité *f* electricity

électrification *f* electrification

électrique *adj* electric; electrical

électrode *f* electrode

électromagnétique *adj* electromagnetic

électron *m* electron

électrostatique *adj* electrostatic

élément *m* component; element; unit; section

élément *m* **modulaire** module

embout *m* end-piece

embout *m* **de câble** cable terminal; cable termination

embout *m* **femelle** socket end

encastrement *m* flush fitting; below surface installation

encastrer *v* embed (to); fit flush (to)

■ **en encastré** = embedded

enclencher *v* engage (to); switch on (to)

enclencher *v* **un circuit** activate a circuit (to); close a circuit (to) (ie activate)

enduit *m* **étanche** sealant

enfiler *v* thread (to); pass wire through (to)

enroulement *m* winding

enrouleur *m* **de câble** extension cable reel

enveloppe *f* **isolante** insulating sheath (of a wire or cable)

enveloppe *f* **protectrice** protective sheath (of a wire or cable)

épissure *f* splice

équipement *m* equipment; fittings; fitments; fitting out

■ **les équipements** = facilities/amenities

équipement *m* **extérieur** exterior fittings

équipement *m* **électrique** electrical fittings

équipotentiel,-elle *adj* equipotential

étanche *adj* humidity-proof; watertight; waterproof

étincelle *f* **électrique** electric spark

étoile *f* star; Y (connection)

faire masse *v* act as earth (to)

farad *m* farad

fermer *v* close (to)

fermer *v* **un circuit** close a circuit (to)

fiabilité *f* reliability; dependability

fiche *f* plug; pin; peg

fiche *f* de connexion connector plug
fiche *f* électrique electric plug
fil *m* wire; filament (of electric bulb); cord
(of electric appliance); thread
fil *m* à plomb plumb line
fil *m* de phase live wire; live conductor
fil *m* hors courant dead wire
fil *m* neutre neutral wire
fil *m* nu bare wire
fil *m* sous tension live wire
fils navettes *mpl* shuttle wires; changeover
wires (commutator)
fixation *f* par collier fixing (a cable) with
clips or collars
fluo *f* fluorescent tube
▪ un tube fluo = a flourescent tube
fluorecent, tube *m* fluorescent tube
fondre *v* un fusible blow a fuse (to)
foudre *f* lightning (see also 'anti-foudre')
fourreau *m* sleeve; pipe; duct; sheath
fréquence *f* frequency
fusible *m* fuse-wire; fuse
fusible *m* à broche plug-in fuse; fuse with
pins
fusible *m* à cartouche cartridge fuse
fusible *m* bon/grillé intact/burnt out fuse
fusible *m* calibré fuse of known rating
fusible *m* principal main fuse
fusible *m* tabatière fuse box; fuse-holder

gaine *f* sheath; conduit; duct; cover
gaine *f* de bourrage inner protective
sheathing of a cable
gaine *f* de câble cable protection sheath;
cable conduit
gaine *f* de protection protective sheath
générateur *m* generator
générateur,-trice *adj* generating
génératrice *f* generator (electrical); direct
current generator
glissière *f* des lumières light track
goulotte *f* trunking; multi-cable housing;
cable ducting; spout
grattoire *m* triangulaire triangular scraper
grille *f* grille; grid (electricity)
griller *v* blow (to) (a fuse); burn out (to) (a
fuse, electric motor)
▪ tous les circuits ont grillé = all the fuses

have blown/burnt out
groupe *m* électrogène electric generating set
groupe *m* générateur electric generating set
guide-fil *m* cable guide

haut voltage *m* high voltage
haute tension; HT *f* high tension; HT
henry *m* henry
hertz *m* hertz
hors courant *adj* dead; no current
hublot *m* bulwark light

ICD *abb*; isolant, cintrable, déformable
insulating, flexible, deformable (conduit)
ICO *abb*; isolant, cintrable, ordinaire
insulating, flexible, ordinary (conduit)
ICT *abb*; isolant, cintrable, transversalement élastique insulating, flexible,
transversally elastic (conduit)
identification *f* des conducteurs identification of conductors (by colour codes) (see
also 'couleur des conducteurs')
impédance *f* impedance
inductance *f* inductance
installation *f* apparente surface-mounted
installation
installation *f* électrique electrical
installation; wiring installation
intensité *f* intensity
inter différentiel *m* circuit breaker (person
sensitive)
interconnecter *v* interconnect (to)
interconnexion *f* interconnection
interférence *f* interference (radio, TV)
interrompre *v* interrupt (to); cut out (to)
interrupteur *m* switch; circuit-breaker
interrupteur *m* à action retardée delayed-
action switch
interrupteur *m* à bascule tumbler switch
interrupteur *m* à distance remote-control
switch
interrupteur à poussoir *m* push-button
switch
interrupteur *m* à relais temporisé time-
delay switch
interrupteur *m* bipolaire two-pole switch
interrupteur *m* de contrôle control switch

interrupteur *m* **de dérogation** override switch

interrupteur *m* **de surcharge** overload device

interrupteur *m* **de va-et-vient** two-way on/off switch (often shortened to 'va-et-vient')

■ **double va-et-vient** = double two-way switch

interrupteur *m* **différentiel** differential switch; safety power-breaker; residual current switch

interrupteur *m* **électronique** electronic switch; touch-sensitive switch

interrupteur *m* **encastré** flush-fitted switch

interrupteur *m* **horaire** time-switch

interrupteur *m* **radio** cordless switch; radio-command switch

interrupteur *m* **unipolaire** single pole switch

ion *m* ion

IRO *abb*; **isolant, rigide, ordinaire** insulating, rigid, ordinary (conduit) (see also 'conduit (nature)')

isolant *m* insulator

isolant,-e *adj* insulating

isolateur *m* insulator

isolateur, isolatrice *adj* insulating

isolation *f* insulation

jeu *m* **(d'un fusible)** blowing (of a fuse)

joule *m* joule

lampadaire *m* standard lamp

lampe *f* lamp; light; bulb

lampe *f* **à fluorescence** fluorescent lamp

lampe *f* **à incandescence** incandescent lamp

lampe *f* **couleur** coloured bulb

lampe *f* **halogène** halogen lamp

lampe *f* **témoin** pilot light; indicator light; warning light

lampe *f* **tubulaire** tube (flourescent)

lave-linge *m* washing machine

lave-vaisselle *m* dishwasher

liaison *f* **équipotentielle** equipotential connection; earthing link (to water pipes, etc)

ligne *f* line

ligne *f* **aérienne** overhead line

ligne *f* **équipotentielle** equipotential line; earthing line

limiteur *m* limiter

limiteur *m* **de courant** current limiter

limiteur *m* **de tension** voltage limiter

lumen *m* lumen

luminaire *m* light; lamp; lighting fitment

luminaire *m* **extérieur** outside lamp/light

lumière *f* light

lumière *f* **artificielle** artificial light

marteau *m* **d'électricien** electrician's hammer

masse *f* earth; mass; ground; metal frame/casing of electrical equipment

massette *f* hammer (heavy)

mesure *f* measurement

mesurer *v* measure (to)

mettre *v* put (to)

mettre *v* **à la masse** earth (to)

mettre *v* **à terre** earth (to)

mettre *v* **en circuit** connect up (to)

microfarad *m* microfarad

minuterie *f* time-switch

mise *f* **à la terre** earth; earthing

monophasé *adj* single phase

montage *m* assembly; coupling; wiring-up; connection; connecting

montage *m* **électrique** circuit scheme or diagram

montage *m* **en parallèle/en série** connection in parallel/in series

montage *m* **en étoile** star- or Y- connection

montage *m* **en étoile-triangle** star-delta connection

montage *m* **encastré** embedded conduit system

moulure *f* moulding; casing (for wires, etc)

navette *f* see 'fils navettes'

neutre *adj* neutral

niveau *m* **à bulle** spirit-level

nominal,-e, -aux *adj* nominal

norme *f* standard; standard specification

nu,-e *adj* bare; not insulated

obturateur *m* blanking plate; blank flange; shutter; cap

ohm *m* ohm

ohmmètre *m* ohmmeter

omnipolaire *adj* all poles

outil *m* **dégainer les câbles** wire stripper

ouverture *f* opening; breaking; disconnecting (a circuit)

panneau *m* panel

panneau *m* **radiant** radiant heating panel

parafoudre *m* lightning-arrester; lightning-protector

parasites *mpl* interference (radio,TV)

parcourir *v* traverse (to); pass (to)

passe-fil *m* grommet

peigne *m* **de répartition** comb distributor (of current)

perceuse *f* drill; electric drill

période *f* period

permitivité *f* permittivity

perméabilité *f* **magnétique** magnetic permeability

phase *f* phase; live (wire)

pile *f* battery

■ **à piles** = battery-operated

pile *f* **sèche** dry battery

pince *f* pliers; tongs; nippers

pince *f* **à becs plats** flat-nose pliers

pince *f* **à becs ronds** round-nose pliers

pince *f* **à dénuder** *f* wire stripper

pince *f* **à dénuder automatique** automatic wire-stripper

pince *f* **à sertir les cosses** pincers for crimping terminal connections

pince *f* **coupante** cutting pliers

pince *f* **coupante diagonale** diagonal cut pliers

pince *f* **coupante en bout** wire-cutters

pince *f* **crocodile** crocodile clip

pince *f* **de fixation** clip

pince *f* **de raccordement** cable connecting clamp

pince *f* **gratte-laque** wire varnish removing tool

pince *f* **multiprise** pliers with adjustable head

pince *f* **plates** flat-nose pliers

pince *f* **rondes** round-nose pliers

pince *f* **universelle** universal pliers

piquet *m* **de terre** earthing spike (metal); earth stake; earthing rod

plafonnier *m* ceiling light

plot *m* contact (elect)

poignée *f* **pare-coups** anti-shock handle (*eg* for masonry chisel)

point *m* point

point *m* **lumineux** light fitting; light point

poire *f* switch (pear-shaped)

poire *f* **électrique** electric switch (pear-shaped)

polarité *f* polarity

pôle *m* pole

■ **2 pôles et terre** = 2 poles (pins) and earth

pôle *m* **moins** minus pole

pôle *m* **négatif** negative pole

pôle *m* **plus** plus pole

pôle *m* **positif** positive pole

ponceuse *f* sander

pontet *m* **plastique** plastic cable clip; plastic conduit clip

porte-cable *m* cable hanger

poser *v* put in place (to)

poser *v* **des fils dans une maison** wire a house (to)

poste *m* post; station; set; installation; unit

poste *m* **d'interconnexion** interconnection substation

poste *m* **de livraison H.T.** high voltage supply substation

poste *m* **de livraison M.T.** medium voltage supply substation

poste *m* **de transformation** transformer substation

potentiel *m* potential

prise *f* hold; socket; point; power point

prise *f* **20A + T(erre)** socket (20A) with earth

prise *f* **à 2 alvéoles sans/avec contact de terre** socket with 2 holes without/with earth

prise *f* **bipolaire (2P)** two-pin socket

prise *f* **bipolaire (2P + T)** two-pin socket with earth

prise *f* **de courant** power point; socket

prise *f* **de courant mâle/femelle** plug-and-socket; power point

prise *f* **de terre** earth

prise *f* **double** double wall socket

prise *f* **multiple** adaptor
prise *f* **murale** wall socket
prise *f* **pour résoir électrique** razor point
programmateur,-trice *m,f* programmable
time-switch
programmation *f* programming; time programme
programmation *f* **par tranche de 2 heures**
programming for 2 hour intervals
programmeur *m* time-switch
projecteur *m* spotlight
PROMOTOLEC *abb.* Association pour la
Promotion de la qualité des Installations
Électriques French Association Monitoring
Electrical Installations
protection *f* protection; circuit protection
protection *f* **anti-foudre** surge protector;
lightning voltage surge protector
protection *f* **des circuits** circuit protection
puissance *f* power; electric power; wattage
puissance *f* **absorbée** power consumption

raccordement *m* connecting; joining;
connection
raccordements *mpl* **enchevêtrés** entangled
connections (wires)
raccorder *v* connect (to); join (to); couple
(to); connect up (to)
rainureuse *f* slot-drilling machine; groove-
cutting machine
récepteur *m* receiver; utiliser of electricity
redresseur *m* rectifier
réglage *m* regulation; setting; adjustment
relais *m* relay
répartir *v* distribute (to)
répartition *f* distribution
repérage *m* marking; marking out; locating
repère *m* marker; benchmark; mark;
indicator
repérer *v* mark (to); mark out (to); to locate
repos (en) out-of-service; resting
réseau *m* network; system; grid
réseau *m* **d'éclairage** lighting system
réseau *m* **interconnecté** network with
multiple supply lines
réseau *m* **primaire en boucle** ring-main
réseau *m* **électrique** electrical network/
system

résistance *f* resistance
résistivité *f* specific resistance; resistivity
rétablir *v* re-establish; restore
rétablir le courant *v* put power back on
again (to)
rhéostat *m* rheostat
ruban *m* **adhésif isolant électrique**
insulating tape, adhesive
ruban *m* **isolant** insulating tape
ruban *m* **isolateur** insulating tape

saignée *f* groove; channel (cut in plaster etc)
saillie *f* ledge; projection
▪ **en saillie** = projecting; surface mounted
sans fil cordless; wireless
schéma *m* diagram; plan; scheme
schéma *m* **de montage** wiring diagram
schéma *m* **d'implantation** installation
diagram (wiring)
secteur *m* sector; local electricity supply area
▪ **le secteur** = mains electricity supply
section *f* section; cross-section
sectionnement *m* isolation (electrical)
severance; opening a circuit; division (into
sections)
sectionneur *m* isolator; isolating switch;
disconnecting switch; separator
sélectivité *f* selectivity
sensibilité *f* sensitivity; threshold of action
séparation *f* separation; isolation prevent-ing
electric shock
seuil *m* threshold
socle *m* socket; base of a lamp; stand
socle *m* **à éclipses** protected (safety) socket;
socket with safety shields
socle bipolaire avec terre (2P+T) *m* bipolar
socket with earth
sol *m* ground; earth (elect); soil
▪ **au sol** = earthed
sonnerie *f* **d'alarme** alarm bell
source *f* source
source *f* **autonome** self-contained source (eg
battery)
source *f* **d'énergie** source of energy
spot *m* spotlight; spot
surcharge *f* overload; overloading
surcharger *v* overload (to)
surintensité *f* **(de courant)** overcurrent;

excess current
surtension *f* overvoltage; excess voltage
survoltage *m* boosting
survolté,-e *adj* stepped up; boosted

tableau *m* board
tableau *m* **(de) répartition** distribution board
tableau *m* **de commande principal** main switch board
tableau *m* **de commutateurs** switch-board
tableau *m* **de distribution** distribution board
tableau *m* **de fusibles** fuse board
TBT; T.B.T.; très basse tension *f* very low tension/voltage
télérupteur *m* remote control switching device
temporisateur *m* timer
temporisation *f* time-delay device; delaying timer
tension *f* voltage; tension
tension *f* **du secteur** mains voltage
terre *f* ground; earth (elect); land; soil
tétrapolaire *adj* four-pole
thermostat *m* thermostat
thermostat *m* **d'ambiance** temperature controller; room thermostat
thermostat *m* **électronique** programmable thermostat
thermostat *m* **à gel** frost stat

thermostat *m* **à horloge** time programmable thermostat
tire-fil *m* pull-through (for cables)
tournevis *m* screwdriver
tournevis *m* **pour vis Phillips™** Phillips™ screwdriver
tournevis *m* **testeur** tester screwdriver

tournevis *m* **vis cruciforme** cross-point tip screwdriver
transformateur *m* transformer
transformateur *m* **reducteur de tension** step-down transformer
transformateur *m* **élévateur de tension** step-up transformer
transmission *f* transmission
triphasé,-e *adj* three-phase
tripolaire *adj* three-pole; triple pole; tripolar
truelle *f* trowel
truelle *f* **berthelet** berthelet trowel; toothed trowel
tube *m* pipe; tube
tube *m* **fluo** fluorescent tube

unifilaire *adj* single wire
uniphasé,-e *adj* single-phase
unipolaire *adj* single-pole
UTE *abb.*; **Union Technique de l'Électricité** UTE French Association publishing electrical installation standards (normes)

variateur *m* dimmer; variable control switch
vérification *f* check; control; test; verification
vérifier *v* verify (to); check (to)
volt *m* volt
voltage *m* voltage
voltage *m* **primaire/secondaire** primary/secondary voltage
voltmètre *m* voltmeter

watt *m* watt

12. PLÂTRIER

accélérateur *m* de prise setting accelerator

accrochage *m* key; keying; roughening to form a key; adhesion

additif *m* additive

agrafe *f* staple; clip; cramp; fastener

baccula *m* lattice of wood strips held together with galvanised wire

bande *f* calicot collée glued calico strip

bande *f* à joint jointing tape; scrim

bouchage *m* stopping; filling up

boucher *v* plug (to); fill (to); plaster over (to); stop (to)

bourrage *m* tamping; stemming; stuffing; filling

bourrer *v* stuff (to); pack (to)

brique *f* plâtrière plasterer's brick (hollow brick readily taking a plaster coat)

calfeutrage *m*; calfeutrement *m* filling; stopping up; draughtproofing

calfeutrer *v* fill (to); stop up (to); draughtproof (to)

carreau *m* de plâtre plaster block (for partitions, etc)

chandelle *f* à crémaillère prop or stay, Acrow ™ type

chaux *f* lime

chaux *f* vive/éteinte quick/slaked lime

chevauchement *m* overlap; overlapping; spanning

cloison *f* partition; partition wall

coffrage *m* coffering; formwork; lining; shuttering

coffrage *m* de plafond ceiling boarding

coffrage *m* en tôle sheet metal casing

coffre *m* case; form (for concrete)

contracter (se) *v* contract (to); shrink (to)

contre-latte *f* counter-lath

contre-latter *v* counter-lath (to)

corniche *f* coving; cornice

corniche *f* en bois wood coving

corniche *f* en plâtre plaster coving

corniche *f* en polystyrène polystyrene coving

corniche *f* en polyuréthane polyurethane coving

corrosion *f* corrosion

couche *f* coat

couche *f* d'approche initial layer of plaster

couche *f* d'impression priming coat

couche *f* de finition finishing coat; setting coat

couche *f* fin thin coat (eg of plaster)

couteau *m* à enduire coating knife; palette knife

couteau *m* à enduire les angles angle trowel

couteau *m* plaquiste wide smoothing knife

crépi *m* plaster rendering; roughcast; wall paint; textured wall paint

crépir *v* apply a textured paint (to); roughcast (to); render (to)

creuser (se) *v* wrinkle (to); form hollows (to)

cric *m* jack; lifting jack; hydraulic jack

cric *m* de charpentier timber jack

crochet *m* hook

crochet *m* de suspension suspension hook; suspender

début *m* de prise start of setting

dilater (se) *v* expand (to); dilate (to); swell (to)

dispositif *f* de suspension suspension piece; suspension arrangement

doublage *m* lining; interior wall facing

dressage *m* dressing (a surface)

éclisse *f* cornière angle bead; angle fishplate

égaliser *v* level (to); make level (to)

enduit *m* coat; coating; rendering; layer

enduit *m* au plâtre épais/fin thick/thin coating of plaster

enduit *m* coupé textured coat

enduit *m* de finition finishing coat

enduit *m* de lissage smoothing coat; floating coat

enduit *m* de lissage plâtre finishing coat; smoothing coat

enduit *m* lisse de plâtre fair-faced plaster

enduit *m* monocouche single coat plaster

enduit *m* plastique grésé smoothed plastic based coat

enduit *m* plâtre projeté mécaniquement plaster coat applied with a mechanical sprayer

enduit *m* **pour joints** jointing coat

enduit m projeté à la machine plaster projected by machine

entraxe *m* **des solives** joist interval; joist spacing

étai *m* **de maçon tubulaire** mason's tubular shore/stay

étaler *v* spread (to); apply (to)

étrésillon *m* **à vérin** prop or stay, Acrow ™ type

exécuter *v* carry out (to); do (to)

exécution *f* carrying out; fulfilment; accomplishment

exécution *f* **des joints** completing the joints; taping the joints

faux plafond *m* false ceiling; suspended ceiling; intermediate ceiling

fente *f* crack; fissure; split

feuillard *m* **d'acier** steel strip; steel or iron strip suspender

fibre *f* **de verre** glass fibre

fil *m* **de cuivre** *m* copper wire

filasse *f* tow

fin, fine *adj* thin; fine (powder); sharp (blade)

fin *m* **de prise** end of setting

fini *m* finish

fissure *f* crack; fissure

gâchage *m* mixing; tempering (with water)

gâche *f* plasterer's trowel (larry)

gâcher *v* temper (to) (plaster); mix (to) waste (to); botch (to)

gobeter *v* roughcast (to)

gobetis *m* first plaster coat; roughing-in coat

gonfler *v* swell (to); expand (to)

grattoir *m* **de plâtrier** plasterer's scraper

grésage *m* smoothing (a surface)

gréser *v* smooth (to) (a surface)

gypse *m* gypsum

hatchette *f* **de plâtrier** lath hammer; plasterer's hammer

hourdage *m* see 'hourdis'

hourder *v* pug (to); deaden (to); deafen (to)

hourdis *m* rough-walling; pugging; layer of rough plaster on a lattice; deadening; deafening material forming the under surface of a floor; rough flooring (eg broken bricks)

jute *m* jute

lambris *m* tongued and grooved board; panelling; cladding

lame *f* blade; strip; lath

lattage *m* lathing

lattage *m* **espacé** spaced lathing

lattage *m* **jointif** close lathing

latte *f* lath

latter *v* lath (to)

latter *v* **une cloison** to lathe a partition (wall)

lattis *m* lathing; lathwork; lagging

lattis *m* **abris** reed lathing; round-reed lathing

lattis *m* **armé** reinforced lathing; wire-tied laths

lattis *m* **canis** split-reed lathing

lattis *m* **en roseaux refendus** split-reed lathing

lattis *m* **en roseaux rond** reed lathing

lattis *m* **espacé** spaced lathing

lattis *m* **jointif** close lathing

lattis *m* **mécanique** laths tied with twisted wire

lattis *m* **métallique** metal lathing; expanded metal lathing

lissage *m* smoothing

lisser *v* smooth (to); make smooth (to)

maille *f* mesh

maille *f* **d'un treillis métallique** mesh of metal lath trellis

mastic *m* **à la chaux** lime putty; plasterer's putty

métal *m* **déployé** expanded metal trellis

mortier *m* **adhésif** adhesive cement (for plaster blocks)

moulure *f* moulding

nervure *f* rib

nervurer *v* rib (to)

ossature *f* frame; framework
ossature *f* cachée hidden framework
ossature *f* métallique metal framework (eg of a suspended ceiling)

palette *f* à enduire coating palette; plasterer's float
pâte *f* à joints joint filler
pâte *f* de remplissage joint filler
peinture *f* murs et plafonds wall and ceiling paint
placoplâtre™ *f* plasterboard
plafond *m* ceiling
plafond *m* à caissons coffered ceiling
plafond *m* en lambris boarded ceiling
plafond *m* lambrissé panelled ceiling; ceiling boarded with lambris
plafond *m* sur canisse reed-lath ceiling
plafond *m* sur contre-lattes ceiling on counter-laths
plafond *m* sur lattes ceiling on laths
plafond *m* surbaissé drop ceiling
plafond *m* suspendu suspended ceiling
plafond *m* traditionnel traditional ceiling (ie plaster ceiling)
plafonnage *m* ceiling; boarded ceiling; ceiling material; ceiling work
plafonnement *m* ceiling ornaments
plafonner *v* construct a ceiling (to); put in a ceiling (to)
plafonneur *m* constructor of ceilings; plasterer
plafonnier *m* ceiling light
plaque *f* sheet; board; slab
plaque *f* à âme alveolée plasterboard with honeycomb core
plaque *f* cartonnée plasterboard with cardboard facing
plaque *f* coupe-feu fire-resistant ceiling board
plaque *f* de plâtre plasterboard; wallboard
plaque *f* de plâtre + laine de roche combined plaster and mineral wool board
plaque *f* de plâtre + laine de verre combined plaster and glass wool board

plaque *f* de plâtre + polystyrène combined plaster and expanded polystyrene board
plaque *f* de staff staff board
plaque *f* mince thin ceiling board
plaque *f* nervurée ribbed board
platoir *m* finishing trowel; rectangular trowel
platoir *m* bout ovale oval-ended smoothing trowel
plâtrage *m* plastering; plaster-work
plâtras *m* plaster debris
plâtre *m* plaster
■ les plâtres *m* plasterwork
plâtre *m* à briqueter plaster for plaster bricks
plâtre *m* à modeler modelling plaster; filling-in plaster
plâtre *m* à mouler plaster for moulding
plâtre *m* à projeter plaster for spraying
plâtre *m* courant ordinary plaster; standard plaster
plâtre *m* de finition finishing plaster
plâtre *m* de moulage plaster of Paris
plâtre *m* de surfaçage plaster to give smooth finish
plâtre *m* fin fine plaster; finishing-coat plaster; setting coat plaster
plâtre *m* gros coarse plaster; first-coat plaster; rendering coat plaster
plâtre *m* lissé trowelled plaster
plâtre *m* pour les enduits extérieurs plaster for outside use
plâtre *m* THD (très haute dureté) very high hardness plaster
plâtrer *v* plaster (to)
plâtrerie *f* plaster-work; plastering
plâtres *m* spéciaux special-purpose plasters
plâtrier *m* plasterer
plâtrière *f* gypsum-quarry; gypsum-furnace
pointe *f* pour plaque de plâtre plaster-board nail
ponçage *m* sanding (down); rubbing down
poutrelle *f* hourdis deadened beam
prêt à l'emploi *adj* ready for use
prise *m* setting (plaster, cement)

raccord *m* join; filling in; point (masonry); touch up (paint)
raccord *m* au plâtre fill in with plaster
rainurer *v* groove (to)

ralentisseur *m* **de prise** setting retarder
ratissage *m* combing; raking
rebouchage *m*; **rebouchement** *m* filling; restopping; stopping up again; filling up again
reboucher *v* fill in (to); fill in again (to)
reboucheur *m* filler; stopping material;
stopper
rétracter (se) *v* shrink (to); retract (to);
contract (to)
riflard *m* plasterer's scraper
rosace *f* ceiling rose

saignée *f* groove (eg on a surface)
sceller *v* seal (to); embed (to)
séchage *m* drying; drying out
sécher *v* dry (to); dry out (to)
serrage *m* tightening; binding; application of
plaster for maximum grip; compaction
sous-face *f* **d'un plancher** underside of a
floor
staff *m* staff; (le staff est un mélange de
filasse et de plâtre = staff is a mixture of tow
and plaster)
support *m* **du plâtre** plaster base; plaster
support

suspendre *v* suspend (to); hang up (to)
suspendu,-e *adj* suspended
suspension *f* suspension; suspending
suspente *f* suspender; suspension piece

taloche *f* plasterer's hawk; float
taloche *f* **à pointes** scratcher; scratch trowel
taloche *f* **plastique pointue** pointed plastic
hawk
talocher *v* float (to)
treillis *m* **céramique** wire netting with
intersections protected by ceramic buttons
treillis *m* **métallique** wire netting; lattice
work; metal trellis
truelle *f* trowel; plasterer's trowel
truelle *f* **à joint** jointing trowel
truelle *f* **berthelet** berthelet trowel; toothed
edge trowel
truelle *f* **bretellée** toothed trowel; serrated
edge trowel
truelle *f* **langue de chat** pointing trowel
truelle *f* **triangulaire** triangular trowel

vermiculite *f* vermiculite

13. PEINTRE-DÉCORATEUR

abrasif *m* abrasive
accessoire *m* accessory
additif *m* additive
adhérence *f* adhesion
adjuvant *m* additive
alcool *m* **dénaturé** methylated spirit;
denatured alcohol
alcool *m* **à brûler** methylated spirit
antigoutte *adj* non-drip
antirouille *f*; also *adj* antirust (paint)
aplanir *v* level (to); smooth out (to)
apprêt *m* priming; size; sizing (with sealer)

apprêt *m* **anti-corrosion** anti-corrosion
primer
apprêter *v* prime (to) (surface for painting);
prepare (to); make ready (to); size (to)
arête *f* arris; edge; ridge
artisan *m* craftsman; artisan
aspérité *f* roughness; unevenness

badigeon *m* distemper; whitewash
badigeonner *v* distemper (to); whitewash
(to)

balai *m* **à encoller** paperhanger's brush
bi-couche *f* double layer; double coat
bicolore *adj* two-tone; bicoloured
bordage *m* plugging and filling prior to wallpapering
bouchage *m* stopping up; obstruction; stoppage; plugging; plugging up; sealing
boucher *v* top up (to); plug (to); plug up (to); seal (to)
bourrelet *m* draught-excluder
brillant,-e *adj* gloss; glossy finish
brosse *f* paintbrush; brush
brosse *f* **à étaler** wallpapering dry brush
brosse *f* **à goudronner** tar-brush
brosse *f* **de tapissier** paperhanging brush
brosse *f* **en fil de fer** wire brush
brosse *f* **métallique** wire brush
brosse *f* **à encoller le papier peint** wallpapering paste brush
brosser *v* brush (to); scrub (to)

calfeutrage *m*; **calfeutrement** *m* filling; filler; draughtproofing; stopping up
calfeutrer *v* fill (to); draughtproof (to); stop up (to)
caoutchouc *m* **mousse** sponge rubber
carreau *m* floor or wall tile; pane (window); tiled floor
carreau *m* **au mur** wall tile
carreau *m* **de carrelage** floor tile
carreau *m* **de faïence** ceramic wall tile
carreau *m* **par terre** floor tile
carrelage *m* tile(d) floor; tiles; tiling
carrelage *m* **de sol** floor tiles; floor tiling
carrelage *m* **mural** wall tiles; wall tiling
carreler *v* tile (to)
carrelette *f* tile cutter
chalumeau *m* blowlamp; blow-torch
chape *f* **d'usure** screed laid as floor surface
chape *f* **de revêtement** screed laid as base for floor covering
chauler *v* whitewash (to) (eg a wall)
ciment *m* **joint carrelage** grouting for tiles
cire *f* wax
cire *f* **d'abeilles** beeswax
cire *f* **liquide bois** wood polish, liquid
ciseau *m* **pour carreaux** tile chisel
ciseaux *mpl* **multi-usages** general purpose scissors

collage *m* gluing
colle *f* glue; paste; wallpaper paste; adhesive
colle *f* **carrelage en pâte** tile adhesive, paste form
colle *f* **de pâte** wallpaper paste
coloris *m* colour; shade
corps *m* body; substance
couche *f* layer; coat (eg of paint)
couche *f* **d'impression** priming coat
couche *f* **de finition** finishing coat; top coat; finishing layer; skimming coat; setting coat (plaster)
couche *f* **de revêtement** layer ready for covering (eg with tiles)
couleur *f* shade; colour
coulis *m* grout
coupe-carreaux *m* tile cutter
coupe-trou *m* hole cutter
couteau *m* cutting knife
couteau *m* **à décaper** stripping knife
couteau *m* **à démastiquer** hacking knife
couteau *m* **à enduire** coating knife
couteau *m* **à lame fixe** cutting knife with fixed blade
couteau *m* **à lame retractable** cutting knife with retractable blade
couteau *m* **à maroufler** pasting knife
couteau *m* **à mastiquer** putty knife; stopping knife
couteau *m* **à palette** palette knife
couteau *m* **de peintre** palette knife
craquelure *f* crackle; fine cracks
crépi *m* masonry paint; textured paint; cement or plaster rendering; roughcast; rendering
crépir *v* render (to); roughcast (to); cover with masonry paint (to)
crépissage *m* rendering; roughcasting; coating with masonry paint
croisillons *mpl* tile-spacers
cutter *m* cutting tool with disposable blades

décapage *m* cleaning (see also décaper); sanding; stripping (eg paint)
décapant *m* tile cleaner; paint stripper
décaper *v* strip (to) (eg paint); clean (to)
décaper *v* **à la sableuse** sandblast (to)

décaper *v* **au chalumeau** burn off (to) (paint)
décaper *v* **au papier de verre** sand (to);
sandpaper (to)
décolorer *v* fade (to)
décorateur *m*; **décoratrice** *f* decorator
(interior)
décoration *f* decoration
décorer *v* decorate (to)
détergent *m* detergent
disque *m* **abrasif** abrasive disc
durable *adj* durable; long lasting

ébarboir *m* triangular scraper
ensemble *m* **d'outils** set of tools
enduire *v* coat (to); cover (to)
enduit *m* coating; coat; rendering
enduit *m* **de jointoiement** grout
enduit *m* **étanche** sealant
enduit *m* **intérieur** interior coating; interior
rendering
ensemblier *m* interior designer
entretien *m* **et brillant des marbres** protector and brightener for marble
éponge *f* sponge
essence *f* **de térébenthine** spirit of turpentine
expansé,-e *adj* expanded; embossed
(wallpaper)

faïençage *m* surface cracking
feuille *f* **abrasive** abrasive sheet
fini *m* finish
finition *f* finishing; finish
fissuration *f* cracking
fissure *f* crack; fissure
foret *m* drill
foret *m* **à percussion** impact drill
foret *m* **hélicoïdal** rotary drill; twist drill
foret *m* **pour carreaux** tile drill
foret *m* **pour le verre** glass drill
foret *m* **pour marteaux perforateurs**
hammer drill
frise *f* frieze

garniture *f* fittings; fitments; lagging; jacket
gratter *v* scrape (to)

grattoir *m* scraper
grattoir *m* **triangulaire** shave-hook; triangular scraper

huile *f* **de lin** linseed oil
huile *f* **de lin bouillie** boiled linseed oil
huile *f* **de lin crue** raw linseed oil
huile *f* **de lin cuite** boiled linseed oil
huile *f* **de teck** teak oil

intérieur *m*; also *adj* interior; inside

lame *f* **de couteau** knife blade
lampe *f* **à souder** blowlamp
laque *f* shellac; lacquer; lac
laquer *v* shellac (to)
laqué blanc *adj* white gloss (finish)
laqué,-e *adj* lacquered
lisser *v* smooth (to)
lustre *f* shine; gloss

machine *f* **à crépir** machine for applying
masonry paint, etc
machine *f* **à encoller le papier peint** wallpaper pasting machine
marbre *m* marble
maroufler *v* paste (to); line (to)
marteau *m* **perforateur** hammer drill
mastic *m* putty; cement
mastic *m* **calfeutrement** stopping putty
mastiquer *v* putty (to); fill in (to); grout (to)
mat,-e *adj* matt
matériau *m*; **matériaux** *mpl* material;
materials
matériau *m* **de revêtement** covering
material; cladding; coating material; lining
material
mélanger *v* mix (to); blend (to)
molette *f* **de tapisserie** wallpaper trimmer
mortier *m* **colle carrelage** adhesive tile
mortar
multicouche *adj* multiple coatings; multicoat

117

nettoyage *m*; nettoiement *m* cleaning; cleansing
nettoyant *m* cleaner
nettoyer *v* clean (to)
neuf, neuve *adj* new
▪ à l'état neuf = as new

pâlir *v* fade (to)
papier *m* à tapisser lining paper (wall); wallpaper
papier *m* peint wallpaper
papier *m* peint lavable et lessivable washable wallpaper
papier *m* peint vinyl vinyl wallpaper
papier-cache *m* adhésif masking tape
papier *m* de tenture wallpaper
parquet *m* parquet floor; wooden floor
parqueter *v* lay a wooden or parquet floor (to)
pavage *m* paving; pavement
peigne *f* à colle carrelage comb for tile adhesive
peindre *v* paint (to)
peindre *v* les boiseries paint the woodwork (to)
peintre *m/f* painter
peintre *m/f* en bâtiment house painter
peintre-décorateur *m* painter and decorator
peinture *f* painting; paintwork; paint
peinture *f* à deux couches two coats of paint
peinture *f* acrylique acrylic paint
peinture *f* antirouille antirust paint
peinture *f* bitumineuse bitumastic paint
peinture *f* brillante gloss paint
peinture *f* crépi masonry paint; textured paint
peinture *f* émulsion emulsion paint
peinture *f* extérieure exterior paint
peinture *f* fraîche!; attention à la peinture! wet paint!
peinture *f* intérieure interior paint
peinture *f* laquée gloss-finish paint; enamel
peinture *f* protectrice protective coating
peinture *f* satineé satin-finish paint
peinture *f* sol floor paint
peinture *f* toiture roof paint

peinture *f* vernissante enamel
perdre son éclat *v* fade (to)
pierre *f* ponce pumice stone
pince *f* à rogner tile clippers
pince *f* coupe carreaux tile cutter pliers
pinceau *m* brush; paint brush
pinceau *m* plat flat brush
pinceau *m* rond à réchampir round brush with shaped bristles
pistolet *m* à mastic mastic gun
ponce *f* pumice
poncer *v* sand (to); sandpaper (to); rub down (to)
préencollé,-e *adj* prepasted
première *f* couche priming coat
protection *f* des marbres protective coating for marble
protéger *v* protect (to)

raclette *f* caoutchouc rubber squeegee
raclette *f* vitre window squeegee
raccord *m* repeat of wallpaper pattern
ragrèage *m* autolissant self-smoothing fix and grout (for floor tiles)
rebouchage *m* filling in; refilling
reboucheur *m* filler
réchampir *v* pick out (to) (with another colour paint)
réchampissage *v* picking out (with another colour paint)
règle *f* à couper le papier peint wallpaper cutting ruler
remettre *v* à neuf renovate (to); refurbish (to)
repeindre *v* repaint (to)
revêtement *m* surface; coating; facing; cladding; covering
revêtement *m* du sol floor covering
revêtement *m* enduit lining
revêtement *m* mural wall covering
revêtement *m* mural imitation carrelage imitation tile wall covering
revêtement *m* mural textile textile-type wall covering
revêtir *v* cover (to); line (to); face (to); coat (to)
rouleau *m* roller; roll (eg of wallpaper)
rouleau *m* "murs et plafonds" wall and

ceiling paint roller
rouleau *m* **crépi** masonry paint roller
rouleau *m* **laqueur souple** emulsion paint
  roller
rouleau *m* **léger** light roller
rouleau *m* **à peinture** paint roller
roulette *f* **pour écraser les joints de papier
peint** seam roller (wallpaper)

satiné,-e *adj.* satin finish
shampooing *m* **parquet** detergent floor
  cleaner
souillure *f* stain; blemish
sous-couche *f* undercoat
spatule *f* spatula
surface *f* **lisse** smooth surface
surface *f* **nue** bare surface; unbroken surface

table *f* **à tapisser** wallpaper pasting table
tampon *m* **à peindre** painting pad
tapisser *v* wallpaper (to); line (to); cover (to)
tapisserie *f* upholstery; wallpaper; tapes-try;

wall covering
tapissier *m* upholsterer
teinte *f* **pour bois** wood stain
teinter *v* stain (to)
temps *m* **de séchage** drying time
tenture *f* hanging
tenture *f* **murale** wall covering
térébenthine *f* turpentine
textile mural *m* wall textile; wall covering;
  wallpaper
toile *f* **de verre** glass cloth; glass fabric

vernir *v* lacquer (to); varnish (to)
vernis *m* varnish
vernis *m* **bateau** boat varnish
vernis *m* **marin** marine varnish
vernissage *m* lacquering; varnishing
vitre *f* pane of glass

white spirit *m* white spirit

14. COULEURS

ambré,-e *adj* amber
ardoisé,-e *adj* slate-coloured
argenté,-e *adj* silver (colour); silvery
âtre *suff* ish (suff); (eg bleu+âtre = bleuâtre
  adj = bluish)
azur *m* azure; sky-blue
azuré, -e *adj* azure; sky-blue

beige *adj* beige
bicolore *adj* bicoloured; two-tone
blanc cerusé *adj* ceruse white
blanc, blanche *adj* white
bleu,-e *adj* blue
bleu ardoise *adj* slate blue
bleu ciel *adj* sky blue
bleu marine *adj* navy blue

bleu outremer *adj* ultramarine
bleu paon *adj* peacock blue
bleu roi *adj* royal blue
bleu vert *adj* blue-green; aquamarine
bleuâtre *adj* bluish
bordeaux *adj* maroon
brillant,-e *adj* bright; brilliant; (eg brillante
  couleur = bright colour)
brun,-e *adj* brown
brunâtre *adj* brownish

cerise *adj* cerise; cherry-red
clair,-e *adj* light; (eg gris clair = light grey)
coloris *m* colour; shade
■ **carte de coloris** *f* = shade card
couleur *f* colour; shade; tint; hue

coleurs

couleurs fondamentales *fpl* primary colours

doré,-e; d'or *adj* golden; gilded; gilt

emeraude *adj* emerald

foncé,-e *adj* dark; (eg bleu foncé = dark blue)
fuchsia *adj* fuchsia colour

granité,-e *adj* granite; grained; (eg granité
  gris = granite grey)
gris,-e *adj* grey
gris acier *adj* steel grey
gris brume *adj* mist grey
gris perle *adj* pearl grey
gris-bleu *adj* blue-grey
grisâtre *adj* greyish

jaunâtre *adj* yellowish
jaune *adj* yellow
jaune canari *adj* canary yellow
jaune citron *adj* lemon yellow
jaune d'or *adj* golden yellow
jaune paille *adj* straw coloured

lavande *adj* lavender
lilas *adj* lilac

marbré,-e *adj* marble; marbled; mottled;
  (e.g. marbré beige = marbled beige)
marine *adj* navy (blue)
marron *adj* brown
mauve *adj* mauve
moucheté,-e *adj* speckled; (eg bleu
  moucheté = speckled blue)

noir,-e *adj* black
nuance *f* shade; hue

orange *m*; *adj* orange

paille *adj* straw-coloured
pâle *adj* pale; light; (eg bleu pâle = pale
  blue; light blue)
pâle violet,-ette *adj* violet (pale violet??)
parme *adj* violet
pastel *adj* pastel; (eg vert pastel = pastel
  green)
pourpre *adj* purple

rosâtre *adj* pinkish
rose *adj* pink
rosé,-e *adj* pink; pinkish
rouge *adj* red
rouge-cerise *adj* cherry-red
rougeâtre *adj* reddish
sable *adj* sand colour
saumon *adj* salmon colour
sombre *adj* dark; (eg vert sombre = dark
  green)
teinte *f* shade; hue; tint
tendre *adj*; **tendresse** *adj* soft; delicate; (eg
  rose tendre/tendresse = soft/delicate rose
  colour
turquoise *adj* turquoise

verdâtre *adj* greenish
vert,-e *adj* green
vert bouteille *adj* bottle green
vert emeraud *adj* emerald green
vert jade *adj* jade green
vert olive *adj* olive green
vert pomme *adj* apple green
vert-de-gris *adj* grey(ish) green
violacé, -e *adj* purplish; mauvish
violet,-ette *adj* purple

[Note: En français, quand la couleur est seul, normalement elle fait fonction d'un nom]

ENGLISH - FRENCH

1. ARCHITECT

according to regulations conformément *adv* aux regléments
additional clause avenant *m*
advance notice préavis *m*
aerial plan of mass plan *m* de masse
allocation répartition *f*
alter (to) modifier (se) *v*; transformer *v*
altitude hauteur *f*
amendment (to a contract) avenant *m*
amount partie *f*
annexe annexe *f*
apartment appartement *m*
appendix annexe *f*
application documents and plans required for the 'permis de construire' dossier *m* de permis de construire
appropriation of ground emprise *f* au sol
architect architecte *m*
architect's fee honoraires *mpl* de l'architecte
architect's instruction to builder ordre *m* de service
architectural diagram of each storey plan *m* de chaque niveau
architectural plan plan *m* de chaque niveau
area of land measured in ares aréage *m*
artisan artisan *m*
aspect aspect *m*
aspect (of a building) exposition *f*; orientation *f*
Association of Architects Ordre *m* des Architectes
association; professional association ordre *m*
availability of services viabilité *f*

back-door porte *f* de derrière; dégagement *m*
basic area of house surface *f* hors œuvre nette; see also 'superficie'
be moved (to) déplacer (se) *v*
block of flats immeuble *m*; immeuble *m* de rapport; immeuble *m* d'appartements
blueprint photocalque *m* bleu
boundary fence clôture *f* de bornage
boudary limit borne *f*
boundary marking bornage *m*
boundary stone or marker borne *f*
break off (to) (a contract) rompre *v*

build (to) bâtir *v*; construire *v*; édifier *v*
builder constructeur *m*
building bâtiment *m*; édifice *m*; aménagement *m*; construction *f*
building contractor entrepreneur *m* de constructions
building fault dommage-ouvrage *m*
building land/site terrain *m* à bâtir
building materials matériaux *mpl* de construction
building permit permis *m* de construire
building site chantier *m* de construction; chantier *m*
building stage with doors and windows completed à la mise hors d'air
building stage with roof completed à la mise hors d'eau
built-up area zone *f* bâtie
business contract (eg building work contract) contrat *m* d'entreprise
buy a house at the plan stage acheter *v* une maison sur plan
bye-laws règlement *m* intérieur

cadastral register cadastre *m*
cadastral survey cadastre *m*
cancellation résiliation *f*
cancellation of a contract résiliation *f* d'un contrat
capacity (eg volume of reservoir) contenance *f*
capital fonds *m*
carpentry menuiserie *f*
central heating chauffage *m* central
certificate of conformity certificat *m* de conformité
certificate of origin certificat *m* d'origine
certificate stating planning and building requirements to be met certificat *m* d'urbanisme
certified report constat *m*
chain measure chaine *f*
chain, surveyor's chaine *f* d'arpenteur
change (to) transformer *v*
change; changeover passage *m*
characteristic propriété *f*
charge servitude *f*
clause clause *f*

clearing défrichement *m*; défrichage *m*
colour couleur *f*; coloris *m*
commune commune *f*
company entreprise *f*
complete (to) achever *v*
component élément *m*; pièce *f*
condition condition *f*
conform to (to) conformer à (se) *v*
conservatory jardin *m* d'hiver; serre *f*
consider (to) projeter *v*
constraint servitude *f*
construct (to) bâtir *v*; construire *v*; édifier *v*
construction construction *f*
construction contract contrat *m* de construction
construction fault or damage dommage-ouvrage *m*; vice *m* de construction
construction stage étape *f* de la construction
constructor constructeur *m*
contract contrat *m*
contract placed with a contractor/company contrat *m* passé à une entreprise
contracting parties parties *fpl* contractantes
control réglementation *f*
convert (to) convertir *v*; aménager *v*
converting; conversion aménagement *m*
cooling-off time délai *m* de réflexion
copy exemplaire *m*
council offices mairie *f*
craftsman artisan *m*
cross-sectional drawing coupe *f* transversale
cubic metre mètre *m* cube
cupboard armoire f
cupboard (built-in) placard *m*

deadline délai *m*
defect défaut *m*; vice *m*; malfaçon *f*
delay délai *m*
delivery date délai *m* de livraison
delivery delay délai *m* de livraison
delivery remise *f*; livraison *f*
demarcation bornage *m*
demolish (to) démolir *v*
demolition démolition *f*
design dessin *m*
designer dessinateur *m*; dessinatrice *f*
detached house maison *f* individuelle
detailed conditions cahier *m* des charges détaillés

detailed estimate devis *m* descriptif
detailed specification cahier *m* des charges détaillés
details of implementation modalités *fpl* de mise en œuvre
develop (to) aménager *v*
developed property propriété *f* bâtie
developing mise *f* au point
development déroulement *m*
diagram schèma *m*; schéme *m*
discount remise *f*
displace (to) déplacer *v*
distraint (legal) saisie *f*
distribution répartition *f*
district commune *f*
divided into plots parcellaire *adj*
document document *m*; pièce *f*
documentation dossier *m*
dominating land (of easements on other land) fonds *m* dominant
dossier dossier *m*
draft (to) (a document) rédiger *v*
draft project avant-projet *m*
drafting (of a document) rédaction *f*
drainage system système *m* de drainage
draughtsman; draughtswoman dessinateur *m*; dessinatrice *f*
draw (to) dessiner *v*
draw up a contract (to) rédiger *v* un contrat
draw up a document (to) établir *v* un document
draw up a report (to) faire *v* un procès-verbal
drawing dessin *m*
drawing board planche *m* à dessin
drawing paper papier *m* à dessin
drawing-up (a document) rédaction *f*
drawing-up a lease rédaction *f* de bail

easement servitude *f*
effecting mise *f* au point
electricity supply alimentation *f* en électricité
element élément *m*
elevation hauteur *f*
enclosed land terrain *m* clos
enclosure clôture *f*
encumbrance servitude *f*
end (to) achever *v*

endorsement avenant *m*
enterprise entreprise *f*
entry (into accounts ledger) passation *f*
equip (to) aménager *v*
erect (to) bâtir *v*; édifier *v*
establish (to) établir *v*
estate fonds *m*; propriété *f*
estate agent agent *m* immobilier
estate free from encumbrances immeuble *m* sans servitudes ni hypothèques
estimate devis *m*
estimate of costs mètré *m*
examination of the request for a permit to build instruction *f* de la demande de permis de construire
excavation terrassement *m*; fouille *f*
exchange controls réglementation *f* des changes
exit dégagement *m*
expert expert *m*
expert appraisal/valuation expertise *f*
exposition exposition *f*; orientation *f*
express (to) énoncer *v*
extension (to a building) annexe *f*
extension of time prolongation *f* de temps

facade façade *f*
facing south/north/east/west exposé au sud/nord/est/ouest
fault défaut *m*; vice *m*
fault (due to bad workmanship) malfaçon *f*
fee honoraires *mpl*
fence; fencing clôture *f*
file dossier *m*
final verification and acceptance that building work has been satisfactorily completed to specification réception *f* des ouvrages/travaux
finalising/settling mise *f* au point
finish (to) achever *v*
fire escape échelle *f* de sauvetage
firm entreprise *f*
fit out (to) aménager *v*
fitted kitchen cuisine *f* équipée
fitting-out aménagement *m*
fix (to) (a price) établir *v*
flaw défaut *m*; vice *m*
for conversion aménager (à) *v*

foreclosure saisie *f*
form formulaire *m*
form; mode modalité *f*
formal demand; formal notice mise *f* en demeure
forwarding transmission *f*
foundations and walls gros œuvre *m*
French Land Commission S.A.F.E.R. (Société Aménagement Foncier et d'Établissement Rural)
front façade *f*
front steps (of house) perron *m*
fund(s) fonds *m*

garage garage *m*
garden jardin *m*
gas supply alimentation *f* en gaz
geometer géomètre *m*
geometrician géomètre *m*
give precise details (to) préciser *v*
glass items vitrerie *f*
glazing vitrerie *f*
gross area of house surface *f* hors œuvre brute
gross habitable floor area surface *f* hors œuvre brute
ground terrain *m*
ground floor rez-de-chaussée *m*; rdc *abb*
guarantee garantie *f*

habitable floor area surface *f* hors œuvre nette (see also 'superficie')
habitable surface area of dwelling surface *f* habitable
heat bridge pont *m* thermique *m*
heating system système *m* de chauffage
hectare (10,000 sq. metres = 2.4711 acres) hectare *m*; ha *abb*
hedge haie *f*; clôture *f*
height hauteur *f*
house plan plan *m* de la maison
house survey visite *f* d'expert
house-builder constructeur *m* de maisons
housing development ensemble *m*; lotissement *m*
housing development (high density) grand ensemble *m*

housing development plan plan *m* d'ensemble
housing estate or site lotissement *m*
housing scheme ensemble *m*

implementation (of a regulation) mise *f* en œuvre
installation plan plan *m* d'installation
instructions prescriptions *fpl*
insurance against building faults assurance *f* dommage-ouvrage
intended usage of premises/dwelling (eg private or commercial) destination *f* du local *f*
interior designer architecte *m* d'intérieur
introduction implantation *f*
invoice facture *f*
ironmonger's (shop) quincaillerie *f*
ironmongery quincaillerie *f*
item in contract prescription *f*; stipulation *f*
items covered by contract éléments *mpl* compris dans le contrat

joinery menuiserie *f*

kitchen unit élément *m* de cuisine

labour main-d'œuvre *f*
labour cost(s) prix/coût *m* de la main-d'œuvre
lack of upkeep défaut *m* d'entretien
ladder échelle *f*
land fonds *m*; terrain *m*
land on which one can build technically and legally terrain *m* constructible
land registry cadastre *m*
land surveying arpentage *m*; levé *m* de terrains
landlord propriétaire *m*
landscape; scenery paysage *m*; paysager, paysagère *adj.*
landscaped garden jardin paysagé *m*; parc *m* paysager *m*
landscaped garden or park parc *m* à l'anglaise *m*
landscaping aménagements *mpl* paysagers

latent or hidden fault/defect vice *m* caché; défaut *m* caché
lawn pelouse *f*; gazon *m*
lay out (to) aménager *v*
lease-back cession-bail *f*
legal flaw or irregularity vice *m* de forme
length longueur *f*
level étage *m*; niveau *m*
locating implantation *f*
location plan plan *m* de situation
logitudinale cross-section coupe *f* longitudinale

main contract contrat *m* principal
main road route *f* nationale
manpower main-d'œuvre *f*
marking out implantation *f*; traçage *m*
means modalité *f*
measure mesure *f*
measurement mètré *m*; métrage *m*
measurement (process) mesurage *m*
measuring tape mètre *m* à ruban
method of construction méthode *f* de construction
method of insulation méthode *f* d'isolement
metal items metallerie *f*
metalwork metallerie *f*
method modalité *f*
methods/terms of payment modalités *fpl* de paiement
metre mètre *m*
metre rule mètre *m*
minutes compte-rendu *m* de séance procès-verbal *m*; procès-verbaux *mpl*
mirror items miroiterie *f*
mode modalité *f*
modern architecture architecture *f* moderne
modernisation rénovation *f*; modernisation *f*
modernise (to) renover *v*; moderniser *v*
modify (to) modifier *v*
move (to) déplacer *v*

negotiate (to) négocier *v*
noise bruit *m*
noise level niveau *m* de bruit
noise rating pondération *f* des bruits
noise reduction réduction *f* de bruit

notary notaire *m*
notary public notaire *m*
notification that permitted building work
 has been completed déclaration *f*
 d'achèvement des travaux; (see also
 'certificat de conformité')

office of mayor mairie *f*
orchard verger *m*
order ordre *m*
ordnance surveyor géomètre *m* du cadastre
origin origine *f*
ornamental lake lac *m* d'agrément
outline (of a project) esquisse *f*
outline drawing ébauche *f*
outline specification devis *m* préliminaire
overall length longueur *f* hors-tout
overall net floor area superficie *f* de
 plancher hors œuvre nette
overestimate surestimer *v*
owner propriétaire *m*
owner (commissioning building work)
 maître *m* d'ouvrage
ownership propriété *f*

parcel (of land) parcelle *f*
part partie *f*; pièce *f*
party (person signing a contract) partie *f*
passage passage *m*
passage (in appartment) dégagement *m*
passing on transmission *f*
payment by cheque règlement *m* par chèque
payment/settlement (eg of an invoice)
 règlement *m*
penalty clause clause *f* pènale
permit to build permis *m* de construire
permit to demolish permis *m* de démolir
piece of land fonds *m* de terre
placing (an order) passation *f*
plan plan *m*; projet *m*; schèma *m*; schéme *m*
plan (to) projeter *v*
plan of elevations plan *m* des facades
plan of local land use Plan *m* d'Occupation
 des Sols
plan of mass plan *m* de masse
plan of site plan *m* d'implantation; plan *m* de
 construction

plan, architectural plan *m* de chaque niveau
plane plan *m*
planning permission permis *m* de construire
planning provision/reqirement disposition *f*
 d'urbanisme
plant with grass (to) gazonner *v*
planting with grass gazonnage *m*;
 gazonnement *m*
plot of land terrain *m*
plot/parcel of land parcelle *f* de terre;
 lotissement *m*
plumbing plomberie *f*
plumbing materials plomberie *f*
possession of jouissance *f*
postponement remise *f*
power supply alimentation *f* en énergie
practicability viabilité *f*
prefabricated construction construction *f* en
 éléments préfabriqués
preliminary estimate devis *m* estimatif
preliminary study avant-projet *m*
premises immeuble *m*
preparation mise *f* en œuvre
prescription prescription *f*
prior notice préavis *m*
private company entreprise *f* priveé
private easements attached to the land/site
 servitudes *fpl* privées grevant le terrain
private entrance dégagement *m* d'entrée
produce a draft agreement/contract (to)
 établir *v* un projet d'accord/de contrat *v*
professional expert *m*
professional report on whether property is
 free of parasites (eg termites etc) constat
 m parasitaire
progress déroulement *m*
progress of building work déroulement *m*
 des travaux
progress of the contract déroulement *m* du
 contrat
progress report compte-rendu *m*
project projet *m*
project (to) projeter *v*
project manager maître *m* d'œuvre
property propriété *f*; biens *mpl* immeubles;
 immobilier *m*
property developer promoteur *m* immobilier
proportional scale échelle *f* proportionnelle
proposed plan avant-projet *m*

proprietor propriétaire *m*
public notice of request for building permit
publicité *f* de la demande de permis de
construire
public utility company entreprise *f* de
service public
pylon pylône *m*

qualified building supervisor (eg architect,
builder) maître *m* d'œuvre qualifié
quantity surveying mètré *m*; métrage *m*
quantity surveyor métreur *m*; métreuse *f*;
métreur-vérificateur *m*
quotation offre *f* de prix

real estate bien *m* fonds
real estate/freehold propriété *f* fonciére
receipt; reception réception *f*
reconditioning remise *f* en état
refurbishment remise *f* en état
registration; registering enregistrement *m*
regulation(s) réglementation *f*; règlement *m*;
règlement *m* intégral
regulations in force réglementation *f* en
vigueur
regulations (instructions) prescriptions *fpl*
renovate (to) renover *v*
renovation rénovation *f*; remise *f* à neuf
repair (to) réparer *v*
repair; repairing réparation *f*
report compte-rendu *m*; rapport *m*; procès-
verbal *m*
request for deferment demande *f* de sursis
requirements for installation (site arrange-
ments) disposition *f* des lieux
rescinding résiliation *f*
residential area quartier *m* résidentiel
restatement mise *f* au point
restoration remise *f* en état; remise *f* à neuf;
restauration *f*; rénovation *f*
restore (to) restaurer *v*
restore (to) (a building) renover *v*
restoring réparation *f*
rider avenant *m*
right of way droit *m* de passage; servitude *f*
de passage
right to draw water droit *m* de puisage

right to pump water (from the ground)
droit *m* de puisage
road; roadway route *f*
roadworks chantier *m*
room (of house) pièce *f*; salle *f*
rough sketch ébauche *f*; esquisse *f*
route route *f*
rules and regulations règlement *m* intérieur
rural/urban district commune *f* rurale/
urbaine

sale and leaseback cession-bail *f*
sample échantillon *m*
scale échelle *f*
scale drawing plan *m*
scale model modèle *m* réduit
schedule (to a contract) annexe *f*
schedule of conditions cahier *m* des charges
scheme projet *m*; schèma *m*; schéme *m*
secondary road route *f* départmentale
section coupe *f*
sectional drawing dessin *m* de coupe
seizure saisie *f*
service (to) (eg a building plot) viabiliser
set of architectural/building plans dossier *m*
de plans
setting mise *f*
setting out implantation *f*
shade coloris *m*; couleur *f*
sharing out répartition *f*
shell (of a building) gros œuvre *m*
shift (to) déplacer *v*
sign (to) signer *v*
signature; signing signature *f*
signing (a contract, deed) passation *f*
signing business contracts passation *f* des
marchés
signing the deed of sale passation *f* de l'acte
site plan plan *m* d'implantation; plan *m* de
situation
site with services laid on terrain *m* viabilisé
■ entièrement viabilisé = fully serviced
site with/without services laid on terrain *m*
avec/sans viabilité
siting implantation *f*
size (of land area) contenance *f*
sketch dessin *m*; esquisse *f*; schèma *m*;
schéme *m*

sketch out (to) ébaucher *v*
slip road voie *f* de dégagement
smooth, well-kept, lawn gazon *m* anglais
solicitor (conveyancing) notaire *m*
solid mass plan plan *m* de masse
sound bruit *m*
source origine *f*
specialist expert *m*
specification devis *m* descriptif ;
    spécification *f*; cahier *m* des charges
specifications prescriptions *fpl* techniques
specifications of a contract stipulations *fpl*
    d'un contrat
specified item (of contract) prescription *f*
specify (to) préciser *v*
square metre mètre *m* carré
stage étage *m*; étape *f*
standing (situation and condition) stand-
    ing *m*
start of building work ouverture *f* de
    chantier
state (to) énoncer *v*
statement énoncé *m*; procès-verbal *m*
statute of limitations prescription *f*
stipulate (to) préciser *v*
stipulation condition *f*
stipulation; item in contract; specified item
    stipulation *f*
storage units éléments *mpl* de rangement
storey étage *m*; niveau *m*
street level rez-de-chaussée *m*; rdc *abb*
structure construction *f*
style style *m*
substruction sous-œuvre *m*
summons mise *f* en demeure
supply (eg of gas, water) alimentation *f*
surface surface *f*; superficie *f*
surface area surface *f*; superficie *f*
surface-clearing (of ground, wood etc.)
    défrichement *m*; défrichage *m*
survey expertise *f*; levé *m*
survey, ground levé *m* de géomètre du
    cadastre; levé *m* de terrain
survey report rapport *m* d'expertise
surveyor expert *m*; géomètre *m*; expert
    géomètre *m*
surveyor (land) arpenteur *m*
surveyor (quantity) métreur *m*; métreuse *f*
surveyor's pole or rod jalon *m*

surveyor's report expertise *f*; levé *m* de
    géomètre
swimming pool piscine *f*

T-square équerre *f* à/en T
tap trade robinetterie *f*
taps and fittings robinetterie *f*
technical regulations prescriptions *fpl*
    techniques
technical specification cahier *m* des charges
    techniques *m*
tenure jouissance *f*
term of contract condition *f*
termination résiliation *f*
terms conditions *fpl;* termes *mpl*
terrace terrasse *f*
terrain terrain *m*
test sample échantillon *m* pour essai
texture texture *f*
third party tiers *m*
time for consideration délai *m* de réflexion
time limit délai *m*
town hall mairie *f*
town planning urbanisme *m*
town ville *f*; commune *f*
tracing paper papier *m* à calquer; papier-
    calque *m*; papier *m* translucide
transform (to) convertir *v*; transformer *v*
transversal cross-section coupe *f*
    transversale
turf gazon *m*
turf (to) gazonner *v*
turf, a motte *f* de gazon (une)
turfing gazonnage *m*; gazonnement *m*

underpin (to) réprendre *v* en sous-œuvre
underpinning sous-œuvre *m*
undersigned (the) soussigné *m*; soussignée
    f; also *adj*
undervalue sous-estimer *v*
undeveloped property propriété *f* non   bâtie
unit component élément *m*
unmetalled road route *f* non goudronnée
use jouissance *f*
using mise *f* en œuvre

valuation of a property expertise *f* d'un bien

129

valuer expert *m*
vendor's title to property origine *f* de propriété
village village *m*

wall (enclosing) clôture *f*
water supply alimentation *f* en eau; distribution *f* d'eau
way the fees are allocated mode *m* de répartition du partage des honoraires

way passage *m*; voie *f*
winter garden; conservatory jardin *m* d'hiver
wood merchant menuiserie *f*
wooded land terrain *m* boisé
wording énoncé *m*; rédaction *f*
work (building) ouvrage *m*; travaux *mpl*
work (finishing) second œuvre *f*
write (to) rédiger *v*

2. EARTHWORKS AND FOUNDATIONS

accelerator accélérateur *m*
access road voie d'accès *f*
adding concrete by pouring bétonnage *m*
additive additif *m*; adjuvant *m*
adjustable stay/support étai *m* réglable
aggregate agrégat *m*; granulat *m*
aggregate, heavy (eg iron shot) granulat *m* lourd
aggregate, light (eg pumice, expanded slag) granulat *m* léger
air-entraining agent entraineur *m* d'air
alignment alignement *m*
anchor (to) ancrer *v*
■ well-anchored = bien ancré
anchorage; anchoring ancrage *m*
angle of friction angle *m* de frottement
angle of slope angle *m* de talus
angledozer angle-dozer *m*
antifreeze additive for concrete antigel *m*
antifrost additive for concrete pare-gel *m*; antigélif *m*
appliance engin *m*
approach ramp rampe *f* d'accès
apron radier *m*
argillaceous argileux,-euse *adj*
artesian well puits *m* artésien

backfill remblai *m*
backfill (to) remblayer *v*
backfilling remblayage *m*; remblaiement *m*
ballast blocaille *f*
bank talus *m*
bank up (to) remblayer *v*
banking up remblai *m*
barrow brouette *f*
barrowful brouettée *f*
barrowing brouettage *m*
barrowload brouettée *f*
base fondation *f*; fondement *m*; sou-bassement *m*
base-plate; footing semelle *f*
base-slab semelle *f*; radier *m*
basement sous-sol *m*; soubassement *m*; cave *f*
basic structure gros œuvre *m*
batter (eg of a wall) talus *m*
batter (to) (eg embankment) taluter *v*
bed assise *f*; lit *m*
bed of concrete lit *m* de béton
beetle dame *f*; demoiselle *f*; masse *f*
blending malaxage *m*; malaxation *f*
block bloc *m*
block of masonry massif *m* de maçonnerie
block (to) bloquer *v*; obstruer *v*; boucher *v*
brace étrésillon *m*

breadth largeur *f*
break (to) concasser *v*
bricklayer's pin chevillette *f* de maçon
bucket seau *m*; godet *m* (d'une chargeuse)
bucket, galvanized-iron seau *m* en tôle galvanisée
bucketful seau *m*
building land terrain *m* à bâtir
building rubble or debris décombres *mpl*
building site chantier *m*; chantier *m* de construction
bulldoze (to) passer *v* au bulldozer
bulldozer bulldozer *m*
bush hammer boucharde *f*
bush hammer finish bouchardage *m*

calcareous clay marne *f*
carcass (of house) cage *f*
carry out earthworks (to) faire *v* des travaux de terrassement
cartage; carting camionage *m*
case coffre *m*
casing (of excavation) blindage *m* par caissons
cast jet *m*
cast to the bank (eg of hole) jet *m* sur berge
cast to the bench jet *m* sur banquette
cast, horizontal jet *m* horizontal
cast, shovel's jet *m* de pelle
caving in éboulement *m*; effondrement *m*
cement ciment *m*
cement (to) cimenter *v*
cement coating; screed chape *f* ciment
cement manufacturer cimentier *m*
cement mortar used for screeding or rendering ragréage *m*
cement, blast-furnace slag ciment *m* de haut fourneau; CHF *abb*
cement, grey ciment *m* gris *m*
cement, high alumina ciment *m* fondu
cement, hydraulic ciment *m* hydraulique
cement, jointing ciment *m* joint
cement, Portland ciment *m* de Portland; ciment *m* Portland; ciment *m* Portland artificiel; CPA *abb*; ciment *m* Portland pur
cement, Portland blast-furnace ciment *m* Portland au laitier; ciment *m* de laitier au clinker; CLK *abb*

cement, pozzolana ciment *m* pouzzolanique
cement, quick-setting ciment *m* à prise rapide
cement, rapid setting ciment *m* prompt
cement, refractory ciment *m* réfractaire
cement, reinforced ciment *m* armé
cement, slag ciment *m* de laitier
cement, slow-setting ciment *m* à prise lente
cement, white ciment *m* blanc
cementation; cementing cimentage *m*; cimentation *f*
cementer (person) cimentier *m*
cementer's pattern marker roller boucharde *f* de cimentier
channel rigole *f*
chipping; chisel-work burinage *m*
chippings (gravel) gravillon(s) *m(mpl)*
chisel burin *m*; burin *m* à froid; ciseau *m*; ciseaux *mpl*
chisel, mason's ciseau *m* de maçon
chiseling burinage *m*
chocking calage *m*
clamping blocage *m*
classification of terrain classification *f* des terrain
clawed spike-lever pied-de-biche *m*
clay argile *f*; argileux,-euse *adj*
clay soil glaise *f*
clay, calcareous marne *f*
cleaning (surface) décapage *m*; ravalement *m*
cleaning down ragrément *m*
clear (to) débarrasser *v*; déblayer *v*; vider *v*
clear away (to) déblayer *v*
clearance déblai *m*
clearance of ground to about 20 cm depth before levelling out décapage *m*
clearing déblai *m*; déblayage *m*; déblaiement *m*; décapage *m*; défrichage *m*; défrichement *m*
clinker clinker *m*; mâchefer *m*
coat couche *f*
coating revêtement *m*; enduit *m*
coffering blindage *m* par caissons; coffrage *m*
cold chisel ciseau *m* à froid; burin *m*; burin *m* à froid
collapse effondrement *m*
column colonne *f*
compact (to) compacter *v*.

compacting; compaction compactage *m*
compress (to) comprimer *v*
compression resistance of concrete
  résistance *f* de béton
compressor compresseur *m*
concrete béton *m*
concrete (to) bétonner *v*
concrete bed forme *f* en béton
concrete block bloc *m* de béton
concrete blocking piece cale *m* en béton
concrete column colonne *f* de béton
concrete floor sol *m* en béton
concete layer dalle *f* de compression
concrete mixer bétonnière *f*
concrete sill appui *m* béton
concrete slab dalle *f* de béton
concrete support appui *m* béton
concrete, bedding béton *m* de propreté
concrete, blinding béton *m* de propreté
concrete, cast in situ béton *m* banché
concrete, cellular béton *m* cellulaire
concrete, highway béton *m* routier
concrete, mass béton *m* de masse
concrete, cellular béton *m* cellulaire
concrete, highway béton *m* routier
concrete, ordinary béton *m* courant
concrete, prestressed béton *m* précontraint
concrete, refractory béton *m* refractaire
concrete, reinforced béton *m* armé; **B.A.** *abb*
concrete, road béton *m* routier
concrete, stressed reinforced béton *m* armé
  sollicité
concrete, universal béton *m* universel
concreting bétonnage *m*
construction worker ouvrier *m* de
  construction
contact pressure pression *f* de contact
continuous strip foundation fondation *f* sur
  semelle continue
contraction retrait *m*; rétrécissement *m*
core test sample (of soil) carotte *f*
  d'enchantillon
corner profile board chaise *f* d'angle
course assise *f*
cover with masonry paint (to) crépir *v*
crab treuil *m*
cribbing boisage *m*
crowbar levier *m*; pince(s)-monseigneur *m*
crowbar, dismantling pince *f* à décoffrer

crush (to) concasser *v*
crushed rock roche *f* concassée
crushed slag laitier *m* concassé
crushed stone roche *f* concassée
cup or bucket of excavator godet *m*
cut tranchée *f*
cut and fill remblai *m* et déblai *m*
cutting déblai *m*
cutting back (agric) ravalement *m*

damp-proof imperméable *adj*
damp-proof course couche *f* d'étancheité;
  couche *f* isolante; couche *f* isolante
  imperméable; lit *m* isolant
damp-proof layer arase *f* étanche
damp-proof membrane membrane *f*
  d'étanchéité
damp-proofing isolation *f* contre l'humidité
darby taloche *f*
debris décombres *mpl*
deep well puits *m* profond
depth profondeur *f*
depth (of excavation) hauteur *f*
depth, excess surprofondeur *f*
deterioration of the foundations
  dégradation *f* des fondations
differential settlements tassements *mpl*
  differentiels
dig (to) bêcher *v*; creuser *v*; fouiller *v*
dig out (to) creuser *v*
dig up (to) déterrer *v*
digger (person) pelleteur *m*
digger, mechanical excavateur *m*; pelle
  mécanique; *f*; pelleteuse *f*
digging creusage *m*; creusement *m*;
  excavation *f*; fouille *f*
disorder désordre *m*
ditch fossé *m*; saignée *f*
drain (to) assécher *v*; vider *v*; drainer *v*
drain off (to) vidanger *v*
drainage; draining asséchement *m*
drainage channel canal *m* d'écoulement
draw up (to) (eg plan) dresser *v*
drawing up dressage *m*; dressement *m*
drawing/plan of situation of site plan *m* de
  situation du terrain
dress (to) (eg stone, wood) dresser *v*
dressing dressage *m*; dressement *m*

drill (to) creuser *v* au marteau-piqueur
drive in piles (to) piloter *v*
drive in, down, out (etc) (to) refouler *v*
driving enfoncement *m*
driving in (eg pile) enfoncement *m*
drying séchage *m*
drying out assèchement *m*
drying time temps *m* de séchage
dump truck camion *f* benne
dumper dumper *m*

earth sol *m*; terre *f*
earth compacter dame *f*
earth levelling machine nivelleuse *f*; engin *m* de nivellement
earth mover engin *m* de terrassement
earth moving equipment engins *mpl* de terrassement
earth platform terre-plein *m*
earth rammer dame *f*; demoiselle *f*
earth transporter engin *m* de transport
earthwork(s) terrassement *m*; travaux *mpl* de terrassement
earthworks labourer; navvy terrassier *m*
embankment remblai *m*; terrassement *m*; talus *m*
empty (to) vidanger *v*; vider *v*
empty out (to) vidanger *v*
equipment appareillage *m*; matériel *m*; matériels *mpl*; also *adj*; outillage *m*
erecting a scaffold échafaudage *m*
examination of the ground reconnaisance *f* des sols
excavate (to) fouiller *v*; excaver v; terasser *v*
excavated material; spoil déblais *mpl*
excavating excavation *f*
excavation déblai *m*; excavation *f*; fouille *f*; terrassement *m*
excavation in rocky ground fouille *f* en terrain rocheux
excavation of rock fouille *f* de rochers
excavation under existing construction fouille *f* en sous-œuvre
excavation work terrasse *f*
excavation, foundation fouille *f* pour fondation
excavation, horizontal passage fouille *f* en excavation; fouille *f* en galerie

excavation, narrow trench (to receive foundation) fouille *f* en rigole
excavation, open fouille *f* à ciel ouvert
excavation, open (levelling) fouille *f* en déblais
excavation, shaft fouille *f* en puits
excavation, shallow fouille *f* en "excavation superficielle"
excavation, trench fouille *f* en tranchée
excavation, underground fouille *f* en excavation; fouille *f* en galerie; fouille *f* souterraine
excavation, well fouille *f* en puits
excavator engin *m* d'excavation; excavateur *m*; pelle *f*; pelleteuse *f*
expansion in bulk foisonnement *m*

fall éboulement *m*
falling in éboulement *m*; effondrement *m*
fill (to) remblayer *v*; combler *v*
fill with rubble (to) (eg wall) bloquer *v*
fill up (to) combler *v*; remblayer *v*
filler (used in cement) filler *m*; fines *fpl*
filling remblayage *m*; remblaiement *m*; remplissage *m*; blocage *m*
filling up remblayage *m*; remblaiement *m*; remplissage *m*
filling up (eg ditch) comblement *m*
finishing; making good ragréage *m*
finishing coat or layer couche *f* de finition
finishing off ragrément *m*
finishing trowel platoir *m*
fix (to) ancrer *v*; poser *v*
flagging dallage *m*
flagging laid on compacted layer of stones hérisson *m*; hérissonage *m*
flatness planéité *f*
float taloche *f*
float (to) talocher *v*
float, devil taloche *f* à pointes
float, plastic taloche *f* plastique
floated work talochage *m*
floating talochage *m*
floating slab floor dalle *f* flottante
floor sol *m*; plancher *m*
floorboard planche *f*
fluidizer fluidifiant *m*; also *adj*
footing semelle *f*

force in (to) refouler *v*
fork fourche *f*
form coffrage *m*; forme *f*
form (for concrete) coffre *m*
formwork coffrage *m*; banche *f*
formwork carpenter coffreur *m*
formwork scraper grattoir *m* de coffrage
formworker's saw scie *f* de coffreur
foundation assise *f*; fondation *f*; fondement *m*
foundation (load distributing element)
semelle *f*
foundation apron radier *m*
foundation block massif *m* de fondation
foundation of next-to-earth compacted
layer of stones, etc hérisson *m*;
hérissonage *m*
foundation on refilled or embanked sites
fondation *f* sur remblais
foundation raft radier *m* de fondation
foundation slippage glissement *m* de la
fondation
foundation, strip fondation *f* par semelle
foundation trench rigole *f*
foundations of a building fondations *fpl* d'un
bâtiment
foundations of a house fondements *mpl*
d'une maison
frame(work) cadre *m*
framework ossature *f*
framing (for concrete work) coffrage *m*
freeze (to) geler *v*
friction frottement *m*
frost gel *m*
frost-free foundation fondation *f* "hors-gel"

gap ouverture *f*
gauging water eau *f* de gâchage
gauze, metal tamis *m* métallique
geotechnical survey étude *f* géotechnique
get rid of (to) débarrasser *v*
giving way enfoncement *m*
grader nivelleuse *f*
gradient rampe *f*
gravel gravier *m*; gravillon *m*
gravel (to) gravilloner *v*
gravel pit gravière *f*
grit gravier *m*
groove saignée *f*

ground terrain *m*; terre *f*
ground, coherent terrain *m* cohérent
ground, detrital terrain *m* détritique
ground, firm terrain *m* ferme; terrain *m*
solide
ground, level terrain *m* à/de niveau; terrain *m*
en palier
ground, powdery terrain *m* pulvérulent
ground, sloping terrain *m* en pente
ground, stony terrain *m* pierreux
ground, unstable terrain *m* instable
ground, waste terrain *m* vague
ground; ground floor sol *m*
gypsum gypse *m*

hammer drill marteau-perforateur *m*
hammer, bush boucharde *f*
hammer, claw marteau *m* arrache-clous
hammer, club massette *f*
hammer, lump massette *f*
hammer, sledge marteau *m* à deux mains;
masse *f*
hammer, stonebreaker's massette *f* de
casseur de pierres
hammer-drill, electric marteau *m* électrique
hammer-pick pioche *f*
hand-barrow brouette *f*
handspike levier *m*
hardcore blocaille *f*; empierrement *m*;
remblai *m*
hardening (eg of cement) durcissement *m*
hardening interval délai *m* de durcissement
hawk taloche *f*
heap tas *m*
height hauteur *f*
hill colline *f*; côté *f*
hoist treuil *m*
hoist, electric treuil *m* électrique
hoisting equipment engins *mpl* de levage
hole fouille *f*; ouverture *f*; trou *m*
hook crochet *m*
hooked tie bar épingle *f*
hydraulic brace étrésillon *m* hydraulique
hydraulic ram, or jack vérin *m* hydraulique

134

ice glace *f*
ice over (to) geler *v*
impermeable imperméable *adj*
impervious imperméable *adj*
impervious layer étanchéité *f*
impervious levelling layer arase *f* étanche
imperviousness étanchéité *f*
inclination inclinaison *f*
incline rampe *f*
incline (to) incliner *v*
increase in bulk (to) foisonner *v*
inflate (to) gonfler *v*
inflation gonflement *m*
initial layer (of plaster or mortar) couche *f* d'approche
insulator isolateur *m*
introduction of steel reinforcement ferraillage *m*

jet jet *m*
joining reinforcements by wiring assemblage *m* des armatures par ligature

labourer ouvrier *m* de chantier
ladder échelle *f*
land terrain *m*; terre *f*
land on which technically and legally one can build terrain *m* constructible
land, enclosed terrain *m* clos
land, waste terrain *m* vague
land, wooded terrain *m* boisé
last course; top course dernière assise *f*
lay (to) poser *v*
lay the foundations of a house (to) poser *v* les fondements d'une maison
layer couche *f*
layer ready for covering (eg with tiles) couche *f* de revêtement
layer ready for use (eg concrete path) couche *f* d'usure
length longueur *f*
level (to) aplanir *v*; dresser *v*
level (to) (eg a wall) araser *v*
level a piece of land (to) aplanir *v* un terrain
level off (to) déblayer *v*
levelling dressage *m*; dressement *m*; nivellement *m*

levelling (soil) ravalement *m*
levelling a site by earth removal déblai *m*
levelling layer of cement or sand below paving or flagstones forme *f*
levelling marker post piquet *m* repère de nivellement
levelling off déblayage *m*; déblaiement *m*
levelling out nivellement *m*
lever levier *m*
liable to wash away affouillable *adj*
lift up (to) soulever *v*
lime chaux *f*
lime, grey chaux *f* gris
lime, hydraulic chaux *f* hydraulique
lime, non-hydraulic chaux *f* aerienne
lime, quick chaux *f* vive
lime, slaked chaux *f* éteinte
lining coffrage *m*
load charge *f*; chargement *m*
load (to) charger *v*
load, permissable charge *f* admissable
load-spreading plate semelle *f* de répartition
loader (machine) chargeur *m*; chargeuse *f*
loading chargement *m*
loading shovel chargeuse *f*
loading strength of a terrain force *f* portante d'un terrain; taux *m* de travail admissable du sol
lorry camion *m*

machine engin *m*
make ready (to) apprêter *v*
marker pin of bricklayer chevillette *f* de maçon
marking out with stakes piquetage *m*
marl marne *f*
masonry paint crépi *m*
mass bloc *m*
mat foundation radier *m*
material matériau *m*; matériaux *mpl*
mattock décintroir *m* à talus; pioche *f* à défricher
measurement of resistance to compression mesure *f* de compression
mechanical scraper scraper *m*
mechanical shovel pelle *f* mécanique
melt (to) dégeler *v*
membrane membrane *f*

mix (to) (mortar/concrete) gâcher *v*
mix (to) (to required consistency) délayer *v*
mixer malaxeur *m*
mixing gâchage *m*; malaxage *m*; malaxation *f*; malaxeur,-euse *adj*
mixing of concrete malaxage *m* du béton
mixing water (for concrete, etc) eau *f* de gâchage
moisten (to) mouiller *v*
mortar mortier *m*
mortar, cement mortier *m* de ciment
mortar, lime mortier *m* de chaux
mortar, lime-cement mortier *m* bâtard
motorised compacter/roller engin *m* de compactage
mould (eg for concrete) moule *m*
mud boue *f*; limon *m*; vase *f*

narrowing rétrécissement *m*
non-erodability by water of the ground carrying the building inaffouillabilité *f* de l'ouvrage
non-erodable ground (by water) sol *m* inaffouillable

open excavation terrassement *m* à découvert
opening ouverture *f*
outer walls gros œuvre *m*
overloading surcharge *f*
oversite concrete radier *m*

packing bourrage *m*
pail seau *m*
pailful seau *m*
parcel (of land) parcelle *f*
pavement dallage *m*
paving dallage *m*
peat tourbe *f*
pebble caillou *m*
pebbly caillouteux,-euse *adj*
peg out (to) implanter *v*; piqueter *v*
permitted tolerance tolérance *f* d'exécution
phenomen of contraction phénomène *m* de retrait

pick pioche *f*
pick-and-claw crowbar levier *m* à pied-de-biche et à pointe
pick-axe pioche *f* ordinaire
pick-mattock décintroir *m* à talus
picket piquet *m*
piece bloc *m*
piece of work ouvrage *m*; œuvre *f*
pier foundation fondation *f* sur puits
pile (of earth, bricks etc) tas *m*
pile pieu *m*; pilot *m*; pilotis *m*
pile (to) piloter *v*
pile driving battage *m* de pieux/pilots; pilotage *m*
pile foundation fondation *f* sur pieux/pilotis
piling pilotage *m*; pilotis *m*
pin épingle *f*
pit fosse *f*; fouille *f*
pitch (slope) inclinaison *f*
place (to) poser *v*
place a frame/form (to) (for concrete) coffrer *v*
plank planche *f*
plant matériel *m*; matériels *mpl*; outillage *m*
plaster debris; rubble plâtras *m*
plastic film damp-proof membrane film *m* plastique étanche
plasticizer plastifiant *m*; fluidifiant *m*; also *adj*
platform terre-plein *m*
plot (of land) terrain *m*
pneumatic drill marteau *m* piqueur; marteau *m* pneumatique
post pieu *m*; piquet *m*
pour (to) (eg concrete, asphalt) couler *v*
pouring (eg concrete) coulage *m*
pozzolana pouzzolane *f*
preparatory work travail *m* préparatoire
prepare (to) apprêter *v*; dresser *v*
preparing dressage *m*; dressement *m*
prise levier *m*
profile board chaise *f* d'implantation
prop étai *m*
prop (to); prop up (to) étayer *v*
propping (up) étayage *m*; étayement *m* étaiment *m*
pump pompe *f*
pump (to); pump out (to) pomper *v*

pump, electric pompe *f* électrique
pumping; pumping out pompage *m*
puzzolana pouzzolane *f*
pylon pylône *m*

raft foundation fondation *f* sur radier
raise (to) soulever *v*
rake râteau *m*
rake (to) ratisser *v*
ram (to) damer *v*; pilonner *v*
rammer dame *f*; demoiselle *f*; engin *m* de damage
ramming bourrage *m*; damage *m*
reinforce (to) armer *v*
reinforced slab floor (concrete) dalle *f* en béton armé
reinforcement armature *f*
reinfocement steel in the foundations or footings aciers *mpl* de la semelle
removal of (excavated) earth évacuation *f* des terres
removal of formwork/shuttering décoffrage *m*
remove (to); clear away (to) débarrasser *v*
render impermeable (to) imperméabiliser *v*
render (to) crépir *v*
rendering crépi *m*; crépissage *m*
repair (to) réparer *v*; reprendre *v*
restart work (to) reprendre *v* les travaux
restoration restauration *f*; ravalement *m*
resurfacing ravalement *m*
retardant retardateur *m*; also *adj*
ribbed/notched steel bar acier *m* crénelé
right angle angle *m* droit
rilling ruissellement *m*
rise rampe *f*
risk of caving in risque *m* d'éboulement
risk of earth-fall risque *m* d'éboulement
risk of giving way risque *m* d'enfoncement
risk of land-slip risque *m* de glissement
risk of sinking (eg foundation) risque *m* d'enfoncement
risk of slippage risque *m* de glissement
roadworks chantier *m*
rock roche *f*
rockfall éboulement *m*
rodding concrete piquage *m*
roll rouleau *m*

roller rouleau *m*
roller, light rouleau *m* leger
roller, road rouleau *m* compresseur
roller, rubber-tyred compacteur *m* à pneus
roughcast crépi *m*
roughcast (to) crépir *v*; hourder *v*; talocher *v*
roughcasting crépissage *m*; ravalement *m*
roughening bouchardage *m*
rubbing (eg with pumice) décapage *m*
rubble blocaille *f*; décombres *mpl*; blocage *m*; déblais *mpl*; gravats *mpl*; gravois *mpl*; moellon *m*; plâtras *m*
rubble-stone blocage *m*; moellon *m*
rubbly blocageux, blocageuse *adj*

sand sable *m*
sand blasting sablage *m*
sand blasting machine sableuse *f*
sand, building sable *m* â bâtir
sand, coarse sable *m* grossier
sand, river sable *m* de rivière
sand, soft sable *m* doux
sand-coloured sable *adj*
sanding sablage *m*
scaffold échafaud *m*
scaffold(ing) échafaud *m*; échafaudage *m*
scouring décapage *m*
scraper, mechanical scraper *m*
scratch trowel; scratcher taloche *f* à pointes
screed chape *f*; chape *f* ciment
screed laid as base for floor covering chape *f* de revêtement
screed laid as floor surface chape *f* d'usure
screed, adherent; monolithic screed chape *f* adhérente; chape *f* incorporée
screed, floating chape *f* flottante
screed, incorporated chape *f* incorporée
screed cap of levelling course chape *f* d'arase
set (to) poser *v*
set up (to) dresser *v*
setting (eg of limes, cements) prise *f*
setting accelerator (for cement/mortar) accélérateur *m* de prise
setting out; layout implantation *f*
setting out the earthworks implantation *f* des terrassements
setting up dressage *m*; dressement *m*

setting, fast prise *f* rapide
setting, slow prise *f* lente
settlement; settling tassement *m*
settlement of the earthwork (remblai)
tassement *m* du remblai
shaft puits *m*
shape forme *f*
sheet metal casing coffrage *m* en tôle
sheeting (wood or metal) used for shoring
blindage *m*
shell (of a building) cage *f*; carcasse *f*; gros
œuvre *m*
shore étai *m*; étançon *m*
shore (to) étayer *v*
shore up (to) blinder *v*; étayer *v*
shoring étaiment *m*; étayage *m*; étayement *m*
shoring arrangement dispositif *m* d'étaiment
shoring of adjoining constructions étaiment
m des constructions voisines
shoring up blindage *m*; étaiment *m*
shoring up with coffers blindage *m* par
caissons
shoring up with prefabricated boards
blindage *m* par panneaux préfabriqués
shoring with horizontal/vertical planking
blindage *m* par planche horizontale/ verticale
shovel pelle *f*
shovel (to); shovel up (to) pelleter *v*
shovel of forged carbon steel pelle *f* forgée
en acier au carbone
shovel, mechanical pelle *f* mécanique
shredder (of undergrowth) broyeur *m*
shrinkage retrait *m*; rétrécissement *m*
shuttering coffrage *m*
shuttering panel panneau *m* de coffrage;
banche *f*
sieve tamis *m*
sieve (to) tamiser *v*
sieve with wooden frame tamis *m* bois
sieving tamisage *m*
sift (to) tamiser *v*
sifting tamisage *m*
silt limon *m*; vase *f*
single strip foundation fondation *f* sur
semelle isolée
sink (to) (a well) creuser *v*
sinking (eg foundation) enfoncement *m*
sinking by piling fonçage *m* au poussage

site plan plan *m* d'implantation; plan *m* de
situation
skimming coat couche *f* de finition
skip benne *f*; skip *m*
slag laitier *m*
sliding glissement *m*
slippage; slipping glissement *m*
slope inclinaison *f*; rampant *m*; rampe *f*;
talus *m*
slope (to) incliner *v*
slope inclination pente *f* de talus
sloped; sloping en forme de talus
smooth out (to) aplanir *v*
smooth steel rod (for reinforcement) rond
m lisse d'acier
smoothing ragrément *m*
soak away puits *m* perdu
soil sol *m*; terre *f*
soil (ordinary) terre *f* végétale
soil cohesion (soil resistance to movement)
cohésion *f* de sol
soil compressibility compressibilité *f* de sol
soil, chalky terre *f* calcaire
soil, clay sol *m* argileux/glaiseux
soil, clayey terre *f* argileuse
soil, sandy terre *f* sableuse
solid earth terre-plein *m*
spade bêche *f*
speed of setting rapidité *f* de prise
spoil; excavated material déblais *mpl*
staging échafaud *m*
stake pieu *m*; piquet *m*
staking out piquetage *m*
stanchion étançon *m*
stay étai *m*; étançon *m*
stay (to) étayer *v*
staying étayage *m*; étayement *m*
steel acier *m*
steel bar barre *f* d'acier
steel bar, distribution acier *m* de répartition
steel rod acier *m*
steel rod reinforcement (for concrete) barre
f d'armature en acier
steel, high-adherence (for reinforcement)
acier *m* à haute-adhérence (HA)
steel, structural acier *m* de construction
stepped foundation fondation *f* en redans
stirrup; joist hanger étrier *m*
stone pierre *f*

stone (pebble) caillou *m*
stone, small (handsize) building moellon *m*
stratum (geol) couche *f*; strate *f*; assise *f*
stressed member élément *m* sollicité
structural concrete topping slab dalle *f* de
  compression
strut étrésillon *m*
subsidence abaissement *m*; affaisement *m*;
  effondrement *m*; subsidence *f*; tassement *m*
subsoil sous-sol *m*; terrain *m* de fondation
substratum sous-sol *m*
substruction sous-œuvre *m*
subterranean souterrain *m*; also *adj*
support étai *m*
support (to) étayer *v*
supporting étaiment *m*; étayage *m*;
  étayement *m*
surface superficie *f*; surface *f*
surface area superficie *f*
surface cut tranchée *f*
surface earthworks terrassement *m* en
  surface
surface finshing with a float talochage *m*
surface waters eaux *fpl* de surface; eaux *fpl*
  superficielles
surface, bearing surface *f* de portée; surface
  f portante
surface, floor (of building) surface *f* des
  étages
surface, smooth surface *f* lisse
surface, support surface *f* d'appui
surface-clearing (of ground, woods etc.)
  défrichement *m* ou défrichage *m*
surveyor's pole or rod jalon *m*
swell foisonnement *m*
swell (to) foisonner *v*; gonfler *v*
swelling foisonnement *m*; gonflement *m*

take back (to) reprendre *v*
tamp (to) damer *v*; pilonner *v*
tamping damage *m*; bourrage *m*
tank bâche *f*; cuve *f*; réservoir *m*
■ water tank = bâche à eau
tarpaulin bâche *f*; toile *f* goudronnée; toile *f*
  à bâche
task œuvre *f*
temper (to) (eg plaster) gâcher *v*
tempering gâchage *m*

terrace terrasse *f*
terrain terrain *m*
textured paint crépi *m*
thaw dégel *m*
thaw (to) dégeler *v*
thickness épaisseur *f*
thin down (to); add water (to) délayer *v*
thin prestressed concrete slab forming base
  of final cast slab prédalle *f*
throw; throwing; cast jet *m*
thrust of the ground poussée *f* des terres
thrusting concrete piquage *m*
tilt inclinaison *f*
tiltdozer tilt-dozer *m*
timber (to) (shoring) blinder *v*
timbering blindage *m*; boisage *m*
timberwork boisage *m*
tipper lorry camion *f* benne
to be set, etc poser (se) *v*
tool outil *m*
tools outillage *m*
top coat couche *f* de finition
topping slab; compression slab dalle *f* de
  compression *f*
total area of a piece of ground masse *f*
  surface d'un terrain
trench fouille *f*; saignée *f*; tranchée *f*
trench (small) rigole *f*
trench (to) fouiller *v*
trench, foundation fouille *f* en rigole
trench, service fouille *f* en rigole
trenching fouille *f*
trowel truelle *f*
trowel, finishing platoir *m*
trowel, round truelle *f* ronde
trowel, scratch taloche *f* à pointes
trowel, toothed truelle *f* dentelée; truelle *f*
  berthelet
tubular stay, mason's étai *m* de maçon
  tubulaire
tufa tuf *m*

underground souterrain *m*; also *adj*
undermine (to) affouiller *v*
underpin (to) (building) reprendre *v* en
  sous-œuvre
underpin (to) (wall) étayer *v*
underpinning reprise *f* en sous-œuvre;

sous-œuvre *m*
unlined excavation fouille *f* non-blindée
uproot (to); unearth (to) déterrer *v*

volcanic lava pouzzolane *f*

wash away (to); erode (to) affouiller *v*
waste material déblais *mpl*; déchet *m*;
déchets *mpl*
water supply alimentation *f* en eau;
approvisionnnement *m* d'eau
water-repellant hydrofuge *m*; also *adj*
water-tightness étanchéité *f*
waterproof imperméable *adj*
waterproof (to) imperméabiliser *v*
waterproof coating revêtment impermeable *m*

waterproofing étanchéité *f*
waterproofness étanchéité *f*
wedging calage *m*
welded steel trellis (for reinforcement)
treillis *m* soudé
well puits *m*
wet (to); dampen (to) mouiller *v*
wheel of barrow roue *f* de brouette
wheel-barrow brouette *f*
width largeur *f*
winch treuil *m*
wire gauze tamis *m* métallique
wire sieve tamis *m* métallique
work travail *m*; œuvre *f*
workability ouvrabilité *f*
worker; workman ouvrier *m*; ouvrière *f*
works travaux *mpl*

3. BUILDER

ABS (plastic) ABS (plastique)
absorb (to) absorber *v*
abut (to) abouter *v*
abutting aboutement *m*
abutment aboutement *m*; pénétration *f*;
butée *f*
accelerator accélérateur *m*
access aperture for cleaning (eg soot box)
orifice *m* de ramonage
access port regard *m*
accessory accessoire *m*
accomplish (to) exécuter *v*
acoustic comfort confort *m* acoustique
act as earth (to) (elect) faire *v* masse
action jeu *m*
adaptor (elect) prise *f* multiple
additive additif *m*; adjuvant *m*
adhere (to) adhérer *v*
adhesion adhérence *f*
adhesive power pouvoir *m* d'adhérence
adjustable prop (Acrow ™ type) étrésillon

m à vis; étrésilon *m* à verin
adjustable stay/support étai *m* réglable
administration gestion *f*
administrative order or decree arrêté *m*
AFNOR; French Industrial Standards
Association AFNOR; Association
Française de Normalisation *f*
against the grain (wood) contre-fil *m*
aggregate agrégat *m*; granulats *mpl*
agreement accord *m*; contrat *m*
air cushion couche *f* d'air
air gap lame *f* d'air
air gap (cavity wall) couche *f* d'air
air grille grille *f* d'aération
air inlet prise *m* d'air
air sample prise *m* d'air
air void vide *m* d'air
air-vent (of fireplace) ventouse *f*
alcove alcôve *f*
align (to) aligner *v*
alignment alignement *m*

alignment by cord (brick laying) alignement *m* au cordeau
alloy alliage *m*
alter (to) modifier *v*; transformer *v*
aluminium aluminium *m*
aluminium foil feuille *f* d'aluminium
alveolate alvéolé,-e *adj*
anchor ancre *f*
anchor (to) ancrer *v*
▪ **bien ancré** = well-anchored
anchor in form of an S ancre *f* en forme d'un S
ancient ancien, ancienne *adj*.
angle bead bourrelet *m* d'étanchéité; éclisse *f* cornière; baguette *f* d'angle
angle between two planes of a curb roof brisis *m*
angle grinder meuleuse *f* angulaire
angle iron cornière *f*; fer *m* cornière; fer *m* d'angle
angle-piece cornière *f*
angle-plate équerre *f* d'angle
annexe annexe *f*
anti-backflow throat (fireplace) gorge *f* anti-refoulante
antirust antirouille *adj*
apartment appartement *m*; logement *m*
aperture orifice *m*
apparatus appareil *m*
appliance appareil *m*
appliances matériel *m*; matériels *mpl*; also *adj*
apply masonry paint (to) crépir *v*
appraisal bilan *m*; expertise *f*
apron radier *m*
apron (of a window) allège *f*
arch arc *m*; cintre *m*; voûte *f*
arch-brick; arch-stone voussoir *m*; vousseau *m*
arching cintrage *m*; voussure *f*
architect architecte *m*
architrave chambranle *m*
archway voûte *f*
area of land measured in ares aréage *m*
arrangement aménagement *m*; dispositif *m*; disposition *f*
arris arête *f*
artesian well puits *m* artésien
article clause *f*

artisan artisan *m*
asbestos amiante *m*; asbeste *m*
ashlar pierre *f* de taille
asphalt asphalte *m*
asphalt (to) asphalter *v*
▪ **asphalté,-e** *adj* = asphalted
aspirator aspirateur *m*
assemblage assemblage *m*
assemble (to) assembler *v*
assembly habillage *m*
assessment bilan *m*
attic grenier *m*; mansarde *f*
avoid (to) éviter *v*
awl alêne *f*; poinçon *m*
axe-hammer hachette *f* de charpentier
axle arbre *m*

back arrière *m*
back-door porte *f* de derrière; dégagement *m*
backfill remblai *m*
backfilling remblaiement *m*; remblayage *m*
backyard arrière-cour *f*
baked clay terre *f* cuite
balcony balcon *m*
ball of string pelote *f* de cordeau
ball-socket cuvette *f* rotule
ballast blocaille *f*
ballcock robinet *m* à flotteur
band bande *f*
band of foam rubber bande *f* de mousse
banisters rampe *f* (d'escalier)
bank (eg of earth) talus *m*
bank (river) rive *f*
banking up remblai *m*; remblaiement *m*; remblayage *m*
barn grange *f*
barrow brouette *f*
bars (window) grille *f*
base base *f*; fondation *f*; fondement *m*; soubassement *m*
base-board plinthe *f*
base-plate semelle *f*
basement soubassement *m*; sous-sol *m*
basic area of house surface *f* hors œuvre nette (see also 'superficie')
basic structure gros œuvre *m*
basic work required on building site (eg drains, electricity, etc) viabilité *f*

bat (half-brick) demi-brique *f*; brique *f* à
   deux quartiers; briqueton *m*
bath baignoire *f*; bain *m*
bathroom salle *f* de bain; sanitaires (les) *mpl*
bathroom appliance appareil *m* sanitaire
bathroom installations sanitaire *m*
bathroom plumbing installation *f* sanitaire;
   sanitaires (les) *mpl*
bathroom suite sanitaires (les) *mpl*
bathrooms, kitchens, shower rooms etc
   pièces *fpl* d'eau
batten liteau *m*; latte *f*; tasseau *m*
batter (of excavation)) talus *m*
batter (of a wall) fruit *m*
be modified (to) modifier (se) *v*
be moved (to) déplacer (se) *v*
be out of plumb/true (to) porter *v* à faux
be set (to), etc poser (se) *v*
be supported by/on (to) porter *v* sur
beam poutre *f*; solive *f*; madrier *m*;
   doubleau *m*
beam encased in terra cotta blocks (floor
   beams) poutrelle *f* en céramique
beam, exposed poutre *f* apparente
beam, small poutrelle *f*
bear (to) porter *v*
bearing coquille *f*
bed assise *f*; lit *m*
bed of concrete lit *m* de béton
bed of pasty mortar bain *m* soufflant de
   mortier
bed of mortar bain *m* de mortier
bed plate plaque *f* d'assise; socle *m*
bedded lité,-e *adj*
bedroom chambre *f*; chambre *f* à coucher
beetle dame *f*; demoiselle *f* de paveur
belt ceinture *f*
bend coude *m*; dévoiement *m*
bend (to) cintrer *v*
bending cintrage *m*
bending; sag flèche *f*
besom balai *m* de bouleau; balai *m* paille de
   riz
bevel biseau *m*
bevel (square) fausse *f* équerre
bevel (to) biseauter *v*
bevel edge biseau *m*
bevelled biseauté,-e *adj*; en biseau;
   chanfreiné,-e *adj*

bevelling biseautage *m*
bicycle shed abri *m* à vélos; garage *m* à
   bicyclettes
bill of quantities; BOQ devis *m* quantitatif
bind (to) lier *v*
binder liant *m*
binding material liant *m*
bit fer *m*
bitumen bitume *m*
bitumen coated enrobé *m* bitumineux
bitumenised paper papier *m* bituminé
bituminous bitumineux,-euse *adj*
blade lame *f*
bleed-tap (of radiator) purgeur *m*
blemish; blister (paint) souillure *f*
blending malaxage *m*
block bloc *m*; cale *f*
block for horizontal/vertical reinforcement
   bloc *m* pour chainage horizontal/vertical
block of flats groupe *m* d'habitations;
   immeuble *m*
block of masonry massif *m* de maçonnerie
block, angle bloc *m* d'angle
block, border planelle *m* de rive
block, breeze parpaing *m*; parpaing *m*
   aggloméré
block, building (part perforated, part
   insulated) planelle *m*
block, cellular concrete bloc *m* de/en béton
   cellulaire
block, column bloc *m* poteau
block, concrete bloc *m* de béton; bloc *m* en
   béton
block, concrete, with air channels parpaing
   m
block, concrete-polystyrene bloc *m*
   ISECO™
block, corner bloc *m* d'angle; bloc *m* poteau
block, edge planelle *m* de rive
block, end bloc *m* d'about
block, fired clay; brick bloc *m* de terre cuite
block, foundation massif *m* de fondation
block, heavy (high-strength) bloc *m* lourd
block, hollow concrete bloc *m* creux en
   béton
block, insulating bloc *m* multifonction
block, ISECO™ bloc *m* ISECO™
block, L-shaped bloc *m* d'angle
block, light bloc *m* léger

block, lintel bloc *m* linteau; bloc *m* pour linteau
block, low-strength bloc *m* léger
block, multifunctional bloc *m* multifonction
block, perforated bloc *m* perforé; bloc *m* B2
block, pillar bloc *m* poteau
block, SIPOREX™ bloc *m* SIPOREX™
block, solid aggregate (standard or light) bloc *m* plein de granulats (courants ou legers)
block, solid concrete bloc *m* plein en béton
block, standard concrete bloc *m* courant en béton
block, terra cotta bloc *m* de terre cuite
block, U-shaped bloc *m* en U
blockage obstruction *f*; blocage *m*
blocking (eg road) blocage *m*
blueprint plan *m*; photocalque *m* bleu
board planche *f*; tableau *m*
board (to) planchéier *v*
board, scaffold planche *f* d'échafaudage
board, skirting plinthe *f*
board, warped planche *f* voilée
boarded ceiling plafond *m* en lambris
boarding planchéiage *m*
body corps *m*
boiler chaudière *f*
bolster ciseau *m* de maçon; ciseau *m* à brique
bolt boulon *m*
bond (arrangement of the components of a wall) appareil *m*
bond (to) appareiller *v*; liaisonner *v*
bond, English appareil *m* anglais
bond, Flemish appareil *m* flamand; appareil *m* hollandais
bond, French appareil *m* français
bond, heading or header appareil *m* de/en boutisses; appareil *m* en travers
bond, irregular (stonework) appareil *m* en opus incertum
bond used at corners (toothing of bricks) appareil *m* en besace
bond, stretcher appareil *m* en panneresse; appareil *m* en long
bond-stone parpaing *m*
bonding appareillage *m*; liason *f*
bonding beam (reinforcement) chaînage *m*
bonding girder chaînage *m*
boot botte *f*

border bord *m*; rive *f*
boring percement *m*; perçage *m*
bossage (shaped face of stone) bossage *m*
botch (to) bâcler *v*; gâcher *v*
boundary fence clôture *f* de bornage
boundary marking bornage *m*
boundary stone or marker borne *f*
bowl, washbasin; WC basin cuvette *f*
bowl (of sink unit) bac *m*; cuve *f*
box-spanner clé *f* à douille
boxing; housing emboîtement *m*
boxroom débarras *m*; cabinet *m* de débarras
brace raidisseur *m*; entretoise *f*; étrésillon *m*
brace (eg of truss) contrefiche *f*
brace (timber frame) écharpe *f*
brace (to) raidir *v*; entretoiser *v*
brace or strut (wind) contrevent *m*
bracket tasseau *m*; support *m*
bracket (for shelf) liteau *m*; gousset *m*
bradawl poinçon *m*
branch-pipe branchement *m*
branching branchement *m*
brass laiton *m*
brass, cast laiton *m* fondu
brazing/hard soldering equipment matériel *m* de brasage *m*
breadth largeur *f*
break (to) casser *v*; briser *v*
breaking load charge *f* de rupture
breast (wall under window ledge) allège *f*
breeze block aggloméré *m*; agglo *abb*; parpaing *m*
brick (to) briqueter *v*; maçonner *v*; murer *v*
brick bolster ciseau *m* à brique
brick bolster with shock-protector handle ciseau *m* de maçon poignée pare-coups
brick dust poussière *f* de brique; brique *f* pilée
brick merchant briquetier *m*
brick paved pavé de brique *adj*
brick pavement pavage *m* en briques
brick paving carrelage *m* en briques
brick up (to) maçonner *v*
brick with horizontal/vertical air holes brique *f* à alvéoles horizontales/verticales
brick, air brique *f* de ventilation; brique *f* évidée
brick, arch brique *f* à couteau
brick, buttered (ie coated with mortar or

plaster on three sides before positioning brique *f* "graissée"

brick, Dutch (clinker) brique *f* hollandaise

brick, facing brique *f* de parement

brick, feather-edged brique *f* à couteau

brick, fire brique *f* réfractaire; brique *f* blanche

brick, fired-clay; brick brique *f* de terre cuite

brick, G- brique *f* à alvéoles; brique *f* G

brick, hollow brique *f* à alvéoles; brique *f* creuse

brick, hollow terra cotta brique *f* creuse de terre cuite

brick, hollow with break joint brique *f* creuse à rupture de joint

brick, insulating brique *f* G

brick, perforated brique *f* à alvéoles; brique *f* creuse; brique *f* perforée

brick, plasterer's brique *f* platrière

brick, pressed brique *f* fabriquée à la presse; brique *f* moulée

brick, refractory brique *f* réfractaire

brick, slag brique *f* de laitier

brick, small briquette *f*

brick, solid brique *f* plein

brick, standard type brique *f* de type courant

brick, terra cotta brique *f* de terre cuite

brick, textured brique *f* rustique

brick, ventilation brique *f* de ventilation

brick, vitrified (ie clinker) brique *f* vitrifiée

brick, white brique *f* blanche

brick, wire-cut brique *f* fabriquée à la filière

brick-making briqueterie *f*

bricklayer briqueteur *m*; maçon *m*

bricklaying briquetage *m*

bricklaying line alignement *m* au cordeau

brickmaker briquetier *m*

brickwork briquetage *m*

brickworks briqueterie *f*

brickyard briqueterie *f*

brickyard worker briquetier *m*

briquette briquette *f*

broach pointerolle *f* de maçon; équarrissoir *m*; broche *f*

broach (to) équarrir *v*

broom balai *m*

broom cupboard placard *m* à balai

broom, garden balai *m* coco

broom, yard balai *m* de piste

brush brosse *f*

brush (to) brosser *v*

bucket seau *m*

bucket, canvas seau *m* en toile

bucket, galvanised-iron seau *m* en tôle galvanisée

bucketful seau *m*

buckle boucle *f*

buckle (to) (metal) voiler *v*

build (to) bâtir *v*; construire *v*; édifier *v*

build higher (to) (eg wall) rehausser *v*

build with bricks (to) briqueter *v*

builder constructeur *m*; entrepreneur *m* de constructions

building bâtiment *m*; bâtisse *f*; construction *f*; édifice *m*

building work ouvrage *m*; travaux *mpl* de construction

building block/stone with embossed face bossage *m*

building fault dommage-ouvrage *m*

building land/site terrain *m* constructible

building paper papier *m* de construction

building permit permis *m* de construire

building rubble décombres *mpl*

building site chantier *m*; chantier *m* de construction; terrain *m* à bâtir

building-contractor; builder entrepreneur *m* de constructions

building/construction materials matériaux *mpl* de construction

built-up area zone *f* bâtie

bulge (to) (eg wall) bomber *v*

bung bouchon *m*

burning off (eg paint) décapage *m*

burr balèvre *f*

bush bague f; douille f; coussinet m; coquille *f*

business firm maison *f* de commerce

butt about *m*

butt (to) abouter *v*; buter *v*

butt-end about *m*

■ en about = abutting

butt-hinge charnière *f*

butt-joint (to) abouter *v*

butt strap éclisse f

butter (to) (eg a brick with mortar) graisser *v*

bye-law arrêté *m* municipal
bye-laws règlement *m* intérieur

cabinet maker ébéniste *m*; menuisier *m* d'art
cable câble *m*
cable duct conduit *m*
cable, buried câble *m* enterré
cable, earthing câble *m* de mise à la terre
cable, electric câble *m*, électrique
cable, multi-wire câble *m* multifilaire
cables canalisation *f*
calico calicot *m*
canalisation canalisation *f*
cane canne *f*
cane, PVC canne PVC *f*
canopy (over a porch) auvent *m*
cantilever encorbellement *m*
cap couronnement *m*; chapeau *f*
capacity (eg volume of reservoir) contenance *f*
carpenter (joiner) menuisier *m*
carpenter (usually roof timbers) charpentier *m*
carpenter's hammer hachette *f* de charpentier
carpentry charpente en bois *f*; menuiserie *f*
carport abri *m* pour la voiture
carry (to) porter *v*
carry out (to) exécuter *v*
cartridge cartouche *f*
case-hardened steel acier *m* cémenté
casement-fastener agrafe *f*
casement window croisée *f*; fenêtre *f* ordinaire
casing (excavation) blindage *m* par caissons;
casing (lagging of tank) enveloppe *f*
casing (of door or window) dormant *m*
casing (of a machine) habillage *m*
cast steel acier *m* fondu; acier *m* moulé
casting fonte *f*
category specification (Norme Française) marquage *m*
caving in éboulement *m*; effondrement *m*
cavity cavité *f*; trémie *f*
ceiling plafond *m*
ceiling board, tongued and grooved lambris *m*
ceiling, boarded plafond *m* en lambris

ceiling, false or suspended faux-plafond *m*
ceiling, intermediate faux-plafond *m*
cellar cave *m*
cellar, small caveau *m*
cellular glass verre *m* cellulaire
cement ciment *m*
cement, adhesive colle *f*; mastic *m*
cement (to) cimenter *v*; mastiquer *v*
cement and fine sand (1:1) mixture barbotine *f*
cement block (parpaing) aggloméré *m*
cement covering chape *f* ciment
cement mortar used for screeding or rendering ragréage *m*
cement or plaster rough rendering crépi *m*
cement, grey ciment *m* gris
cement, high alumina ciment *m* fondu
cement, jointing ciment *m* joint
cement, Portland ciment *m* Portland
cement, pozzolana ciment *m* pouzzolanique
cement, quick-setting ciment *m* à prise rapide
cement, rapid setting ciment *m* prompt
cement, reinforced ciment *m* armé
cement, slag ciment *m* de laitier
cement, slow-setting ciment *m* à prise lente
cement, white ciment *m* blanc
cementation; cementing cimentage *m*; cimentation *f*
central heating chauffage *m* central
centre centre *m*
centering centrage *m*
ceramic céramique *adj*
certificate of conformity certificat *m* de conformité
certificate stating planning and building requirements to be met certificat *m* d'urbanisme
cesspool fosse *f* d'aisances; puisard *m*; puits *m* perdu
chain chaîne *f*
chain, measuring chaîne *f* d'arpenteur
chain, surveyor's chaîne *f* d'arpenteur
chain-link chaîne *f* à maillons
chaining (surveying) chaînage *m*
change changement *m*
change (to) transformer *v*; changer *v*
changeover passage *m*
channel rigole *f*; conduite *f* (pour câbles)

characteristic propriété *f*
charge (elect) charge *f*
chase saignée *f*
chase (to) faire *v* passer dans la saignée;
ciseler *v*; rainurer *v*
chasing rainurage *m*
check plate plaque *f* d'arrêt
cheek joue *f*
chimney cowl with rain protector aspirateur
m statique pare-pluie
chimney opening trémie *f* de cheminée
chimney piece cheminée *f*
chimney stack souche *f*
chimney sweep's brush hérisson *m*
chimney sweeping kit kit *m* de ramonage
chink lézarde *f*
chip éclat *m*; épaufrure *f*
chipboard panneau *m* de particules;
aggloméré *m*; agglo *abb*
chipping (action) burinage *m*
chippings gravillon(s) *m*
chisel burin *m*; ciseau *m*; ciseaux *mpl*
chisel (to) ciseler *v*
chisel, cold burin *m*; ciseau *m* à froid
chisel, side or skew biseau *m*
chiselling burinage *m*
chrome steel acier *m* chromé
chromium chrome *m*
chromium plated chromé,-e *adj*
chromium plating chromage *m*
circuit (elect) circuit *m*
■ **electric circuit** = circuit électrique
circuit diagram schéma *m* de câblage
circuit wiring câblage *m* de circuit
circuit-breaker interrupteur *m*; coupe-
circuit *m*
cistern citerne *f*; réservoir d'eau *m*
cistern cuve *f*.
civil engineering génie *m* civil
cladding lambris *m*; matériau *m* de revêtement; revêtement *m*
cladding (eg with shingles) bardage *m*
clamp agrafe *f*; bride *f*; bride *f* à capote;
valet *m* d'établi; serre-joint *m*
clamp (to) serrer *v*; brider *v*; cramponner *v*
clamp, mason's serre-joint *m* de maçon
clamp nail cheville *f* de moise
clamping blocage *m*; bridage *m*
clarification mise *f* au point

clasp (to) agrafer *v*
clause clause *f*
claw-bar pied-de-biche *m*
clawed spike-lever pied-de-biche *m*
clay argile *f*
clay soil sol *m* argileux/glaiseux
clean down (brickwork) (to) ragréer *v*
cleaning décapage *m*; nettoyage *m*; nettoiement *m*; ramonage *m*; ravalement *m*
cleaning aperture (eg of soot box) orifice *m*
de ramonage *m*
cleaning down ragrément *m*
cleaning plug (of a flue) tampon *m* de
ramonage *m*
cleansing assainissement *m*; nettoyage *m*;
nettoiement *m*
clear (to) vider *v*
clearance (eg of soil) déblai *m*
clearance (between parts) jeu *m*
clearing défrichement *m*; défrichage *m*;
décapage *m*
cleat; strip of wood tasseau *m*; languette *f* de
bois
cleave (to) (eg wood) fendre *v*
cleaver merlin *m*
clinker mâchefer *m*; clinker *m*; scorie *f*
clip clip *m*; patte *f*; pince *f* de fixation
clip (for conduits) patte d'attache *f*
clip (to) attacher *v*
closer brique *f* d'appoint
closet cabinet *m*
coating, exterior enduit *m* extérieur
coating, interior enduit *m* intérieur
coastal zone zone *f* littorale
coat enduit *m*
coat (eg paint) couche *f*
coat (to) enrober *v*
coat, finishing couche *f* de finition
coat, hot application (eg of bitumen) enduit
m d'application à chaud; EAC *abb*
coat, keying couche *f* d'accrochage; gobetis
m; couche *f* d'approche
coat, priming couche *f* d'impression;
première couche *f*
coat, scratch (of mortar rendering) couche
f d'accrochage
coat, setting (plaster) couche *f* de finition
coat, size or sizing enduit *m*; apprêt *m*
coat, skimming couche *f* de finition

coat, top (paint) couche *f* de finition
coating (rendering, screed) chape *f*
coating enduit *m*; enrobage *m*; enrobement *m*; revêtement *m*
coating knife couteau *m* à enduire
coating knife for angles couteau *m* à enduire les angles intérieures
coating material matériau *m* de revêtement
coating of fill-in material (eg plaster, mortar) solin *m*
coating of tar enduit *m* de goudron
coating, exterior enduit *m* de façade
coating, protective peinture *f* protectrice
coating, waterproof revêtment *m* imperméable *m*
coffer (to) coffrer *v*
coffered ceiling plafond *m* à caissons
coffering blindage *m* par caissons; coffrage *m*
collapse effondrement *m*
collar bride *f*
collector collecteur *m*
colour couleur *f*; coloris *m*
colouring material colorant *m*
column colonne *f*; pilier *m*
comb crête *f*
combining tube convergent *m*
communal sewerage system réseau *m* communal d'assainissement
community charge taxe *f* d'habitation
company entreprise *f*
complete (to) achever *v*
completion work second œuvre *m*
component élément *m*
compress (to) comprimer *v*
conceal (to) voiler *v*
concrete béton *m*
concrete (to) bétonner *v*
concrete bonding beam chaînage *m* béton
concrete cast in situ béton *m* banché
concrete layer dalle *f* de compression
concrete mixer bétonnière *f*
concrete poor in cement béton *m* maigre
concrete rich in cement béton *m* gras
concrete sill appui *m* béton
concrete support appui *m* béton
concrete topping slab dalle *f* de compression
concrete, aerated béton *m* cellulaire
concrete, bedding béton *m* de propreté

concrete, blinding béton *m* de propreté
concrete, cast in situ béton *m* coulé sur place
concrete, cellular béton *m* cellulaire
concrete, formed béton *m* banché
concrete, ordinary cement béton *m* aggloméré
concrete, oversite; concrete raft radier *m*
concrete, precast béton *m* precoulé
concrete, prestressed béton *m* précontraint
concrete, refractory béton *m* réfractaire
concrete, reinforced béton *m* armé; B.A. *abb*
concrete, reinforced stressed béton *m* armé sollicité
concrete, standard béton *m* courant
concrete, universal béton *m* universel
concrete, waterproofed béton *m* hydrofuge
concreting bétonnage *m*
condensation condensation *f*
condition condition *f*
conduit conduit *m*; conduite *f*; tuyau *m*
conduit (wiring/cable) canalisation *f*
connecting raccord *m*; raccordement *m*
connecting the telephone raccordement *m* au réseau
connecting to the drains raccordement *m* aux égouts
connecting-up branchement *m*
connection branchement *m*; joint *m*; raccord *m*
connection to local electricity supply branchement *m* sur le secteur
conservatory jardin *m* d'hiver; serre *f*
consider (to); plan (to) projeter *v*
constraint astreinte *f*
construct (to) bâtir *v*; construire *v*; édifier *v*
construction construction *f*
construction fault or damage dommage-ouvrage *m*
construction fault/defect vice *m* de construction
construction possible (physical conditions and official authorisation) constructible *adj*
construction stage étape *f* de la construction
construction worker ouvrier *m* de construction
constructor constructeur *m*
contact (elect) plot *m*

147

contract contrat *m*
contraction rétrécissement *m*
contractor entrepreneur *m*; entreprise *f*
contribution (financial) apport *m*
contrivance dispositif *m*
control réglementation *f*
conversion aménagement *m*
convert (to) aménager *v*; convertir *v*
▪ **à aménager** = for conversion
convert into (to) convertir en *v*
converting aménagement *m*
cooker cuisinière *f*
cooker, coal-fired cuisinière *f* à charbon
cooker, electric cuisinière *f* électrique
cooker, gas cuisinière *f* à gaz
cooling-off period délai *m* de réflexion
cope (to) (a wall) chaperonner *v*
coping chaperon *m*; couronnement *m*; crête *f*
copper cuivre *m*
copper plate plaque *f* de cuivre
corbel corbeau *m*
cord cordeau *m*
cord (of electric appliance) fil *m*
cordless telephone téléphone *m* sans fil
cordon cordon *m*
cork bouchon *m*; liège *m*
cork sheet plaque *f* de liège
cork slab plaque *f* de liège
corner coin *m*
corner chain bonding (of alternate courses) chainette *f* d'angle
corner-plate équerre *f* d'angle
corner-post montant *m* d'angle
cornice corniche *f*; voussure *f*
cottage chaumière *f*; villa *f*
cotter pin clavette *f*
council offices mairie *f*
counter compteur *m*
coupling accouplement *m*; joint *m*; raccord *m*
course assise *f*
▪ **dernière assise** = last course
course, cross-jointed assise *f* à joints croisés
course, corbel chapeau *m*
course, damp-proof couche *f* d'étanchéité; couche *f* isolante imperméable
course, string cordon *m*
court cour *f*
courtyard cour *f*

courtyard, inner cour *f* intérieure
courtyard, small courette *f*
courtyard, stone cour *f* empierrée
cove corniche *f*
cover abri *m*; couverture *f*; enveloppe *f*
cover (to) couvrir *v*
cover (to) (eg with wallpaper) tapisser *v*
cover strip bande *f* de recouvrement; couvre-joint *m*
cover with cement (to) enrober *v*
cover with zinc (to) zinguer *v*
covered porch reached by an outside staircase perron *m*
covering habillage *m*; recouvrement *m*; revêtement *m*
covering material matériau *m* de revêtement
covering of the underside of a roof sous-toiture *f*
covering plate bande *f* de recouvrement; couvre-joint *m*
coving corniche *f*; voussure *f*
cowl (chimney ventilator) aspirateur statique *m* de toit
crab treuil *m*
crack fente *f*; fissure *f*; lézarde *f*
cracking fissuration *f*
crackle (fine cracks) craquelure *f*
craftsman artisan *m*
cramp bride *f*; crampon *m*; patte *f*; patte *f* à scellement
cramp (to) cramponner *v*
cramp-iron crampon *m*
crest crête *f*
crevice lézarde *f*
cross té *m* double
cross (to) traverser *v*
cross connection té *m* double
cross-bar traverse *f*
cross-beam traverse *f*
cross-file feuille *f* de sauge
cross-tie traverse *f*
crossing traversée *f*
crosspiece barre *f* transversale
crowbar levier *m*; pince *f*; pinces *fpl*; pince *f* à levier; pince(s)-monseigneur *m*
crowbar, dismantling pince *f* à décoffrer
crowbar, pick-and-claw levier *m* à pied-de-biche et à pointe
crowning couronnement *m*

crush (to) concasser *v*
crushed rock/stone roche *f* concassée
crushing écrasement *m*
cubic metre mètre *m* cube
cupboard armoire *f*; placard *m*
current courant *m*
current, alternating courant *m* alternatif
curve cintre *m*
curve (to) cintrer *v*
cut tranchée *f*
cut (to) couper *v*
cut (to) (stone) tailler (se) *v*
cut off (to) (level) araser *v*
cut up wood (to) aménager *v* du bois; débiter *v*
cut-off (to) couper *v*
cut-out (elect) coupe-circuit *m*
cutting (excavation) déblai *m*
cutting edge (of a tool) fil *m*
cutting into sections tronçonnage *m*; tronçonnement *m*
cuttting back (agric) ravalement *m*
cylinder-jacket enveloppe *f* de cylindre
cylindrical boiler chaudière *f* cylindrique

dado (wall) lambris *m* d'appui
dado (wall, window) soubassement *m*
daily fine for delay astreinte *f*
damage dommage *m*
damages dommages *mpl* et intérêts; dommages-intérêts *mpl*
damp proof imperméable *adj*
damp-proof course couche *f* d'étanchéité; couche *f* isolante imperméable; lit *m* isolant
damp-proof covering revêtement *m* d'étanchéité
damp-proof strip ruban *m* d'étanchéité
damp-proofing isolation contre *f* l'humidité
damping humidification *f*
darby (float) taloche *f*
dead shore étai vertical *m*
deaden (to) hourder *v*
deadening material hourdis *m*
deadline délai *m*
deafen (to) hourder *v*
deal bois *m* blanc; madrier *m*
debris décombres *mpl*
decorate (to) décorer *v*; garnir *v*

decorator (interior) décorateur *m*; décoratrice *f*
deep well puits *m* profond
deepening refouillement *m*
default défaut *m*
defect défaut *m*; vice *m*
defect (due to bad workmanship) malfaçon *f*
defect, latent/hidden défaut *m* caché
deflection déviation *f*
deflection of slab/slab floor flèche *f* d'une dalle
deformation déformation *f*
delay délai *m*
delivery date délai *m* de livraison
demarcation bornage *m*
demolish (to) démolir *v*
density densité *f*
dependence dépendance *f*
deposit (to) (money) déposer *v*; verser *v*
deposition of coating on interior wall of a flue chemisage *m*
depth épaisseur *f*; profondeur *f*
depth, excess surprofondeur *f*
design dessin *m*
designer dessinateur *m*; dessinatrice *f*
details détails *mpl*
deterioration of the foundations dégradation *f* des fondations
develop (to) aménager *v*
developing, perfecting mise *f* au point
development (progress) déroulement *m*
deviation déviation *f*
device dispositif *m*
diagram schéma *m*; schème *m*
diameter diamètre *m*
difference écart *m*
dig (to) fouiller *v*; excaver *v*; creuser *v*
digger, mechanical excavateur *m*; pelle *f* mécnique: pelleteuse *f*
digging excavation *f*; fouille *f*
dimension dimension *f*
discharge (output) débit *m*
discharge (elect) décharge *f*
discharge évacuation *f*
discharge/disposal of waste water décharge *f* des eaux usées
discontinuous joint rupture *f* de joint
displace (to) déplacer *v*

displacement forward or backward décalage *m*

disposition disposition *f*

dissociating layer couche *f* de désolidarisation

distance between floor supports portée *f* d'un plancher

distemper badigeon *m*

distemper (to) badigeonner *v*

ditch fossé *m*; saignée *f*

dividing wall/partition cloison *f* de distribution

division cloison *f*

documentation dossier *m*

dognail crampon *m*

door porte *f*

door frame dormant *m*; bâti *m* de porte; châssis *m* de porte, huisserie *f*

door opening baie *f* de porte

door post montant *m* de porte; poteau *m* d'huisserie; chambranle *m*

door sill seuil *m*

door, back porte *f* de derrière

door, front porte *f* d'entrée

door, landing porte *f* palière

door, open-lattice porte *f* à claire-voie

door, sliding/folding porte *f* coulissante/pliante

doorstep seuil *m*

doorway porte *f*; seuil *m*

dossier dossier *m*

dot point *m*

double coat bi-couche *f*

double door or gate porte *f* à deux battants

double glazing double *m* vitrage

double half-round file feuille *f* de sauge

double layer bi-couche *f*

double row of tiles/slates forming eaves doublis *m*

doubling doublage *m*

downpipe chute *f*; descente *f*; tuyau *m* de descente

downpipe, cast iron chute *f* en fonte

draft scheme avant-projet *m*

drain drain *m*; égout *m*; tuyau *m* d'écoulement

drain (to) vider *v*

drain clearing kit kit *m* de débouchage

drain cock purgeur *m*; robinet *m* purgeur

drain off (to) (water, oil) vidanger *v*

drainage drainage *m*; écoulement *m*

drainage ditch fossé *m* collecteur

draining; drainage drainage *m*; assainissement *m*; asséchement *m*

draught (eg of a fire) tirage *m*

draught-hole (of fire, furnace) ventouse *f*

draughtproof (to) calfeutrer *v*

draughtproofing calfeutrage *m*; calfeutrement *m*

draughtsman; draughtswoman dessinateur *m*; dessinatrice *f*

draw (to) tracer *v*; dessiner *v*

draw up (to) (document) établir *v*

draw up plans (to) tirer *v* des plans

drawing dessin *m*; plan *m*

drenching douche *f*

dress (stone) (to) tailler *v*; dégauchir *v*

dressed stone moellon *m* traité

dresser (eg for plaster) rabotin *m*

drier séchoir *m*

drift broche *f*; broche *f* de maçon

driftpin broche *f*

drilling percement *m*; forage *m*

drip throat goutte *f* d'eau

dripstone (archit) larmier *m*

drive in piles (to) piloter *v*

drive in, down (etc) (to) refouler *v*

driver, pile sonnette *f* de battage

driving in (eg pile) enfoncement *m*

drop chute *f*

dry rot pourriture *f* sèche

drying séchage *m*

drying out asséchement *m*

drying shed séchoir *m*

duct conduite *f*

ducting conduite *f*

dump (to) (rubbish) déposer *v*

dump truck dumper *m*; camion *m* benne

dust poussier *m*; poussière *f*

dwelling habitation *f*

dwelling place lieu *m* d'habitation

dyke mur *m* en pierres sèches; digue *f*

earth sol *m*; terre *f*

earth (elect) masse *f*; sol *m*; terre *f*

earth platform terre-plein *m*

earth-moving equipment engins *mpl* de ter-

rassement
earth-rammer dame *f*; demoiselle *f* de
paveur
▪ **10 kg rammer** = une dame de 10Kg
earthenware grès *m*
earthenware (glazed) faïence *f*
earthenware drainpipe conduit *m* en grés
earthenware factory faïencerie *f*
earthwork(s) terrassement *m*
eaves avant-toit *m*
eaves égout *m*; égout *m* du bord du toit;
rive *f*
edge arête *f*; bord *m*; chant *m*; rebord *m*;
rive *f*
edge of break arête *f* de bris
edge-plate (of lock) rebord *m*
edifice édifice *m*
efflorescence efflorescence *f*
elastomeric covering revêtment *m* élastomère
elbow coude *m*
electric hoist treuil *m* électrique *m*
electric plug/socket prise *f* de courant (mâle
/femelle)
electric water heater chauffe-eau *m* électrique
electrical fittings équipement *m* électrique
electrician électricien *m*
electricity électricité *f*
electricity supply alimentation *f* en électricité *f*
element élément *m*
elevation élévation *f*; hauteur *f*
embank (to) remblayer *v*
embankment remblai *m*; terrassement *m*
embed (to) encastrer *v*; sceller *v*
embedding encastrement *m*; scellement *m*
emery cloth toile *f* émeri
emery paper papier *m* d'émeri
emission (eg of gas, steam) dégagement
employing mise *f* en œuvre
empty vide *m*
empty (to) vidanger *v*; vider *v*
empty out (to) vidanger *v*
empty space vide *m*
emptying (draining) asséchement *m*
enamel peinture *f* laquée; peinture *f*
vernissante
encase (to) enrober *v*

encasing enrobage *m*; enrobement *m*
enclose (to) enrober *v*
enclosed land terrain *m* clos
enclosing enrobage *m*; enrobement *m*
enclosure clôture *f*
end (to) (eg work) achever *v*
engineer ingénieur *m*
enterprise entreprise *f*
entrance entrée *f*; porte *f* d'entrée
entry entrée *f*
equip (to) aménager *v*; équiper *v*
equipment appareillage *m*; matériel *m*;
matériels *mpl*; also *adj*; outillage *m*
erect (to) bâtir *v*; édifier *v*
erect a scaffold (to) échafauder *v*
erecting a scaffold échafaudage *m*
erecting a wall montage *m* d'un mur
establish (to) établir *v*
estate propriété *f*
estimate devis *m*
estimate of quantities and costs métré *m*
estimate, detailed devis *m* descriptif
estimate, preliminary devis *m* estimatif
evacuation évacuation *f*
excavate (to) fouiller *v*
excavating excavation *f*
excavation déblai *m*; excavation *f*; fouille *f*;
terrassement *m*
excavation in rocky ground fouille *f* en
terrain rocheux
excavation of rock fouille *f* de rochers
excavation under existing construction
fouille *f* en sous-oeuvre
excavation, trench fouille *f* en tranchée
excavation, underground fouille *f* souterraine
excavator pelleteuse *f*; excavateur *m*
execute (to) exécuter *v*
exit; passageway dégagement *m*
expand (to) dilater *v*
expanded polystyrene polystyrène *m*
expansé
expanded slag laitier *m* expansé
expansion dilatation *f*
expansion in bulk foisonnement *m*
expansion joint joint *m* de dilatation; joint *m*
glissant
expert expert *m*
expert valuation/appraisal expertise *f*

exposed beams poutres *flp* apparentes
expropriation or requisitioning of ground emprise *f* au sol
exterior extérieur *m*; also *adj*
exterior fittings équipement *m* extérieur
exterior/interior fixtures aménagements *mpl* extérieurs/intérieurs

facade façade *f*
face pan *m*; parement *m*; paroi *f*
face in imitation brickwork (to) briqueter *v*
face of an anvil table *f* d'une enclume
face of wall parement *m* d'un mur
face (to) parementer *v*; revêtir *v*
facilities/amenities les équipements *mpl*
facing revêtement *m*
facing (eg of wall) parement *m*
failure to pay défaut *m* de paiement
fair-faced plaster enduit *m* lisse de plâtre
fall chute *f*
fall éboulement *m*
falling in éboulement *m*; effondrement *m*
fan ventilateur *m*
fan, electric ventilateur *m* électrique
fan, extractor ventilateur *m* extracteur
fanlight imposte *f*; vasistas *m*
farm buildings or sheds bâtiments *mpl* de ferme/d'exploitation
farmyard cour *f* de ferme
fascia panneau *m*
fasten (to) agrafer *v*; attacher *v*; cramponner *v*; fixer *v*; lier *v*
fastener attache *f*
fastening fermeture *f*; fixation *f*; patte *f*
fastening together (eg flanges) bridage *m*
fault défaut *m*; malfaçon *f*; vice *m*
fault, flaw (in metal) paille *f*
feather (shaft-key) clavette *f*; languette *f*
feather (tongue on board) languette *f*
feather-edge biseau *m*
feed alimentation *f*
felt feutre *m*
felt, bitumised feutre *m* bitumisé
felt, roofing carton *m* bitumé
felting feutrage *m*; feutre *m*
fence clôture *f*
fence post piquet *m* de clôture
fence (to) clôturer *v*

fencing clôture *f*
ferrule virole *f*
ferrule for boiler tubes virole *f* pour tubes de chaudière
fibrocement fibrociment *m*
filament (of electric bulb) fil *m*
file (papers) dossier *m*
file (tool) lime *f*
fill (to) remblayer *v*
fill (to) (eg crack) reboucher *v*; calfeutrer *v*
fill (to) (eg ditch) combler *v*
fill up (to) combler *v*; remblayer *v*
filled (with a filler) fillerisé,-e *adj*
filler reboucheur *m* calfeutrage *m*; calfeutrement *m*
filler (used in cement) filler *m*
fillet bandelette *f*
fillet-gutter solin *m*
filling blocage *m*; calfeutrage *m*; calfeutrement *m*; remplissage *m*; remblaiement *m*; remblayage *m*
filling in (of crack) rebouchage *m*
filling up remplissage *m*
filling up (eg ditch) comblement *m*
fillister (rebate) feuillure *f*
filter gravel gravier *m* de filtrage
final levelling course (of bricks/stones) arasement *m* (des briques/pierres)
final rendering enduit *m* de ragréage
finalising/settling (business) mise *f* au point
fine cracks craquelure *f*
fine-tuning mise *f* au point
finish finition *f*
finish (to) achever *v*; finir *v*
finish off (to); make good (to) ragréer *v*
finishing finissage *m*; finition *f*
finishing layer couche de finition *f*
finishing off ragrément *m*; travaux *mpl* de finition
finishing works second œuvre *m*
fire back contrecœur *m*
fire base plaque *f* foyère
fire gap écart *m* au/de feu
fire resistance résistance *f* au feu
fire-bucket seau *m* d'incendie
fire-proof(ing) ignifuge *adj*
fire-proofing agent ignifuge *m*
fire-retardant ignifuge *m*; also *adj*
fireback contre-feu *m*

fireplace cheminée *f*
firm entreprise *f*; maison *f*
fishpond réservoir *m*; bassin *m*
fissure fente *f*; fissure *f*
fit (to) équiper *v*
fit flush (to) encastrer *v*
fit out with (to) garnir *v*
fitments équipement *m*; garniture *f*
fitter appareilleur *m*
fitting out équipement *m*; aménagement *m*
fittings appareillage *m*; équipement *m*;
    garniture *f*
fix (to) ancrer *v*; poser *v*; attacher *v*
fix (to) (a price) établir *v*
fixation; fixing fixation *f*
fixed frame (door or window) bâti *m*
    dormant
fixing anchor ancre *f* de maintien
fixing clip attache *f* de fixation
fixing collar collier *m* de fixation
flag dalle *f*
flag, small dallette *f*
flagging dallage *m*
flagging laid on compacted stones
    foundation hérisson *m*; hérissonnage *m*
flagstone dalle *f*
flange bride *f*; joue *f*
flap trappe *f*
flat appartement *m*; logement *m*
flat roof terrasse *f*; toit *m* en terrasse; toit *m*
    plat
flatness planéité *f*
flaw vice *m*; défaut *m*; paille *f*
flexibility (of metal) liant *m*
flexing/flexure flèche *f*; flexion *f*
flight of stairs rampe *f*; rampe *f* d'escalier;
    volée *f* d'escalier
float taloche *f*
float (to) talocher *v*
float, devil taloche *f* à pointes; gratton *m*
float, plastic taloche *f* plastique
floating slab floor dalle *f* flottante
floor sol *m*; plancher *m*
floor (to) planchéier *v*
floor covering revêtement *m* de sol
floor joist solive *f* de plancher
floor (storey) étage *m*;
floor tiling carrelage *m* de sol
floor, concrete sol *m* en béton

floor, first/second premier/deuxième
    étage *m*
floor, ground rez-de-chaussée *m*; rdc *abb.*
floor, heated plancher *m* chauffant
floor, lower ground (of shop) sous-sol *m*
floor, solid plancher *m* solide
floorboard lame *f* de parquet; planche *f*
flooring plancher *m*; planchéiage *m*;
    revêtement *m* de sol; sol *m*
flow débit *m*; écoulement *m*
flow of electricity écoulement *m* d'électricité
flue carneau *m*; conduit *m*; conduit *m* de
    cheminée; conduit *m* de fumée; tuyau *m*
flue block boisseau *m*
flue block, concrete boisseau *m* en béton
flue block, perforated boisseau *m* avec
    alvéoles
flue block, solid boisseau *m* plein
flue block, terra cotta boisseau *m* de terre
    cuite
flue brush hérisson *m*
flue crown couronnement *m*
flue entry pipe (from boiler) buse *f* d'entrée
flue for burners of multiple fuels conduit *m*
    polycombustible
flue for single fuel burner conduit *m* mono-
    combustible
flue unified with supporting wall along full
    height conduit *m* accolé
flue, asbestos cement conduit *m* en amiante
    ciment
flue, boiler carneau *m* de chaudière
flue, completely self-supporting conduit *m*
    isolé
flue, reinforced concrete conduit *m* en béton
    arm
flue, self-supporting but tied to indepen-
    dent wall conduit *m* adossé
flue-shutter tablier *m*
flush fitting encastrement *m*
flush the toilet (to) tirer *v* la chasse
flushing cistern of WC chasse *f* d'eau
foam rubber mousse *f* expansée
foamed slag laitier *m* expansé
footing empattement *m*; semelle *f*
footing-block plate-forme *f*
force in (to) refouler *v*
foreman chef *m* d'équipe; chef *m* de chantier;
    contremaître *m*

form coffrage *m*; forme *f*
formwork coffrage *m*; banche *f*
foul water piping/sewer tuyauterie *f* des eaux usées
foundation fondation *f*; fondement *m*; assise *f*
foundation (load distributing element) semelle *f*
foundation excavation fouille *f* pour fondation
foundation of next-to-earth compacted layer of stones hérisson *m*; hérissonnage *m*
foundation or service trench fouille *f* en rigole
foundation raft radier *m*
foundation trench rigole *f*
foundation wall jambage *m*
foundation, pile fondation *f* sur pieux/pilotis
foundations of a building fondations *fpl* d'un bâtiment
foundations of a house fondements *mpl* d'une maison
foundations, walls and floors etc grosœuvre *m*
fragment éclat *m*
frame bâti *m*; cadre *m*; dormant *m*
frame (of door or window) huisserie *f*; châssis *m*; dormant *m*; chambranle *m*
frame(work) (of house, building) charpente *f*; carcasse f
frame, iron pan *m* de fer
frame, timber (eg wall, partition) pan *m* dc bois
framework bâti *m*
framework cadre *m*; châssis *m*; ossature *f*
framework, metal ossature *f* métallique
framing bâti *m*; cadre *m*
freestone pierre *f* de taille
freezing point point *m* de congélation
French Gas Board Gaz *m* de France; GDF *abb*
french window porte-fenêtre *f*
friction frottement *m*
frog indentation in brick clé *f*
front entrance (archit) portail *m*
front steps (of a house) perron *m*
fulcrum point *m* d'appui
funnel entonnoir *m*

furnace four *m*; fourneau *m*; chaudière *f*
furring coyau *m*
furring-piece (of a roof) coyau *m*
fuse fusible *m*; coupe-circuit *m* à fusible
fuse-box boîte *f* à fusibles
future development zone zone *f* d'aménagement différé

G coefficient coefficient *m* G
G-clamp bride *f* à capote
G-clamp, mason's serre-joint *m* de maçon
gable pignon *m*
■ gabled = à pignon
galvanized steel acier *m* galvanisé
galvanize (to) galvaniser *v*
■ galvanized = galvanisé
gang équipe *f*
gap écart *m*; écartement *m*; ouverture *f*; vide *m*; décalage *m*
garage garage *m*
garden jardin *m*
garden level rez-de-jardin *m*
garden rubbish détritus *mpl* de jardin
garnish (to) garnir *v*
gas gaz *m*
gas supply alimentation *f* en gaz
gas, bottled gaz *m* en bouteille
gas, mains gaz *m* de ville
gas, propane/butane gaz *m* propane/butane
gate porte *f*
gate, double portail *m*
gate, metal grille *f*
gate, metal double portail *m* métallique
gate-post montant *m* de porte
gauge (template) gabarit *m*; gabari *m*
gauze tamis *m* métallique
general conditions conditions *fpl* générales
geometer; geometrician géomètre *m*
geyser chauffe-bain *m*
girder poutre *f*; ferme *f*; solive *f*
girder, small poutrelle *f*
girderage poutrage *m*; poutraison *f*; solivage *m*
give precise details (to) préciser *v*
giving way enfoncement *m*
glass cloth voile *f* de verre
glass fibre fibre *f* de verre
glass items vitrerie *f*

glass paper papier *m* verré; papier *m* de verre
glass wool laine *f* de verre; laine *f* minerale de
 verre
glasshouse serre *f*
glazier vitrier *m*
glaziery vitrerie *f*
glazing vitrerie *f*; vitrage *m*
glazing fillet (eg of putty) solin *m*
glue colle *f*
glue gun pistolet *m* à colle
gluing collage *m*
grain (of wood) fil *m*
granit granit(e) *m*
granulometry granulométrie *f*
grating grille *f*
gravel gravier *m*; gravillon *m*; cailloutis *m*;
 sable *m* (not common)
gravel (to) empierrer *v*
gravel (to) (eg road, path) gravilloner *v*
gravel chippings gravillons *mpl* concassés
gravelling cailloutage *m*
grease (to) graisser *v*
greenhouse serre *f*
grid (electricity) grille *f*; réseau *m*
grille grille *f*; grillage *m*
grind (to) (eg tool) meuler *v*
grip prise *f*; serrage *m*
grit gravier *m*; grès *m*
groove rainure *f*; saignée *f*
groove (eg beading, pulley) gorge *f*
groove (to) rainurer *v*
groove of a screw vide *m* d'une vis
grooved surface rainurage *m*
grooving rainurage *m*
ground sol *m*; terrain *m*; terre *f*
ground floor sol *m*
ground floor flat rez-de-chaussée *m*;
 rdc *abb*
ground level pipework canalisation *f*
grout coulis *m*; enduit *m* de jointoiement
grout (to) jointoyer *v*; mastiquer *v*
grouting jointoiement *m*
grouting (for tiles) ciment *m* joint
gutter gouttière *f*
gutter (road) caniveau *m*
gutter (roof) chéneau *m*
gypsum gypse *m*

habitable floor area surface *f* hors œuvre
 nette; (see also 'overall net floor area')
habitable surface area of dwelling surface *f*
 habitable
hacksaw scie *f* à métaux
half-brick demi-brique *f*; brique *f* à deux
 quartiers
half-header mulot *m*
half-round pointing trowel fer *m* à joint
 demi-lune
half-timbered colombage *m*
hall (of a château) salle *f*
hallway entrée *f*
hammer drill marteau-perforateur *m*
hammer, adze-eye marteau *m* américaine
 avec arrache-clous *m*
hammer, bricklayer's marteau *m* à briques
hammer, caulking marteau-matoir *m*
hammer, claw marteau *m* à dent; marteau *m*
 américaine avec arrache-clous; marteau *m* à
 panne fendue
hammer, club massette *f*
hammer, cutting- décintroir *m* de maçon
hammer, fitter's marteau *m* d'ajusteur
hammer, lath hachette *f* de plâtrier
hammer, lump massette *f*
hammer, mason's massette *f* de maçon
hammer, mason's cutting- décintroir *m* de
 maçon
hammer, mason's stone- têtu *m* de maçon
hammer, pick marteau *m* à piquer; martelette *f* à pic; marteau *m* à pioche
hammer, power marteau-pilon *m*
hammer, scaling marteau *m* à piquer
hammer, scapling smille *f*
hammer, slater's tille *f* de couvreur; marte-
 let *m*
hammer, sledge marteau *m* à deux mains;
 masse *f*; masse *f* couple
hammer, small martelette *f*
hammer, stonebreaker's massette *f* de
 casseur de pierres
hammer-drill, electric marteau *m* électrique
hammer-pick pioche *f*
hand-barrow brouette *f*
hand-rail lisse *f*
handspike levier *m*
hardboard panneau *m* de fibres dures;
 Isorel™ *m*

hardcore blocaille *f*; empierrement *m*
hardened steel acier *m* trempé
hardening (eg cement) durcissement *m*
hardening interval délai *m* de durcissement
hardware quincaillerie *f*
harm dommage *m*
hatch trappe *f*
hatchet hachette *f*
haunch voutain *m* d'une poutrelle
hawk taloche *f*
hazard aléa *m*
head (eg of downpipe) hotte *f*
head (of a hammer) tête *f*; corps *m*
head of water chute *f* d'eau
header boutisse *f*
heading-bond appareil *m* de/en boutisses; appareil *m* en travers
heading-course assise *f* de boutisses
heap tas *m*
hearth âtre *m*; foyer *m*
heat bridge pont *m* thermique
heat comfort confort *m* thermique
heat loss déperdition *f* calorifique/thermique
heat recovery récupération *f* de chaleur
heater calorifère *m*; (also *adj*); réchauff-eur *m*
heater, hot-air calorifère *m* à air; réchauffeur *m* d'air
heater, hot-water calorifère *m* à eau
heating chauffage *m*
heating pipe tube *m* de chauffage
heavy aggregate (eg iron shot) granulat *m* lourd
heavy-duty flex câble *m*
hectare (10,000 sq. metres = 2.4711 acres) hectare *m*; **ha** *abb*
hedge haie *f*
height hauteur *f*
height (person) taille *f*
height above sea-level hauteur *f* au-dessus du niveau de la mer
heighten (to) rehausser *v*
heightening rehaussement *m*
hessian toile *f* de jute
hidden fault/defect vice *m* cache
high density housing development grand ensemble *m*
■ **high-rise flats** = les grands ensembles
higher-care tolerance of execution

exécution *f* soignée
highway system voirie *f*
hinge charnière *f*
hinge, cabinet fiche *f*
hinge, split paumelle *f*
hip (roof) croupe *f*
hip-bath baignoire *f* sabot
hire (to) louer *v*
hoist treuil *m*
hoisting equipment engins *mpl* de levage; appareil *m* de levage
hold prise *f*
holdfast patte *f*; patte à scellement *f*; clou à patte *m*
holding serrage *m*
hole ouverture *f*; trou *m*; fouille *f*
hollow (ground) entonnoir *m*
honeycombed alvéolé,-e *adj*
hood (eg cooker) hotte *f*
hook crochet *m*; agrafe *f*; esse *f*
hook (to) agrafer *v*
hopper-head hotte *f*
horizontal passage excavation fouille *m* en excavation; fouille *f* en galerie
horizontal side piece of door or window traverse *f*
hose tuyau *m*
hosepipe tuyau *m* d'arrosage
hot water tank ballon *m* d'eau chaude
hot-air heating chauffage *m* à air chaud
hot-water boiler chaudière *f* à eau chaude
house bâtiment *m*; maison *f*; pavillon *m*; habitation *f*
house drainage assainissement *m* d'habitation
house painter peintre *m* en bâtiment
house, detached maison *f* individuelle
house, dwelling maison *f* d'habitation
house, five-roomed maison *f* de 5 pièces
house, half-timbered maison *f* à colombage
house, new maison *f* en neuf
house, old house maison *f* en ancien
house, previously owned maison *f* en ancien
house, private maison *f* d'habitation
house, three-storeyed maison à deux étages
house-builder constructeur *m* de maisons
housing encastrement *m*; logement *m*; emboîtement *m*
housing development ensemble *m*

housing development plan plan *m*
d'ensemble
housing scheme ensemble *m*
humidification humidification *f*
hydrant prise *f* d'eau
hydraulic brace étrésillon *m* hydraulique

illumination éclairage *m*
imitation tile wall covering revêtement *m*
mural imitation carrelage
immersion heater chauffe-eau *m* à élément
chauffant; thermoplongeur *m*
impermeable imperméable *adj*
impervious imperméable *adj*
impervious levelling layer arase *f* étanche
imperviousness étanchéité *f*
implementation (of a regulation) mise *f* en
œuvre
implements (tools) outillage *m*
in a slope form en forme de talus
in addition en plus
in bulk en vrac
in quantity en gros vrac
in the clear (measurements) dans-œuvre
adv (opposite to 'hors-œuvre')
inclination fruit *m*; inclinaison *f*
incline (to) incliner *v*
increase in bulk (to) foisonner *v*
independent screen écran *m* d'indépendance
industrial effluent eaux *fpl* résiduaires
infiltration infiltration *f*
inflammable inflammable *adj*
initial layer of plaster or mortar couche *f*
d'approche; gobetis *m*
injury dommage *m*
inlet/intake prise *f*
inside intérieur *m*; also *adj*
inside (measurement) dans-œuvre *adv*
(opposite to 'hors-œuvre')
inspection hole regard *m*; trou *m* de regard
install fitments (to) équiper *v*
installation branchement *m*
insulating material introduced by
projection (eg spraying) isolation *f* par
projection
insulating plasterboard Placoplâtre™ *m*
insulating tape ruban *m* isolant
insulation isolation *f*; isolement *m*

insulation material isolant *m*
insulation with composite panels isolation *f*
par panneaux composite
insulation with polyester/polyurethane
isolation *f* polyester/polyuréthane
insulation, sound isolation *f* acoustique;
isolation *f* phonique
insulation, thermal isolation *f* thermique
insulator isolant *m*; isolateur *m*
insurance against building faults assurance
f dommage-ouvrage
intended use of a building destination *f* d'un
bâtiment
interior intérieur *m*;. also *adj*
interior rendering enduit *m* intérieur
interior surface/face paroi *f*
interjoist space (floor) entrevous *m*
interval décalage *m*
introduction of metal liner tube into
existing flue tubage *m*
introduction (siting) implantation *f*
iron fer *m*
iron framework (for concrete reinforcement) ferraillage *m*
iron scale paille *f* de fer
iron, cast fer *m* de fonte; fonte *f*; fonte *f* de
fer
iron, pig fonte *f*; fonte *f* brute
iron, wrought fer *m* forgé
ironmongery quincaillerie *f*
ironwork, ornamental serrurerie *f* d'art
irregular bonding (eg of stones) appareil *m*
en opus incertum
irrigation channel fossé *m* d'irrigation
isolation isolation *f*; isolement *m*
isolating layer couche *f* de désolidarisation
items covered by the contract éléments *mpl*
compris dans le contrat

jack arch voutain *m* de plancher
jacket enveloppe *f*; garniture *f*
jamb jambage *m*
jamb of a fire-place jambage *m* d'une
cheminée
jamb-lining chambranle *m*
jamb-post jambage *m*; montant *m*
jamb-post of a doorway jambage *m* d'une
baie de port

job tâche *f*
join (to) assembler *v*
join together (to) (with tie, strap) lier *v*
joiner menuisier *m*
joiner's workshop menuiserie *f*
joinery menuiserie *f*
joining assemblage *m*; raccordement *m*
joint assemblage *m*; joint *m*
joint (to) assembler *v*
joint cover couvre-joint *m*
joint ring; sealing ring bague *f* d'étanchéité
joint tape bande *f* à joint
jointer fer *m* à joint
jointer, mason's mirette *f* de maçon; spatule *f* de maçon
jointing jointoiement *m*; assemblage *m*
jointing (eg of pipes) emboîtement *m*
joist solive *f*
joisting solivage *m*
junction branchement *m*; jonction *m*

key clef *f*; clé *f*; clavette *f*
key (eg for plaster, paint) accrochage *m*
key (to) accrocher *v*
keyhole trou *m* de serrure
keying accrochage *m*
kitchen cuisine *f*
kitchen cupboard placard *m* de cuisine
kitchen range cuisinière *f*
kitchen sink évier *m*
kitchen unit bloc-cuisine *m*; élément *m* de cuisine
kitchen, fitted cuisine *f* équipée
kraft ™ paper papier *m* kraft

L-iron cornière *f*; équerre *f*; fer *m* cornière, fer *m* d'angle
labour main-d'œuvre *f*
labour force main-d'œuvre *f*
labourer ouvrier *m* de chantier; travailleur *m*; terrassier *m*; manœuvre *m*
lack of upkeep défaut *m* d'entretien
ladder échelle *f*
lag (to) calorifuger *v*; garnir *v*
lagging calorifugeage *m*
lagging (material) enveloppe *f*; garnissage *m*; garniture *f*

lagging (eg boiler) habillage *m*
laminated lamellé,-e *adj*; laminé,-e *adj*
land terrain *m*; terre *f*
land on which technically and legally one can build terrain *m* constructible
land with/without services laid on terrain *m* avec/sans viabilité
landing (of a staircase) palier *m*
landing-trimmer (staircase) chevêtre *m* sous la marche palière
landlord propriétaire *m*
lap recouvrement *m*
lap (to) recouvrir *v*
lath latte *f*
lattice claire-voie *f*; claires-voies *fpl*
lattice-work treillis *m*
lawn pelouse *f*
lay (to) poser *v*
lay (to) (eg mortar) étaler *v*
lay (to) (a wooden or parquet floor) parqueter *v*
lay bricks (to) briqueter *v*; maçonner *v*; murer *v*
lay down (to) déposer *v*
lay out (to) aménager *v*; tracer *v*
lay pipes (to) poser *v* des tuyaux
lay the foundations of a house (to) poser *v* les fondements d'une maison
layer couche *f*; lit *m*
layer of air lame *f* d'air
layer ready for covering (eg with tiles) couche *f* de revêtement
layer ready for use (eg concrete path) couche *f* d'usure
layer, impervious étanchéité *f*
layer, insulating couche *f* isolante
layer, isolation couche *f* de glissement
layer, multiple multicouche *adj*
layer, non-adherent couche *f* de glissement
layer, slip couche *f* de glissement
laying double doublage *m*
laying floors/flooring pose *f* des sols
lead (metal) plomb *m*
lead flashing (roof) revêtement *m* de plomb
lead sheet feuille *f* de plomb; plomb *m* en feuille
lead-pot (of plumber) poêle *f*
leading plombage *m*
leadwork plomberie *f*

lean-to appentis *m*
ledger (scaffolding) filière *f*; moise *f*
legal flaw or irregularity vice *m* de forme
length longueur *f*
length/strip (of wallpaper) lé *m*
level niveau *m*
level (to) aplanir *v*
level (to) (eg a wall) araser *v*
level a piece of land (to) aplanir *v* un terrain
level course assise *f* de niveau
**levelling layer of bedding cement or sand
  for paving or flagstones** forme *f*
levelling arasement *m*; nivellement *m*
levelling course (of a wall) arase(s) *f(pl)*;
  arasement *m*
lever levier *m*
lift (to) enlever *v*
lifting élévation *f*
lifting loop boucle *f* de levage
light aggregate (eg pumice, expanded slag)
  granulat *m* léger
light source source *f* de lumière
lighted ceiling plafond *m* lumineux
lighting éclairage *m*
lighting system réseau *m* d'éclairage
lime chaux *f*
lime, grey chaux *f* grise
lime, high-calcium chaux *m* blanche
lime, hydraulic chaux *f* hydraulique
lime, non-hydraulic chaux *f* aérienne
lime, quick- chaux *f* vive
lime, slaked chaux *f* éteinte
lime, slaked (for building work) chaux *f*
  aérienne éteinte pour le bâtiment;
  CAEB *abb*
lime, white chaux *m* blanche
limestone pierre *f* à chaux; pierre *f* calcaire
limit; boundary borne *f*
limits tolérance *f*
line cordeau *m*
line (to) garnir *v*; revêtir *v*; chemiser *v*;
  tapisser *v*
line of supports file *f* d'étais
linen cupboard armoire *f* à linge
liner; lining partition cloison *f* de doublage
lining doublage *m*; garnissage *m*; lambris
  m; revêtement enduit *m*
lining (eg of a well) cuvelage *m*;
  cuvellement *m*

lining a flue by inserting a metal flue liner
  tubage *m*
lining material matériau *m* de revêtement
lining paper (wall) papier *m* à tapisser
lining revêtement *m*
lintel linteau *m*
lintel tied to a reinforcing beam linteau *m*
  continu; linteau *m* filant
lintel with boot linteau-botte *m*
lintel, internal contre-linteau *m*
lintel, isolated linteau *m* isolé
lintel, large span linteau *m* de grande portée
lintel, prefabricated linteau *m* préfabriqué
lintel, short span linteau *m* de petite portée
lip balevre *f*
live wire (elect) fil *m* sous tension; phase *f*
livestock buildings bâtiments *m* d'élevage
load charge *f*
load distribution plate semelle *f* de
  répartition
loadbearing element élément *m* porteur
loadbearing section élément *m* porteur
local electricity supply area secteur *m*
locating; siting implantation *f*
lock serrure *f*
lock-staple gâche *f*
lock-work serrurerie *f*
locksmith serrurier *m*
lodge (to) (a document) déposer *v*
loft grenier *m*; comble *m*
long bend or elbow coude *m* prolongé
loop boucle *f*
loose en vrac
loose materials matériaux *mpl* en vrac
loss perte *f*; dommage *m*
lounge salon *m*; séjour *m*
lower (to) (eg ceiling) surbaisser *v*
lowering abaissement *m*
lug sill appui *m* à oreilles
lump bloc *m*
lump hammer massette *f*
lump of plaster plâtras *m*

machinery appareil *m*; outillage *m*
mahogany acajou *m*
▪ **made of mahogany** = en acajou
main drain drain *m* collecteur
main drain (sewage) collecteur *m* à l'égout

main home résidence *f* principale
main residence habitation *f* principale
main sewer collecteur *m* principal; collecteur *m* à l'égout; égout *m* collecteur; grand collecteur *m*
mains drainage tout-à-l'égout *m*
make clear (to) préciser *v*
make even or level (to) araser *v*
make plans for (to) (eg a house, garden) dresser *v* les plans de
make ready (to) apprêter *v*
mallet maillet *m*
mallet, caulking maillet *m* de calfat
mallet, rubber maillet *m* caoutchouc
management gestion *f*
manhole regard *m*; trou *m* d'homme
manhole cover plaque *f* d'égout
manor house (small) gentilhommière *f*
manpower main-d'œuvre *f*
mansard roof toit *m* en mansarde
mantelpiece; mantelshelf manteau *m* (de cheminée); tablette *f* (de cheminée); cheminée *f*
marble marbre *m*; marbrier,-ière *adj*
marble slab plaque *f* de marbre
margin tolérance *f*
marking marquage *m*
mason maçon *m*
mason's jointer mirette *f* de maçon; spatule *f* de maçon
mason's level niveau *m* de maçon
mason's pin chevillette *f* de maçon
mason's plumb plomb *m* de maçon
mason's pointed chisel broche *f* de maçon; pointerolle *f* de maçon
mason's rule règle *f* de maçon
mason's set square équerre *f* de maçon
mason's straight-edge règle *f* de maçon
masonry maçonnerie *f*; murage *f*; bâtisse *f*
masonry paint applicator machine *f* à crépir
mass bloc *m*; masse *f*
massive structure masse *f*
massive structure of the building masse *f* de l'édifice
material; materials matériau *m*; matériaux *mpl*
mattock pioche *f*; pioche-hache *f*; décintroir *m* à talus
mattock (grubbing) pioche *f* à défricher

measure with a spirit level (to) niveler *v*
measurement dimension *f*; métrage *m*; métré *m*
measuring métrage *m*
measuring tape mètre *m* à ruban
mechanical resistance résistance *f* mécanique
mechanically controlled ventilation ventilation *f* mécanique contrôlée; VMC. *abb*
melting fonte *f*
member piéce *f*; élément *m*
membrane membrane *f*
membrane, damp-proof membrane *f* d'étanchéité
mend réparer *v*
mending réparation *f*
mesh treillis *m*
metal (to) (eg road) empierrer *v*; caillouter *v*
metal flue pipe conduit *m* métallique
metal items, grilles etc métallerie *f*
metal trellis beam (concreted for floor support) poutrelle *f* en treillis
metal wall tie patte *f* métallique
metalling (road) cailloutage *m*
metalwork métallerie *f*; serrurerie *f*
meter compteur *m*
meter, electricity supply compteur *m* électrique
meter, gas compteur *m* à gaz
meter, water compteur *m* à eau
method système *f*
method of constructing wall from randomly placed stones (moellons) blocage *m*
metre mètre *m*
metre rule mètre *m*
mezzanine; mezzanine floor mezzanine *f*
mild steel acier *m* doux
mildew moisissure *f*
mineral fibre fibre *f* minérale
mix (to) (by adding water to plaster, etc) gâcher *v*
mix (to) (to required consistency) délayer *v*
mixing gâchage *m*; malaxage *m*
mixing tray (eg for mortar) bac à *m* gâcher
modern house villa *f*
modernisation rénovation *f*
modernise (to) rénover *v*
modify (to) modifier *v*
moisten (to) mouiller *v*

mortar adhesive for cellular concrete blocks mortier *m* colle pour béton cellulaire

mortar fixative (for tiles) mortier *m* colle; ciment *m* colle

mortar joints laid using metal former joints *mpl* au cadre

mortar mortier *m*

mortar, average mortier *m* moyen

mortar, bonding mortier *m* de liaison

mortar, cement mortier *m* de ciment

mortar, fat mortier *m* gras; mortier *m* riche

mortar, fine mortier *m* fin

mortar, finishing mortier *m* fin

mortar, hydraulic mortier *m* hydraulique

mortar, lean mortier *m* maigre

mortar, lime mortier de *m* chaux

mortar, lime-cement mortier *m* bâtard

mortar, masonry mortier *m* normal

mortar, medium mortier *m* moyen

mortar, ordinary mortier *m* normal

mortar, rapid setting mortier *m* rapide

mortar, refractory mortier *m* refractaire

mortar, universal mortier *m* universel

mortar, white mortier *m* blanc

moss mousse *f*

mould moisissure *f*

mould (eg for concrete) moule *m*

moulding moulure *f*

move (to) déplacer *v*

movement apart écartement *m*

mud limon *m*; vase *f*; boue *f*

mullion meneau *m*

nail clou *m*; pointe *f*

nail (to) clouer *v*

nail, clamp cheville *f* de moise

narrowing rétrécissement *m*

natural bed (of stone) lit *m* de carrière

natural drainage écoulement *m* naturel

necessary steps démarches *fpl* nécessaires

neck opening (flue) goulet *m*

netting treillis *m*

network réseau *m*

new neuf, neuve *adj*

▪ as new = à l'état neuf

nickel nickel *m*

no entry passage *m* interdit

noise bruit *m*

noise level niveau *m* de bruit

noise rating pondération *f* des bruits

noise reduction réduction *f* de bruit

non-conductor (of heat) calorifuge *m*; also *adj*

non-decayable packing-piece/wedge cale *f* imputrescible

non-packaged vrac (en)

non-packaged materials matériaux *mpl* en vrac

nook coin *m*; recoin *m*

normal tolerance of execution exécution *f* courante

nosing nez *m*

nosing of step (staircase) nez *m* de marche

notification that permitted building work has been completed déclaration *f* d'achèvement des travaux

nozzle; nose-piece buse *f*

nylon fibre mesh quadrillage *m* en fil de nylon

obstruction obstruction *f*; bouchage *m*

office bureau *m*; cabinet *m*

old ancien, ancienne *adj*

old house logement *m* en ancien

one hundred square metres are *m*

open excavation (levelling) fouille *f* en déblais

open framework (timber) châssis *m* de charpente

open-lattice gate or door porte *f* à claire-voie

open-work claire-voie *f*; claires-voies *fpl*

open-work fence claire-voie *f*; claires-voies *fpl*

opening ouverture *f*; orifice *m*; baie *f*

order (administrative) arrêté *m*

ordinary courant,-e *adj*

ordnance surveyor géomètre *m* du cadastre

orifice orifice *m*

ornamental tree arbre *m* d'agrément

out of plumb hors d'aplomb

out of square hors d'équerre

outbuilding dépendance *f*; annexe *f*

outer frame châssis *m* de charpente

outer walls gros œuvre *m*

outflow écoulement *m*

outlet décharge *f*; orifice *m* de sortie
outline (of a project) esquisse *f*
outline sketch ébauche *f*
outline specification devis *m* préliminaire
outside extérieur *m*; also *adj*
outside measurement hors-œuvre *m,inv*;
(opposed to 'dans- œuvre')
outwork; annexe hors *m* d'œuvre
overall length longueur *f* hors-tout
overall net floor area superficie *f* de
plancher hors œuvre nette
overall width largeur *f* hors-tout
overestimate (to) surestimer *v*
overflow; overflow-pipe trop-plein *m*
overlap recouvrement *m*
overlapping recouvrement *m*
overloading surcharge *f*
overmantel (fireplace) trumeau *m*
overvalue (to) surestimer *v*
overvalue a house for sale (to) surestimer *v*
une maison à vendre
owner propriétaire *m*
■ former owner = ancien propriétaire
owner (commissioning building work)
maître *m* d'ouvrage
ownership propriété *f*

pack (to) (a gland) garnir *v*
packing bourrage *m*; garnissage *m*
packing with plaster and tow bourrage *m* au
plâtre et filasse
packing-piece cale *f*
pad; support; stud plot *m*
pail seau *m*
pailful seau *m*
paint peinture *f*
paint (to) peindre *v*
paint spray gun pistolet à peinture *m*
paint the woodwork (to) peindre *v* les
boiseries
paint, antirust peinture *f* antirouille
paint, bitumastic peinture *f* bitumineuse
paint, emulsion peinture *f* emulsion
paint, gloss/satin-finish peinture *f* laqueé/
satineé *f*
paint, masonry crépi *m*; peinture *f* crépi
paintbrush brosse *f*; pinceau *m*
painter peintre *m/f*

painter and decorator peintre-décorateur *m*
painting peinture *f*
paintwork peinture *f*
paling clôture *f*
pane of glass carreau *m* de verre, carreau *m*;
vitre *f*
panel panneau *m*
panel (to) lambrisser *v*
panel (to) (in wood) boiser *v*
panel, composite insulation panneau *m*
composite
panel, insulation, faced both sides
panneau *m* "sandwich"
panel, polstyrene plaque de *f* polystyrène
panel, rigid plaque *f* rigide
panel, single material insulation panneau *m*
simple
panelled ceiling plafond *m* lambrissé
panelling boiserie *f*; lambris *m*; lambrissage *m*
pantry arrière-cuisine *f*
parapet of a roof terrace (acroter)
acrotère *m*
parcel (of land) parcelle *f*
parget (to) crépir *v*
pargetting chemisage *m*; crépissage *m*;
crépi *m*
parquet floor parquet *m*
part pièce *f*
part of wall between sill and floor allège *f*
partition cloison *f*; paroi *f*
partition (to) cloisonner *v*
partition liner cloison *f* de doublage
partition wall cloison *f*; cloison mitoyenne *f*
partition wall of staircase échiffre *m*
partition wall support raidisseur *m*
partition with honeycomb core cloison *f* à
âme alvéolée
partition, dividing cloison *f* de distribution
partition, glass/glazed cloison *f* vitrée
partition, wood cloison *f* en bois
partitioning cloisonnage *m*
pass through (to) traverser *v*
passage passage *m*
passage (in appartment) dégagement *m*
passage through traversée *f*
paste colle *f*; pâte *f*
pave (to) daller *v*
pavement dallage *m*; pavage *m*

pavilion pavillon *m*
paving dallage *m*; pavage *m*
paving stone dalle *f*; lauze *f*
paving with slate slabs dallage *m* en ardoise
payment in full règlement *m* intégral
peat tourbe *f*
pebble caillou *m*
pebbledash cailloutage *m*
pebble paving cailloutage *m*
pebble-work cailloutage *m*; rocaillage *m*
pebble; pebble-stone galet *m*
pedestal socle *m*
peg chevillette *f*; taquet *m*; fiche *f*
penalty astreinte *f*
penalty clause clause *f* pénale
penetration ferrule virole *f* de penetration
penthouse (roof) appentis *m*
perfecting mise *f* au point
perlite; pearlite perlite *f*
permit to build permis *m* de construire
permit to demolish a building permis *m* de
   démolir
permitted tolerance tolérance *f* d'exécution
perpend parpaing *m*
perpendicular plomb (à)
pick-axe pioche *f*; pioche *f* ordinaire
pick-mattock décintroir *m* à talus
picket piquet *m*
picture window baie *f* vitrée
piece pièce *f*
piece of joinery/carpentry menuiserie *f*
piece of work œuvre *f*
pier (wall between two openings)
   trumeau *m*
pier (brickwork) pied-droit *m*; piédroit *m*
piercing percement *m*
pile (heap) tas *m*
pile (constr) pieu *m*; pilot *m*
pile (to) piloter *v*
pile driving battage *m* de pieux/pilots;
   pilotage *m*
piling pilotage *m*; pilotis *m*
pillar colonne *f*; pilier *m*
pillar (of arch) pied-droit *m*; piédroit *m*
pin cheville *f*; chevillette *f*; fiche *f*; plot *m*
pin and chain (scaffolding) broche *f*
   imperdable
pin, mason's chevillette *f* de maçon
pin, round chevillette *f* ronde

pin, square chevillette *f* carrée
pincers pince *f*; pinces *fpl*; tenaille(s) *f*(pl)
pinion pignon *m*
pins, line chevillettes *fpl* de maçon
pipe conduite *f*; tube *m*; tuyau *m*; conduit
   m; buse *f*; canalisation *f*; tubulure *f*
pipe cutter coupe-tube *m*
pipe/piping, copper tuyau *m* en cuivre
pipe fitter poseur *m* de tuyaux; tuyauteur *m*
pipe wrapping revêtement *m* des tubes
pipe, earthenware tuyau *m* en terre
pipe, overflow tuyau *m* de trop-plein
pipe, plastic tuyau *m* en plastique
pipe-slick lissoir *m* à tuyau
pipe-smoother lissoir *m* à tuyau
pipe-strap patte *f* à crochet
pipes canalisation *f*; tuyauterie *f*
pipes (main) canalisation *f*
pipes and fittings tuyauterie *f*
pipework canalisation *f*
pipework installation tuyauterie *f*
piping tuyau *m*; tuyauterie *f*
pistol, spray (paint) pistolet *m*
pit fosse *f*
pitch bitume *m*
pitch (slope) inclinaison *f*; chute *f*
pitch of roof chute *f* de comble; pente *f*;
   rampe *f* de chevrons
pitcher (chisel) ciseau *m* de maçon
place point *m*
place (to) poser *v*
place a frame for (to) (eg concrete)
   coffrer *v*
place edge to edge placer *v* bord à bord
place shuttering (to) coffrer *v*
plan plan *m*; projet *m*; schéma *m*; schème *m*
plan (to) projeter *v*
plan to do (to) projeter *v* de faire
plan, building plan *m* de construction
plan, frontage or front elevation plan *m* de
   la façade
plan, house plan *m* de la maison
plan, raised (of building) élévation *f*
plan, siting (for house) plan *m* d'implantation de la maison sur le terrain
plan, structural plan *m* de masse; plan *m*
   masse
plan/drawing of situation of site plan *m* de
   situation du terrain

plane plan *m*
plane down (to) araser *v*
plane, nosing nez *m* de marche
planeness planéité *f*
planer raboteuse *f*; aplanisseur *m*; aplanisseuse *f*
planing machine raboteuse *f*; machine *f* à raboter
plank planche *f*; madrier *m*
planning permission permis *m* de construire
planning provision/requirement disposition *f* d'urbanisme
plant appareil *m*; matériel *m*; matériels *mpl*
plaster plâtre *m*
plaster (to) plâtrer *v*
plaster debris plâtras *m*
plaster filling between ceiling joists auget *m*
plasterer plâtrier *m*
plasterer's hammer hachette *f* de plâtrier
plastering plâtrage *m*
plastic film damp-proof membrane film *m* plastique étanche
plastic trough (plastering) auge *f* plastique
plate (sheet metal) tôle *f*
plate, cover plaque *f* de protection
plate, finger plaque *f* de propreté
plate, foundation plaque *f* d'assise
plate, reinforcing plaque *f* de renfort
plate, stiffening plaque *f* de renfort
platform plate-forme *f*; terre-plein *m*
plating (of metal) doublage *m*; placage *m*
play jeu *m*
pliers pince *f*; pinces *fpl*
pliers, flat-nosed pinces *fpl* plates
plinth socle *m*
plot (of land) terrain *m*; parcelle *f* de terre
plug bouchon *m*; cheville *f*; fiche *f*; plot *m*
plug (to); plug up (to) boucher *v*
plugging; plugging up bouchage *m*; colmatage *m*
plugging-in branchement *m*
plumb plomb *m*
plumb-bob plomb *m*; plomb *m* de maçon
plumb-line fil à plomb *m*; plomb *m*
plumber plombier *m*
plumber's workshop plomberie *f*
plumbing plombage *m*; plomberie *f*; robinetterie *f*

plywood bois *m* contreplaqué
pneumatic drill marteau *m* piqueur; marteau *m* pneumatique
point point *m*
point (to) (masonry) jointoyer *v*
point of support point *m* d'appui
pointing jointoiement *m*; gobetis *m*
pointing after wall has been built rejointoiement *m*
pointing as wall is built jointoiement *m*
pointing tool, flat fer *m* à joint plat
pointing tool, half-round fer *m* à joint demi-lune *m*
pole poteau *m*
polyester sheet/membrane film polyester *m*
polyethylene polyéthylène *m*
polystyrene pellets billes *f* de polystyrène
polyurethane polyuréthane *m*
polyvinyl chloride; PVC polychlorure *m* de vinyl
porch; porchway porche *m*
porosity porosité *f*
portal portail *m*
possession propriété *f*
post poteau *m*; montant *m*; piquet *m*
post, anchor poteau *m* d'ancrage
post, boundary poteau *m* de bornage
post, door poteau *m* d'huisserie
post, inertial poteau *m* d'inertie
post, jamb- poteau *m* d'huisserie
post/pole, telegraph poteau *m* télégraphique
pour (to) (eg concrete, asphalt) couler *v*
pouring (eg concrete) coulage *m*
power (elect) courant *m*
power point (plug/socket) prise *m* de courant (mâle/femelle)
power point (elect) prise *f*
power supply alimentation *f* en énergie
pozzolana pouzzolane *f*
practicability viabilité *f*
pre-lintel prélinteau *m*
prefabrication préfabrication *f*
preliminary plan avant-projet *m*
preparation mise *f* en œuvre
preparation and placing of steel frames ferraillage *m*
preparatory study of constructional project avant-projet *m*
preparatory work travail *m* préparatoire

prepare (to) apprêter *v*
prestressed (concrete) précontraint,-e *adj*; also *m*
prestressed concrete beam poutrelle *f* précontrainte
prime (to) (a pump) amorcer *v*
priming coat première *f* couche
prior work travail *m* préparatoire
prise levier *m*
private company entreprise *f* privée
private entrance dégagement *m* d'entrée
proceed by stages (to) procéder *v* par paliers
produce a draft agreement/contract établir *v* un projet d'accord/de contrat
professional expert *m*
progress déroulement *m*; avancement *m*
progress of building work déroulement *m* des travaux; avancement *m* des travaux
progress of the contract déroulement *m* du contrat
progress report compte *m* rendu d'avancement des travaux
project plan *m*; projet *m*
project (to) projeter *v*
project manager maître *m* d'œuvre
projecting en saillie; saillant,-e *adj*
prop étai *m*
prop (to) étayer *v*; buter *v*
property propriété *f*
proportional composition of mortar mix dosage *m* de mortier
propping étayage *m*; étayement *m*
proprietor propriétaire *m*
protected chimney (with cover slab) souche *f* protegée
protected facade façade *f* abritée
protection abri *m*
protection against fire protection *f* incendie
protection against impacts or shocks protection *f* aux chocs
provision (eg of water) apport *m*
provision clause *f*
public building édifice *m* public
pug (to) hourder *v*
pugging hourdage *m*; hourdis *m*
pull down (to) démolir *v*
pumice ponce *f*
pump pompe *f*
pump, circulating pompe *f* de circulation

pump, electric pompe *f* électrique
punch emporte-piece *m,inv*
punching poinçonnage *m*; poinçonnement *m*
purlin filière *f*; panne *f*; panne *f* filière
purpose for which building is to be used destination *f* d'un bâtiment
put in a window pane (to) poser *v* une vitre
put up a shelf (to) poser *v* un rayon
putty mastic *m*
putty (to) mastiquer *v*
putty, glazier's mastic *m* de vitrier
putty, iron mastic *m* de fer
putty, lime mastic *m* à la chaux
putty, stopping mastic *m* calfeutrement
PVC sheet feuille *f* de PVC

qualified building supervisor (eg architect, builder) maître *m* d'œuvre qualifié
queen-closer (half a brick cut along its length) mulot *m*
quoin voussoir *m*; vousseau *m*
quotation devis *m*

rabbet feuillure *f*
rabbet (to) feuiller *v*
raft foundation radier *m* de fondation
rafter chevron *m*
raftering chevronnage *m*
rail rail *m*
railings grille *f*
rain-water tank citerne *f*
rainwater downpipe descente *f*
raise (to) (ceiling) rehausser *v*
raising (a wall) montage *m*
rake râteau *m*
rake (of a wall) fruit *m*
rake out (to) (mortar joints) dégarnir *v*
raking out (mortar joints) dégradation *f*
raking shore étai *m* incliné
ram (to) damer *v*; pilonner *v*
rammer dame *f*; demoiselle *f* de paveur
■ 10Kg rammer = une dame de 10Kg
ramming bourrage *m*; pilonnage
rapid drying sèche *m* rapidement
rates taxe *f* d'habitation
razor point prise *f* pour résoir électrique

ready-mix concrete béton *m* prêt à l'emploi
ready-mix rendering enduit *m* prêt à gâcher
ready-mixed concrete béton *m* préparé
ready-to-use single coat rendering mono-couche *f* prêt à l'emploi
real estate/freehold propriété *f* fonciére
rear arrière *m*
rebate feuillure *f*
rebate (to) feuiller *v*
receiver (tank) collecteur *m*
recess (of a masonry joint) refouillement *m*
recess; nook recoin *m*
redevelopment rénovation *f*
refilling (eg cracks) rebouchage *m*
refractory hood hotte *f* refractaire
refurbish (to) remettre *v* à neuf
refuse déchet *m*; déchets *mpl*; détritus *mpl*
refuse collection ramassage *m* des ordures
refuse tip décharge *f*
regrout (to) rejointoyer *v*
regrouting rejointoiement *m*
regulate (to) régler *v*
regulation(s) règlement *m*; réglementation *f*
regulations in force réglementation *f* en vigueur
reinforced concrete beam poutre *f* en béton armé
reinforced slab floor (concrete) dalle *f* en béton armé
reinforcement chainage *m*
reinforcement (for concrete) armature *f*
reinforcement cage armature *f* de chainage
removal évacuation *f*
removal of (excavated) earth évacuation *f* des terres
removal of air (ventilation) évacuation *f* d'air
removal of formwork décoffrage *m*
removal of shuttering décoffrage *m*
remove (to) enlever *v*
render (to) enduire *v*; hourder *v*; plâtrer *v*
render impermeable (to) imperméabi-liser *v*
render with cement mortar (to) enduire *v* au mortier de ciment; hourder *v* au mortier de ciment
render, rough (to) crépir *v*
rendering crépi *m*; crépissage *m*; enduit *m*

rendering of facade enduit *m* de façade
renovate (to) rénover *v*; remettre *v* à neuf
renovation rénovation *f*
rent (to) louer *v*
repaint (to) repeindre *v*
repair (to) réparer *v*
repair (to) (masonry) remaçonner *v*
repairing réparation *f*
repoint (to) rejointoyer *v*
repointing rejointoiement *m*
report compte rendu *m*
reservoir réservoir *m*
residence résidence *f*
residue résidu *m*
resilient base-plate semelle *f* résiliente
resilient joint joint *m* résilient
rest appui *m*
restatement mise *f* au point
restoration ravalement *m*; rénovation *f*; restauration *f*
restore (to) ragréer *v*; restaurer *v*; rénover *v*
restored building bâtiment *m* restauré
restoring réparation *f*
resurface (to) refaire *v* la surface
resurfacing ravalement *m*
reveal jouée *f*
ridge arête *f*
ridge (of roof) crête *f*; faîtage *m*; faîte *f*
ridge beam faîte *f*; madrier *m* de faîtage
ridge tile faîtière *f*
right of way droit *m* de passage; servitude *f* de passage
right to draw water (eg from river, well) droit *m* de puisage
rim bord *m*; rebord *m*
ring bague *f*
ring-bolt boucle *f* d'amarrage
ring-main (elect) réseau *m* primaire en boucle
rise rampe *f*
riser (of staircase) contremarche *f*
rising damp infiltration *f*
risk of caving in risque *m* d'éboulement
risk of earth-fall risque *m* d'éboulement; risque *m* de glissement
risk of giving way risque *m* d'enfoncement
risk of sinking (eg foundation) risque *m* d'enfoncement
risk of slippage risque *m* de glissement

rivet rivet *m*
rivet (to) riveter *v*
road gully avaloir *m* de chaussée
roadworks chantier *m*
rock roche *f*
rock garden jardin *m* de rocaille
rock wool laine *f* minerale de roche
rockery jardin *m* de rocaille
rod tige *f*
rolled steel acier *m* laminé; acier *m* marchand
rolled steel joist poutrelle *f* en acier laminé
rolled-iron girder poutre *f* en fer laminé
roller rouleau *m*
roller, light rouleau *m* léger
roller, paint rouleau *m* à peinture
roof toit *m*; toiture *f*; couverture *f*
roof board; roof sheathing vorlige *f*
roof light vélux ™ *m*
roof space comble *m*; combles *mpl*
roof terrace toiture-terrasse *f*
roof tiler couvreur *m*
roof timbers combles *mpl*; ferme *f*
roof truss/trussing charpente *f* de comble; ferme *f*; combles *mpl*
roof ventilator ventilateur *m* de toit
roof, French comble *m* mansardé
roof, mansard mansarde *f*; comble *m* mansardé *m*; toit *m* à la mansarde
roof-light, opening tabatière *f;* vélux™ *m*; fenêtre *f* de toit
roofer couvreur *m*
roofing couverture *f*; toiture *f*
roofing stone lauze *f*
roofing, thatched couverture *f* de chaume
roofing, tiled couverture *f* en tuiles
room salle *f*
room (of house) pièce *f*
room, boiler chaufferie *f*
room, box débarras *m*
room, dining salle à manger *f*
room, laundry buanderie *f*
room, linen lingerie *f*
room, living salle *f* de séjour; séjour *m*; salon *m*; living *m*
room, lumber cabinet *m* de débarras; débarras *m*
room, main pièce *f* principale
room, shower salle *f* d'eau; salle *f* de douches

room, sitting salon *m*
room, spare/guest chambre *f* d'amis
room, utility buanderie *f*
rough sketch esquisse *f*
rough-casting crépissage *m*
rough-walling hourdage *m*
roughcast crépi *m*; hourdis
roughcast (to) crépir *v*; hourder *v*
roughcast (to) (masonry) hérissonner *v*
roughcasting crépissage *m*
roughening bouchardage *m*
roughness aspérité *f*
row rang *m*; rangée *f*
rub (to) frotter *v*
rub down (to) poncer *v*
rubber tubing tuyau *m* en caoutchouc
rubber, foam mousse *f* de caoutchouc
rubbing frottement *m*
rubbish détritus *mpl*; ordures *fpl*
rubbish chute vide-ordures *m*
rubbish dump décharge *f*; voirie *f*
rubble blocage *m*; blocaille *f*; décombres *mpl*; gravats *mpl*; gravois *mpl*; moellonage *m*; plâtras *m*
rubble-stone moellon *m*
rubble-work moellonage *m*
rubbly blocageux, blocageuse *adj*
rule (to) régler *v*
rules and regulations règlement *m* intérieur
rust rouille *f*
rustproofing traitement *m* antirouille

S-plate ancre *f* en forme d'un S
S-shaped pipe connector esse *f*
sacking toile *f* à sac
saddle patte *f* d'attache
sagging affaissement *m*; flèche *f*; flexion *f*
saltpeter salpêtre *m*
sand sable *m*
sand paper papier *m* verré; papier *m* de verre
sand pistol pistolet *m* de sablage
sand, building sable *m* à bâtir
sand, coarse sable *m* grossier
sand, soft sable *m* doux
sand-coloured sable *adj*
sand-pit sablière *f*
sandblaster (machine) sableuse *f*
sandblasting sablage *m*; décapage *m*

sander ponceuse *f*
sanding ponçage *m*
sandstone grès *m*
sanitary sanitaire *adj*
sanitary engineering génie *f* sanitaire
sash window fenêtre *f* à guillotine
saw for cellular concrete scie *f* pour bêton cellulaire
saw for soft stone and plaster scie *f* pour pierre tendre et plâtre
saw, formworker's scie *f* de coffreur
saw-blade lame *f* de scie; feuille *f* de scie
sawing up tronçonnage *m*; tronçonnement *m*
scabble (to) smiller *v*
scaffold boards platelage *m* d'echafaud
scaffold(ing) échafaud *m*; échafaudage *m*
scaffolding on trestles échafaudage *m* sur tréteaux
scale drawing plan *m*; dessin *m* à l'échelle
scantling (timber) volige *f*
scapple (to) smiller *v*
scheme projet *m*; schéma *m*; schème *m*
scouring décapage *m*
scraper, wall riflard *m* de maçon
screed chape *f*; chape *f* ciment
screed laid as base for floor covering chape *f* de revêtement
screed laid as floor surface chape *f* d'usure
screed, adherent chape *f* incorporée
screed, adherent (opposed to floating screed) chape *f* adhérente
screed, detached chape *f* rapportée
screed, finishing enduit *m* de ragréage
screed, floating chape *f* flottante
screed, incorporated chape *f* incorporée
screed, levelling layer of chape *f* d'arase
screed, monolithic chape *f* adhérente; chape *f* incorporée
screed, non-adherent chape *f* rapportée
screen écran *m*
screen (to) (sift) cribler *v*; tamiser *v*
screen (to) (elect) blinder *v*
screening (elect) blindage *m*
screw vis *f*
screw (to) visser *v*
screwdriver tournevis *m*
screwed plug/cap bouchon *m* à vis
scrim bande *f* à joint
scrub (to) brosser *v*; frotter *v*

scullery arrière-cuisine *f*
seal (to) boucher *v*; sceller *v*
sealant enduit *m* étanche
sealing bouchage *m*; scellement *m*
season timber (to) sécher *v* les bois
seasoning (wood) séchage *m*
second home résidence *f* secondaire
second or middle coat of mortar/plaster corps *m* de l'enduit
sectional drawing dessin *m* de coupe
sector secteur *m*
security device dispositif *m* de sécurité
separation layer couche *f* de désolidarisation
septic tank fosse *f* septique
set (to) poser *v*
set square équerre *f*; équerre *f* à dessin
setting (of cement, etc) prise *f*
■ rapid/slow setting = prise rapide/lente
setting accelerator (eg for mortar) accélérateur *m* de prise
setting up implantation *f*
setting-out line cordeau *m* traceur
settle (to) (a bill, a problem) régler *v*
settlement (eg of ground) tassement *m*
settlement of account arrêté *m* de compte
settlement/payment (eg of an invoice) règlement *m*
settling tassement *m*
sewage eaux *fpl* d'égout; eaux *fpl* usées
sewage disposal assainissement *m*
sewer égout *m*
sewerage system réseau *m* d'égouts
shade (colour) coloris *m*
shaft (driving) arbre *m*
shaft excavation fouille *f* en puits
shallow excavation fouille *f* en "excavation superficielle"
shank tige *f*
shape forme *f*
shear cisaillement *m*
shear (to) (eg metal) cisailler *v*
shed remise *f*; appentis *m*; chai *m*; abri *m*
sheet feuille *f*; plaque *f*; tôle *f*
sheet copper tôle *f* de cuivre
sheet iron tôle *f*
sheet iron cover plaque *f* en tôle
sheet lead plomb *m* en feuille
sheet of glass feuille *f* de verre

sheet, corrugated metal tôle *f* ondulée
sheet, galvanised iron tôle *f* zinguée; tôle *f* galvanisée
sheet, stainless steel tôle *f* d'acier inoxydable
sheeting (wood or metal) blindage *m*
shelf rayon *m*; étagère *f*; planche *f*
shell (of a building) carcasse *f*; cage *f* d'une batisse; gros œuvre *m*
shellac laque *f*
shellac (to) laquer *v*
shelter abri *m*
shift équipe *f*
shift (to) déplacer *v*
shingle bardeau *m*
shore étai *m*; étançon *m*; butée *f*
shore (to) étayer *v*; blinder *v*; buter *v*
shore (to); shore up (to) étançonner *v*
shoring étaiement *m*; étayage *m*; étayement *m*
shoring arrangement dispositif *m* d'étaiement
shoring of adjoining constructions étaiement *m* des constructions voisines
shoring up blindage *m*
shoring up with coffers blindage *m* par caissons
shoring up with prefabricated boards blindage *m* par panneaux préfabriqués
shoring with vertical planking blindage *m* par planche verticale
shoulder or upstand (roof terrace) costière *f*
shovel pelle *f*
shovel (to) pelleter *v*
shovel up (to) pelleter *v*
shovel's cast jet *m* de pelle
shovel, mechanical pelle *f* mécanique; pelleteuse *f*
shower douche *f*
shower tray bac *m* de douche
shower unit bloc-douche *m*
shrinkage retrait *m*; rétrécissement *m*
shutter volet *m*; contrevent *m*
shuttering coffrage *m*
shuttering panel banche *f*
side pan *m*; paroi *f*
side-timber filière *f*; panne *f*
sieve tamis *m*
sieve (to) tamiser *v*

sieve with wooden frame tamis *m* bois
sieving tamisage *m*
sift (to) tamiser *v*
sifting tamisage *m*
silicone sealant pistol pistolet *m* pour mastic au silicone
sill appui *m*; seuil *m*
silt limon *m*; vase *f*
sink bac *m*; évier *m*
sink unit bloc-evier *m*
sink, single/double évier *m* à un bac/deux bacs; évier *m* simple/double
sinking (eg of foundations) enfoncement *m*
sinking by piling fonçage *m* au poussage
sinter, calcareous travertin *m*
siphon siphon *m*
site foreman chef *m* de chantier
site with services laid on terrain *m* viabilisé
siting implantation *f*
size dimension *f*; taille *f*
size (of land area) contenance *f*
size (to) (eg plaster surface) apprêter *v*
size; sizing (sealing) apprêt *m*; enduit *m*
skeleton; frame ossature *f*
sketch dessin *m*; esquisse *f*; schéma *m*; schème *m*
skim coat enduit *m* pelliculaire
skip benne *f*
skirting plinthe *f*
skylight claire-voie *f*; tabatière *f*; fenêtre *f* à tabatière; lucarne *f*; châssis *m* vitré
slab dalle *f*
slab, concrete dalle *f* de/en béton
slab, small dallette *f*
slab (eg slate) table *f*
slack; play jeu *m*
slag laitier *m*; scorie *f*
slag, crushed laitier *m* concassé
slag, granulated laitier *m* granulé
slant pente *f*
slate, roofing ardoise *f*
slate (to) ardoiser *v*
slate-coloured ardoisé,-e *adj*
slater couvreur *m*
sliding glissement *m*
slip joint joint *m* de dilatation
slip road voie *f* de dégagement
slippage; slipping glissement *m*
slope pente *f*; inclinaison *f*; rampant *m*;

rampe *f*; talus *m*
slope, lower, of Mansard roof brisis *m*
slope (of a roof) égout *m*; pente *f*
slope (to) incliner *v*
sloped en forme de talus
sloping en pente; rampant,-e *adj*
sloping roof appentis *m*
slot rainure *f*
slot-drilling machine rainureuse *f*
small arch voutain *m*
small bottle of bluc powder (mason's marking powder) biberon *m* de poudre bleu
small cracks (appearing on the surface of a coating or rendering) faïençage *m*
small shelf planchette *f*
smoke-pipe conduit *m* de fumée
smooth (to) lisser *v*; adoucir *v*; ragréer *v*
smooth out (to) aplanir *v*
smoothing lissage *m*; ragrément *m*
smoothness lisse *m*
soak away puits *m* perdu
soaking douche *f*
socket (elect) prise *f*
socket (housing) logement *m*
socket outlet (elect) socle *m*
socketing emboîtement *m*
soffit soffite *m*; sous-face *f*
soil sol *m*; terre *f*
soil pipe tube *m* d'égout; tuyau *m* d'égout
soil, chalky terre *f* calcaire
soil, clayey terre *f* argileuse
soil, sandy terre *f* sableuse
sole (of a plane) semelle *f* d'un rabot
solid earth terre-plein *m*
soot suie *f*
soot box (of flue) boîte *f* à suie
sound bruit *m*
sound proofing isolation *f* acoustique; insonorisation *f*
source source *f*
space between écartement *m*
space between joists solin *m*
spacing piece entretoise *f*
spade bêche *f*; pelle *f*
spalling épaufrure *f*
span portée *f*
spandrel (staircase) coquille *f*
spanner clé *f*; clef *f*

spatula spatule *f*
specialist expert *m*
specification spécification *f*; devis *m*; cahier *m* des charges
specification, detailed devis *m* descriptif
specify (to) préciser *v*
spike; spike-nail broche *f*
spindle (mechan) arbre *m*
spirit level niveau *m* à bulle (d'air)
spirit level with one base plate niveau *m* à bulle 1 semelle
spline clavette *f*
splinter écharde *f*; éclat *m*; épaufrure *f*
split fente *f*
split pin clavette *f* fendue
splitting wedge coin *m* éclateur
spoil déblais *mpl*
spot tache *f*
spread (out) (to) étaler *v*
spring (of arch) naissance *f*
spring (mechan) ressort *m*
spring (water) source *f*
springing-course (of an arch) assise *f* de retombée
square équerre *f*
square (to) équarrir *v*
square file lime *f* carrée; carreau *m*
square metre mètre *m* carré
stack (chimney) souche *f*
stack covered with raised slab souche *f* protegée
stage étage *m*; étape *f*; niveau *m*
staggered en quinconce
staging (scaffolding) échafaud *m*; échafaudage *m*
stain tache *f*
stainless (steel) inoxydable *adj*
stainless steel acier *m* inoxydable
stair cavity; stair well trémie *f*
stair rail rampe *f*
stair well cage *f* d'escalier; jour *m*
staircase escalier *m*
staircase, private or back escalier *m* de dégagement
staircase, spiral escalier *m* en colimaçon
staircase, spiral escalier *m* tournant
stairway escalier *m*
stake pieu *m*; piquet *m*; tasseau *m*
stanchion étançon *m*

stand; pedestal; plinth socle *m*
standard courant,-e *adj*; norme *f*;
(NF = Norme Française)
staple clou *m* à deux pointes; agrafe *f*;
crampon *m* (à deux pointes)
staple gun agrafeuse *f*
start (to) amorcer *v*
start (to) (eg engine) démarrer *v*
start up (to) démarrer *v*
start work (to) se mettre *v* à l'ouvrage
statement of accounts bilan *m*
stay étai *m*; étançon *m*
staying étayage *m*; étayement *m*
steel acier *m*
steel frame reinforcement for concrete
ferraillage *m*
steel joist solive *f* en acier
steel wool laine *f* d'acier; paille *f* de fer
steepness (eg of a staircase) raideur *f*
stem tige *f*
step (action) démarche *f*
step (of stair) marche *f*; pas *m*
steps (leading to an entrance) perron *m*
stick (to) adhérer *v*
sticking on a layer (eg of PVC sheeting)
marouflage *m*
stiffen (to) raidir *v*
stiffener pièce *f* de renfort; raidisseur *m*
stipulate (to) préciser *v*
stipulation clause *f*; condition *f*
stone caillou *m*; pierre *f*; roche *f*; moellon *m*
stone (buhrstone) meulière *f*
stone bonding (wall) appareillage de
pierre *m*
stone random bonding (according to
natural shape) appareil *m* en opus
incertum
stone chippings éclats *mpl* de pierre
stone pier jambage *m*
stone quarry carrière *f*
stone wall built with "meulières" mur *m* en
meulières
stone wall construction moellonage *m*
stone with almost parallel faces meulière *f*
plaquette
stone with dressed face meulière *f* piquée
stone, building pierre *f* de taille; pierre *f* à
bâtir
stone, corner pierre *f* angulaire

stone, cut- pierre *f* de taille
stone(s), small caillasse *f*
stone, local pierre *f* du pays
stone, pumice pierre *f* ponce
stone, small irregular-shaped moellon *m*
stone, small, lightly dressed moellon *m*
smillé
stone, small, roughly dressed moellon *m*
brut
stone, soft pierre *f* tendre
stone, uncut pierre *f* non-taillée
stone, whet- pierre *f* à aiguiser
stone-built cottage or house maison *f* de/en
pierre(s)
stonemason tailleur *m* de pierre
stoneware grès *m*; grès *m* cérame; faïence *f*
stonework maçonnerie *f*
stop up (to) boucher *v*; calfeutrer *v*
stopcock robinet *m* d'arrêt; robinet *m* de
fermeture
stoppage bouchage *m*; obstruction *f*
stopper bouchon *m*
stopping up bouchage *m*; rebouchage *m*;
calfeutrage *m*; calfeutrement *m*
storage stockage *m*
storage on (building) site stockage *m* sur le
chantier
storage units éléments *mpl* de rangement
store room cellier *m*; réserve *f*
storey étage *m*; niveau *m*
storm drain/sewer égout *m* pluvial
stove cuisinière *f*; poêle *m*; calorifère *m*;
also *adj*;
stove, solid-fuel cuisinière *f* à charbon
strain déformation *f*
stranded wire câble *m* métallique
strap armature *f*; bretelle *f*; feuillard *m*;
lien *m*
straw paille *f*
street level rez-de-chaussée *m*; rdc *abb*
strength, breaking résistance *f* à la rupture
strength, compressive résistance *f* à l'écrase -
ment *f*; résistance *f* à la compression
strength, crushing résistance *f* à
l'écrasement; résistance *f* à la compression
strength, tensile résistance *f* à la traction
strength, ultimate résistance *f* à la rupture
stress contrainte *f*; effort *m*; sollicitation *f*;

charge *f*
stress (to) solliciter *v*
stressing sollicitation *f*
stretcher (stonework) carreau *m*
stretcher bond appareil *m* en long; appareil
m en panneresse
stretcher-bond (stone) appareil *m* à carreau
stretching-course assise *f* de carreaux
strike plate (lock) gâche *f*
string course (masonry) bandeau *m*
strip bande *f*; lame *f*
strip (eg of iron, steel) feuillard *m*
strip (fillet) bandelette *f*
strip of parquet flooring lame *f* de parque
strip of wood languette de bois *f*; tasseau *m*;
baguette *f*
stripping décapage *m*
structural steel acier *m* de construction
structure construction *f*; ossature *f*
strut barre *f* transversale; contrefiche *f*;
étrésillon *m*
strut/prop jambe *f* de force
stuck-on layer marouflage *m*
stud montant *m*; plot *m*
studio atelier *m*
study cabinet *m* d'étude; bureau *m*
subfoundation; substructure soubassement *m*
subsidence effondrement *m*; affaisement *m*
subsoil sous-sol *m*
substance corps *m*
substratum sous-sol *m*
substruction sous-œuvre *m*
subterranean souterrain *m*; also *adj*
sullage eaux *fpl* usées
sump puisard *m*
supply alimentation *f*; apport *m*
supply system réseau *m* d'alimentation
support appui *m*; étai *m*; point *m* d'appui;
soutènement *m*; support *m*; butée *f*
support (to) étayer *v*; porter *v*
support bracket patte *f* de maintien; patte *f*
de support
support for persienne tapée *f*
supporting étayage *m*; étayement *m*;
soutènement *m*
surbase (to) (eg vault) surbaisser *v*
surface superficie *f*; surface *f*

surface (to) faire *v* surface
surface area superficie *f*; surface *f*
surface condensation condensation *f*
superficielle
surface cut tranchée *f*
surface finishing with a float (eg concrete)
talochage *m*
surface, bare surface *f* nue
surface, bearing surface *f* de portée; surface *f*
portante
surface, floor (of building) surface *f* des
étages
surface, smooth surface *f* lisse
surface, support surface *f* d'appui
surface, unbroken surface *f* nue
surface-clearing (of ground, wood etc.)
défrichement *m*; défrichage *m*
surface-condensation condensation *f* par
surface
surround ceinture *f*
surrounding railing grille *f* de clôture
survey expertise *f*; levé *m*; levé *m* de
géomètre
survey report rapport *m* d'expertise
surveying arpentage *m*; métrage *m*
surveying, quantity métrage *m*; métré *m*
surveyor expert *m*; expert *m* géomètre;
geomètre *m*; métreur *m*; métreuse *f*
surveyor (land) arpenteur *m*
surveyor, quantity métreur *m*; métreuse *f*
suspended ceiling plafond *m* suspendu
suspender bretelle *f*
sweeping a chimney or flue ramonage *m*
swell foisonnement *m*
swell (to) foisonner *v*
swelling foisonnement *m*
swimming pool piscine *f*
switch (elect) interrupteur *m*
switch off (to) (elect) couper *v*
switch on (to) (electrical appliance)
démarrer *v*
switch on (to) (light) allumer *v*
system réseau *m*; système *f*
system of roads voirie *f*
system, sewerage système *f* d'égouts

T connection té *m* de raccordement
T-coupling, oblique té *m* à tubulure oblique

T-cramp agrafe *f* à T
T-iron équerre *f*
T-square double équerre *f*; équerre *f* en T;
  équerre *f* à T; équerre *f* en té; té *m* de
  dessin
table table *f*
table (flange of a girder) semelle *f*
table/tread of a girder table *f* d'une poutre
tail in (to) encastrer *v*
tail trimmer (joist) solive *f* d'enchevêtrure
tail-pipe (of a cock) tubulure *f*
tailing encastrement *m*
take stock of (to) faire *v* le bilan de
tamp (to) damer *v*; pilonner *v*
tamping damage *m*; pilonnage *m*; tassement *m*
tank citerne *f*; cuve *f*; réservoir *m*
tank, fuel-oil cuve *f* à mazout *f*
tap robinet *m*
tap trade robinetterie *f*
tap, mixer robinet *m* mélangeur/mitigeur
taper driftpin broche *f* conique
tapping branchement *m*
taps and fittings robinetterie *f*
tar bitume *m*; goudron *m*
tar-brush brosse *f* à goudronner
tarpaulin bâche *f*; toile *f* à bâche; toile *f*
  goudronnée
task tâche *f*; œuvre *f*
tautness (eg of rope) raideur *f*
team équipe *f*
temper (to) (plaster) gâcher *v*
tempering (eg plaster) gâchage *m*
template gabarit *m*; calibre *m*
template (beam) traverse *f*
term of contract condition *f*
terminal (elect) borne *f*
terra cotta terre *f* cuite
terrace terrasse *f*
terrace garden terrasse-jardin *f*
terrace with zero slope (below 1% slope)
  terrasse *f* à pente null
terrace, flat terrasse *f* plate
terrace, inaccessible terrasse *f* inaccessible
terrace, sloping terrasse *f* rampante
terrain terrain *m*
terrazzo granito *m*; terrazzo *m*; sol *m* de
  mosaïque
textured brick brique *f* rustique

textured wall paint crépi *m*
thatched cottage chaumière *f*; maison *f* à toit
  de chaume
thatched cottage, small chaumine *f*
thermal characteristics caractéristiques *fpl*
  thermiques
thermal loss factor coefficient *m* G
thick épais *m*; also *adj*
thickness épaisseur *f*; épais *m*; also *adj*
thickness of a board rive *f* d'une planche
thimble virole *f*
thin down (to) (eg concrete with water)
  délayer *v*
**thin prestressed concrete slab forming base
  of composite slab** prédalle *f*
thread fil *m*
three-coat plastering/rendering enduit *m* en
  trois couches
threshold (of a door) seuil *m*
throat (of chimney) gorge *f*
throat (of fireplace) avaloir *m*
throat, drip (window sill) goutte *f* d'eau
through-lounge séjour *m* double
tie-bar entrait *m*; tirant *m*
tie-beam entrait *m*; tirant *m*
tie-rod entrait *m*
tightener; tensioner raidisseur *m*
tightening serrage *m*
tile (floor) carreau *m*
tile (roof) tuile *f*
tile (wall) carreau *m*; plaquette *f*
tile (to) carreler *v*
tile adhesive ciment *m* colle
tiled floor carrelage *m*
tile, border (wall tile) listel *m*
tile, ceramic carreau *m* de faïence
tile, curved tuile *f* creuse/romaine/ronde
tile, floor carreau *m* de carrelage; carreau *m*
  par terre
tile, floor (glazed) grès *m* émaillé
tile, floor (vitrified clay) grès *m* cérame
tile, plaster carreau *m* de plâtre
tile, ridge tuile *f* faîtière
tile, Roman tuile *f* romaine
tile, roof tuile *f*
tile, terra cotta carreau *m* de terre cuite
tile, wall carreau *m* au mur
tile-cutting machine machine *f* à couper;
  coupe-tuiles *m*

tiling carrelage *m*

tilt inclinaison *f*

timber bois *m*; bois *m* de charpente

timber (to) (an excavation) blinder *v*

timbering (an excavation) blindage *m*

time for consideration délai *m* de réflexion

time limit délai *m*

tipper lorry benne *f*; camion *m* benne

tolerance tolérance *f*

tommy-bar broche *f*

tongs pince *f*; pinces *fpl*; tenaille(s) *f (pl)*

tongue (carpentry) languette *f*

tool outil *m*

tools outillage *m*

toothed dresser (eg for plaster) rabotin *m*

toothing (masonry) appareil *m* en besace; harpe *f*

tow filasse *f*

town hall mairie *f*

town planning urbanisme *m*

trace (to) tracer *v*

transform (to) convertir *v*; transformer *v*

transom traverse *f*; meneau *m* horizontal; linteau *m*; traverse *f* d'imposte

trap purgeur *m*

trap door trappe *f*

trap door access to attic/loft trappe *f* accès combles

trap-door for cleaning flue trappe *f* de ramonage

traverse (to) traverser *v*

travertine travertin *m*

tray bac *m*

tread (of a girder) semelle *f*

tread width (stairs) emmarchement *m*

tree arbre *m*

trellis treillis *m*

trench fouille *f*; saignée *f*; tranchée *f*

trench (small) rigole *f*

trenching fouille *f* (en rigole)

trim (to) (eg metal) parer *v*

trim (to) (edges) dégraisser *v*; rogner *v*

trim joists (to) enchevêtrer *v* des solives

trim level (to) araser *v*

trimmer chevêtre *m*; enchevêtrure *f*

trimmer-beam chevêtre *m*

trimming-joist chevêtrier *m*

trough bac *m*; auge *f*

trough, plastic auge *f* plastique

trowel truelle *f*

trowel, flat pointing fer *m* à joint plat

trowel, half-round, pointing fer *m* à joint demi-lune

trowel, laying-on platoir *m*

trowel, plasterer's gâche *f*

trowel, round truelle *f* ronde

trowel, scratch taloche *f* à pointes

trowel, serrated truelle *f* dentelée

trunking (elect) moulure *f*

truss ferme *f*

try square équerre *f* à lame d'acier

tube tube *m*; tuyau *m*

tubing tubage *m*; tube *m*; tuyauterie *f*

tubular stay, mason's étai *m* de maçon tubulaire

tungsten carbide cutter molette *f* au carbure de tungstène

turn (in chimney, etc) dévoiement *m*

two-metre rule, wood double mètre *m* bois

tying walls liasonnement *m* des parois

type of pointing type *m* de joint

under-floor space vide *m* sanitaire

undercoat sous-couche *f*

underface; underside sous-face *f*

underground souterrain *m*; also *adj*

underground excavation fouille *m* en excavation; fouille *f* en galerie

underpin (to) reprendre *v* en sous-œuvre

underpinning reprise *f* en sous-œuvre; sous-œuvre *m*

undertaking entreprise *f*; œuvre *f*

unevenness aspérité *f*

unit bloc *m*; élément *m*

unscrew (to) dévisser *v*

upright montant *m*

urban development zone zone *f* à urbaniser en priorité

use (to) utiliser *v*; se servir (de) *v*

vacuum vide *m*

vacuum cleaner aspirateur *m*

valley (roof) noue *f*; noulet *m*

valley-gutter noue *f*; noue *f* encaissée

valley-rafter noue *f*; chevron *m* de noue;

noulet *m*
valve clapet *m*; soupape *f*
valuation of a property expertise *f* d'un bien
vapour barrier (eg membrane) pare-vapeur *m*
variation écart *m*
vault voûte *f*; cave *m*
vaulted cellar cave *m* voûtée
vaulted/arched ceiling plafond *m* voûté
vegetable garden jardin *m* potager; jardin *m*
velux™ vélux™ *m*
veneer feuille *f* de placage; placage *m*
veneer (to) plaquer *v*
veneering placage *m*
vent pipe from boiler to flue buse *f* d'entrée
ventilated ceiling plafond *m* diffuseur d'air
ventilated chimney top turbine *f* statique
ventilation ventilation *f*
ventilation conduit conduit *m* de ventilation
ventilator ventilateur *m;* aérateur *m*
veranda véranda *f*
vermiculite vermiculite *f*
vertical mortar joints staggered from row to row joints *mpl* croisés
vertical shore étai *m* vertical
vertical side of opening in facade tableau *m*
vertical trap (eg of flue) purgeur *m* vertical
villa pavillon *m*; villa *f*
void (archit) vide *m*
voussoir voussoir *m*; vousseau *m*

wainscot (to) lambrisser *v*
wainscoting lambris *m*; lambrissage *m*; boiserie *f*
waiting period délai *m*
wall mur *m*; cloison *f*; clôture *f*; paroi *f*
wall (to) murer *v*
wall built from small stones (moellons) mur *m* en moellons
wall covering revêtement *m* mural
wall liner cloison *f* de doublage
wall tie patte *f* de liason
wall tie with water drip patte *f* de liasonnement avec goutte d'eau
wall ties chainage *m*
wall up (to) murer *v*
wall, back façade *f* arrière
wall, baffle mur *m* d'écran

wall, base(ment) mur *m* de soubassement
wall, bearing mur *m* portant; mur *m* porteur
wall, blank/blind mur *m* orbe
wall, block mur *m* en agglomérés; mur *m* en parpaings
wall, breast-high mur *m* d'appui; mur *m* de parapet; mur *m* de soutènement
wall, bulged mur *m* bombé; mur *m* bouclé
wall, bulging muraille *f* qui pousse
wall, carrying a staircase; string wall mur *m* d'échiffre
wall, cavity mur *m* creux; mur *m* double
wall, common mur *m* mitoyen
wall, composite mur *m* composite
wall, cross (load bearing) mur *m* de refend
wall, double mur *m* double
wall, drystone mur *m* en pierres sèches
wall, enclosing mur *m* de clôture
wall, exterior non-load bearing mur *m* de remplissage
wall, exterior, classified type I to IV mur *m* extérieur, type (I à IV)
wall, façade mur *m* de façade
wall, flank mur *m* en retour
wall, front façade *f*; mur *m* de face
wall, gable mur *m* pignon
wall, high or thick muraille *f*
wall, hollow mur *m* à double cloison/paroi
wall, honeycomb mur *m* de brique alvéolé
wall, interior load-bearing mur *m* de refend
wall, internal/external paroi *f* interne/externe
wall, lining contre-mur *m*
wall, load-bearing mur *m* portant; mur *m* porteur
wall, low muret *m*; murette *f*
wall, mortar-bound stone mur *m* en pierres maçonnées
wall, non load-bearing mur *m* non porteur
wall, outer mur *m* d'enceinte; contre-mur *m*; parement *m* extérieur
wall, outer/surrounding mur *m* de clôture
wall, parapet mur *m* de parapet
wall, partition mur *m* de cloison
wall, party mur *m* mitoyen
wall, pebble-stone mur *m* en galets
wall, retaining mur *m* de retenue; mur *m* de revêtement; mur *m* de soutènement; mur *m*

de terasse
wall, return mur *m* en retour
wall, side façade *f* latérale; mur *m* latéral
wall, single mur *m* simple
wall, single thickness mur *m* simple
wall, type I or type IV mur *m* de type I ou IV
wall-plate sablière *f*; plate-forme *f*; solive *f* en ferme; semelle *f*
wallboard, lining cloison *f* de doublage
walling murage *f*
wallpaper papier *m* peint; tapisserie *f*
wallpaper (to) tapisser *v*
wallpaper paste colle *f*; colle *f* de pâte
wallpaper pasting table table *f* à tapisser
wallpaper, vinyl papier *m* peint vinyl
wallpaper, washable papier *m* peint lavable et lessivable
wallplug cheville *f*
walls of an excavation parois *fpl* de fouille
wardrobe armoire *f*
warp (to) se déformer *v*; voiler *v*
warping déformation *f*
wash-basin cuvette *f*; lavabo *m*
washer rondelle *f*
wastage gaspillage *m*; déperdition *f*
waste (excavation spoil) déblais *mpl*
waste (rubbish) déchet *m*; déchets *mpl*
waste (to) gaspiller *v*
waste pipe trop-plein *m*
water eau *f*
water butt tonneau *m* (pour l'eau de pluie)
water retaining rétenteur *m* d'eau
water supply alimentation *f* en eau; approvisionnement *m* d'eau
water tank citerne *f*; réservoir *m* d'eau
water, cold/hot eau *f* froide/chaude
water, drinking eau *f* buvable/potable
water, fresh eau *f* douce
water, soft/hard eau *f* douce/dure
water, spring eau *f* de source
water, tap eau *f* de distribution
water, town/mains eau *f* de ville
water, waste eaux *fpl* usées
water-closet (WC) WC *m*
water-heater chauffe-eau *m*
water-repellant hydrofuge *m*; also *adj*
water-resisting hydrofuge *m*; also *adj*
water-tight lining revêtment *m* étanche
water-tightness étanchéité *f*

waterproof imperméable *adj*
waterproof (to) imperméabiliser *v*; étancher *v*
waterproof joint joint *m* d'étanchéité
waterproofing étanchéisation *f*; imperméabilisation *f*
waterproofness étanchéité *f*
way voie *f*; passage *m*
WC WC *m*
WC basin cuvette *f* de WC
WC seat siège *m* de cabinet (see abattant)
wedge cale *f*; coin *m*; taquet *m*
wedge, splitting coin *m* éclateur
wedge, timber-splitting coin *m* à fendre le bois
wedging coinçage *m*
welded trellis (reinforcement) treillis *m* soudé
well puits *m*
well excavation fouille *f* en puits
wet (to) mouiller *v*
wet rot pourriture *f* humide
wetting humidification *f*
wheel-barrow brouette *f*
white stain (eg from efflorescence) tache *f* blanchâtre
whitewash badigeon *m*
whitewash (to) badigeonner *v*
whitewood bois *m* blanc
width largeur *f*
width (of cloth) lé *m*
winch treuil *m*
wind-brace contrevent *m*
window fenêtre *f*; baie *f*; croisée *f*
window opening baie *f* de fenêtre
window pane vitre *f*
window, casement fenêtre *f* ordinaire
window, dormer lucarne *f*; fenêtre *f* mansardée
window, french fenêtre *f* ordinaire; fenêtre *f* à la française
window, sash fenêtre *f* à guillotine
window-frame dormant *m*; châssis *m*
window-ledge rebord *m* de la fenêtre
window/door sill appui *m* de fenêtre/porte
windowsill rebord *m* de la fenêtre
wine cellar chai *m*
winter garden; conservatory jardin *m* d'hiver

wire fil *m*
wire brush brosse *f* en fil de fer; brosse *f* métallique
wire fencing grillage *m*
wire gauge filière *f*
wire gauze tamis *m* métallique; toile *f* métallique
wire mesh grillage *m*
wire mesh fencing grillage *m*
wire netting grillage *m*; treillis *m*; treillis *m* métallique
wire rope câble *m* métallique
wire sieve tamis *m* métallique
wire wool paille *f* de fer
wiring diagram schéma *m* de câblage
wood bois *m*
wood fibre fibre *f* de bois
wood, green bois *m* vert
wood, solid bois *m* massif
wood, unseasoned bois *m* vert
wood, worm-eaten bois *m* vermoulu; bois *m* mouliné
wooded land terrain *m* boisé
wooden floor parquet *m*
woodland pays *m* boisé; bois *m*

woodwool-cement slab fibragglo *m*
woodwork boiserie *f*
woodworm eaten state vermoulure *f*
woodworm holes vermoulure *f*
work travail *m*; œuvre *f*; ouvrage *m*
work/works travaux *mpl*
work (to) travailler *v*
worker ouvrier *m*; travailleur *m*; travailleuse *f*
working (of machinery) marche *f*
workman ouvrier *m*
workmanship exécution *f*; main-d'œuvre *f*
workshop atelier *m*
worm-eaten vermoulu,-e *adj*
worm holes vermoulures *fpl*

yard cour *f*; jardin *m*
year of construction année *f* de construction

zigzag quinconce (en)
zinc zinc *m*
zinc flashing (roof) revêtement *m* de zinc

4. CARPENTER AND JOINER

abutting aboutement *m*
across travers *m*
■ **saw/cut across** = scier/couper en travers
add (to) rapporter *v*
adhere (to) adhérer *v*
adhesion adhérence *f*
adhesive colle *f*
adjust (to) délarder *v*
adjustment ajustement *m*; ajustage *m*; réglage *f*
adze herminette *f*
aeration aération *f*
air (to) aérer *v*
air damper volet *m* d'aération
air vent (roof) châtière *f*; trou *m*

air-vent at roof-ridge level lanternau *m*
alley passage *m*; ruelle *f* coursive *f*
aluminium frames/framework menuiserie *f* aluminium
angle brace étresillon *m*; entretoise *f*
angle brace; corner brace aisselier *m*
angle clamp; angle cramp presse *f* d'angle
angle iron équerre *f*
angle strip (wood) baguette *f* d'angle
anti-parasite treatment traitement *m* anti-parasite
apparatus dispositif *m*; appareil *m*
apron (of a window) allège *f*
arch cintre *m*
architrave chambranle *m*; architrave *f*

arrest arrêt *m*
arris arête *f*
assemble (to) assembler *v*
assembly; assembling assemblage *m*
**assembly of tongued-and-grooved boards
with beaded edge** assemblage *m* à
baguette
attic grenier *m*; mansarde *f*
auger tarière *f*
avert (to) empêcher *v*
axe hache *f*; cognée *f*
axe-hammer hachette *f* de charpentier
axle arbre *m*; axe *m*

back-to-back adossé,-e *adj*
backing-strip (as floor support) lambourde *f*
balance (to) balancer *v*
balance/dance a stair step (to) balancer *v*
une marche d'escalier
balanced step marche *f* balancée; marche *f*
dansante
balcony balcon *m*
ball peen (of a hammer) panne *f* bombée
baluster balustre *m*; barreau *m*
balustrade balustrade *f*
balustrade of a stair rampe *f*
bandsaw scie *f* à ruban; scie *f* sans fin
banister balustre *m*; barreau *m*
banister rail main *f* courante
banisters rampe *f* d'escalier
bar barre *f*; barreau *m*
barefaced tenon tenon *m* bâtard
base socle *m*
base-board plinthe *f*
batten latte *f*; barre *f*; liteau *m*; tasseau *m*;
volige *f*
batten (to) voliger *v*
battening voligeage *m*
baulk (of timber) poutre *f*
bay baie *f*; travée *f*
bead baguette *f*
beading baguette *f*; parclose *f*
beam poutre *f*; madrier *m*; solive *f*
beam (small) poutrelle *f*
beam support appui *m* des poutres;
corbeau *m*
beam, collar entrait *m;* entrait *m* retroussé;

faux *m* entrait
beam, cross- entretoise *f*; longrine *f*;
traverse *f*
beam, exposed poutre *f* apparente
beam, main poutre *f* maîtresse; poutre *f*
principale
beam, main support poutre *f* maîtresse
beam, principal poutre *f* principale
beam, raised tie- entrait *m* retroussé
beam, reinforced concrete poutre *f* en béton
armé
beam, ridge faîte *m*; faîtage *m*; panne *f*
faîtière
beam, tie- blochet *m*; entrait *m*; tirant *m*;
moise *f*
beam, trimmer chevêtre *m*
beam, trussed poutre *f* armée; poutre *f* à
treillis
beam, under-braced, trussed poutre *f* sous-
bandée
beams solivage *m*
beams, set of, radiating from a centre
enrayure *f*
bearer support *m*
bearing repos *m*; appui *m*
bed (to) sceller *v*
belt sander ponceuse *f* à bande
bench établi *m*
bench plane rabot *m* d'établi
bench rabbet plane guillaume *m* d'établi
bend (to) cintrer *v*
bevel biseau *m*; chanfrein *m*
■ **bevelled** = en biseau
bevel (to) biseauter *v*
bevelled edge arête *f* chanfreinée
bevelling biseautage *m*
binder (wooden roof) entrait *m*
binding-piece moise *f*
bit (drill) mèche *f*; trépan *m*
blade lame *f*
blemish défaut *m*
block bloc *m*
block (on main rafter) échantignole *f*
block; sandpaper block cale *f*
blockboard latté *m*; panneau *m* latté
board planche *f*; plateau *m*; ais *m*
board (to) planchéier *v*
board with melamine surface plateau *m*
melaminé *m*

board, small tablette *f*
boarding palissade *f*; planchéiage *m*
bolt boulon *m*
bolts and nuts boulons *mpl* et écrous *mpl*
bolt (casement) crémone *f*
bolt (eg door) verrou *m*
bolted joint assemblage *m* par boulons
bond (to) liaisonner *v*
bore calibre *m*
bore (to) percer *v*
boring perçage *m*; percement *m*
bow window; bay window fenêtre *f* en saillie
bowed or deflected piece of wood affaisée *f*
box boîte *f*; caisson *m*
boxing emboîtement *m*
brace jambe *f* de force
brace (corner) moise *f*
brace (diagonal) entretoise *f*; étrésillon *m*
brace (of a timber frame) décharge *f*; écharpe *f*
brace (of steel roof truss) bielle *f*
brace (of truss) contrefiche *f*
brace (to) moiser *v*
brace, carpenter's rachet vilebrequin *m* de menuisier
brace or strut contrevent *m*
braced armé,-e *adj*; renforcé,-e *adj*
bracing armature *f*; moisage *m*
bracket console *f*; tasseau *m*
bracket (for shelf) liteau *m*; gousset *m*
bracket for fixing wood to concrete équerre *f* pour fixation sur béton
brad pointe *f*; clou *m* sans tête
brad-punch chasse-clou *m*; chasse-pointe *m*
bradawl poinçon *m*
breadth largeur *f*
break (to) briser *v*
break-iron (of plane) contre-fer *m*
break line (eg of a mansard roof) ligne *f* de bris
bridging piece étrésillon *m*; entretoise *f*
bridle joint joint *m* anglais
broom cupboard placard *m* à balai
buckling déformation *f*; gauchissement *m*
building work ouvrage *m*; travaux *mpl*
built-in cupboard armoire *f* arasée
bull's-eye window œil-de-bœuf *m*

bung bouchon *m*
butt about *m*
▪ **abutting** = en about
butt (to) abouter *v*
butt-end about *m*
butt-hinge charnière *f*
butt joint joint *m* bout à bout; joint *m* en bout; joint *m* plat
butt-joint (to) abouter *v*
butt-jointing aboutement *m*
butt-strip couvre-joint *m*

cabinet maker ébéniste *m*; menuisier d'art *m*
cabinetwork ébénisterie *f*
calibre calibre *m*
calipers compas *m*
calipers, vernier pied *m* à coulisse
canopy auvent *m*
cant (out of plumb) dévers *m*
carpenter charpentier *m*; menuisier *m*
carpenter's bench établi *m* de charpentier
carpenter's clamp valet *m*; sergent *m*
carpenter's hammer hachette *f* de charpentier
carpenter's pencil crayon *m* de charpentier
carpenter's square équerre *f* de menuisier
carpenter's/joiner's pincers tenaille *f* de menuisier
carpentry charpente *f* en bois; menuiserie *f*
carry away (to) enlever *v*
carry out (to) exécuter *v*
case caisson *m*
case (of a lock) boîte *f*
casement or Cremona bolt crémone *f*
casement window croisée *f*
casing caisson *m*; chambranle *m*; dormant *m*
cat-flap châtière *f*
catch fermeture *f*
ceiling plafond *m*; plafonnage *m*
ceiling coving corniche *f*
ceiling material plafonnage *m*
ceiling rose rosace *f*; rosace *f* de plafond
cement mastic *m*; ciment *m*
centering cintre *m*
centre milieu *m*; noyau *m*
centre-bit mèche *f* à trois pointes; mèche *f*

anglaise
centre-punch pointeau *m*
certificate of conformity of manufacture to given standards certificat *m* de suivi et marquage
chain mortising machine mortaiseuse *f* à chaine
chain vice étau *m* à chaine
chainsaw scie *f* à chainette; tronçonneuse *f*
chalk a line battre *v* une ligne
chamfer chanfrein *m*
chamfer (to); bevel (to) chanfreiner *v*
chamfer-stop arrêt *m* de chanfrein
chimney opening trémie *f* de cheminée
chimney trimmer linçoir *m*
chipboard aggloméré *m*; agglo *abb*; panneau *m* de particules; panneau *m* de copeaux
chipboard faced with melamine panneau *m* mélaminé
chipboard with melamine surface panneau *m* de particules surfacé mélaminé
chipping burinage *m*; éclat *m*
chisel ciseau *m*
chisel (to) ciseler *v*
chisel, bevel-edged ciseau *m* biseauté
chisel, cold burin *m* à froid; burin *m*
chisel, double mortise bédane *m* double
chisel, firmer ciseau *m* à bois
chisel, framing bédane *m*
chisel, mortise bédane *m*; burin *m*
chisel, side biseau *m*
chisel, skew biseau *m*
chiselling burinage *m*; ciselure *f*
chock cale *f*; coin *m*
chocking calage *m*
chock (to) caler *v*
cladding revêtement *m*; bardage *m*
cladding board bardeau *m*; lambris *m*
clamp agrafe *f*; crampon *m*; serre-joint *m*
clamping blocage *m*; serrage *m*
clean down (to) ragréer *v*
clean off (to) (eg floor) replanir *v*
cleaning down ragrément *m*
cleaning off (flooring) replanissage *m*; replanissement *m*
clearance jeu *m*; jour *m*
cleat languette *f* de bois; taquet *m*
cleave (to) refendre *v*

cleaving refente *f*
cleft fente *f*; gerce *f*
clip clip *m*
close/exact fit ajustement *m* précis
close/tight fit ajustement *m* serre
closed fretwork chantournement *m* fermé
closing fermeture *f*
closing up serrage *m*
coach bolt or screw tire-fond *m*
coating of fill-in material (eg plaster, mortar) solin *m*
coefficient of contraction coefficient *m* de rétractibilité
collar bride *f*; collet *m*; collier *m*
collar beam entrait *m*; entrait *m* retroussé; faux *m* entrait
comb crête *f*
combined saw-set and marking knife rénette *f* (de charpentier)
commode step (staircase) marche *f* cintrée; marche *f* courbe
compass (drawing) compas *m*
connect (to) relier *v*
connecting piece raccord *m*
connecting rod bielle *f*
connection raccord *m*; liason *f*
construct (to) fabriquer *v*; construire *v*
construction fabrication *f*; construction *f*
contact adhesive colle *f* contact
contract (to); narrow (to) resserrer (se) *v*
conventional carpentry signs used to differentiate pieces of wood établissement *m*
convert (to) aménager *v*
▪ **for conversion** = à aménager
corbel corbeau *m*
cord cordeau *m*
cord (of electric appliance) fil *m*
core âme *f*; noyau *m*
cork bouchon *m*
corner coin *m*
cornice corniche *f*
cotter pin clavette *f*
counter gauge (to) contre-jauger *v*
counter lath contre-latte *f*
countersink fraise *f*; fraisure *f*
countersink (to) fraiser *v*
countersink-bit fraise *f*
countersinking fraisage *m*

couple (to) relier *v*
coupling piece (metal) raccord *m*
cover fourrure *f*
cover strip couvre-joint *m*
cover strip (wood) parclose *m*
cover-piece fourrure *f*
cover-plate fourrure *f*
covering habillage *m*
covering piece couvre-joint *m*
coving corniche *f*
crack gerce *f*
cramp crampon *m*; patte *f* à scellement
crest crête *f*
crest (of roof) faîtage *m*
cross-bar traverse *f*
cross-cut saw scie *f* de travers
cross grain en bois d'about
cross-piece entretoise *f*; étrésillon *m*;
traverse *f*; barre *f* transversale
cross-wall mur *m* de refend
crosswise en travers
crown-post (roof timbers) poinçon *m*
cupboard armoire *f*; placard *m*
curb roof comble *m* brisé
curve (eg arch) cintre *m*
curve (to) cintrer *v*
curved lintel linteau *m* courbe
custom-made fait sur commande *adj*
cut coupe *f*; entaille *f*
cut (to) couper *v*; découper *v*; entailler *v*
cut a piece of wood along its length to alter
cross- section (to) délarder *v*
cut diagonally (to) (wood) débillarder *v*
cut down to size (to) blanchir *v*
cut into sections (to) tronçonner *v*
cut off (to) araser *v*; couper *v*; tronçonner *v*
cut out (to) découper *v*
cut up (to) débiter *v*; découper *v*;
tronçonner *v*
cutter fraise *f*
cutter, roughing fraise *f* à dégrossir
cutter, slabbing fraise *f* à dégrossir
cutter, slot fraise *f* pour rainures
cutting coupe *f*; découpage *m*; taillage *m*
cutting (board) edgewise division *f* sur
champ
cutting (board) flatwise division *f* sur plat
cutting angle angle *m* de coupe

cutting box boîte *f* à coupe
cutting edge (of a tool) fil *m*; arête *f* de
coupe; arête *f* tranchante
cutting into sections tronçonnage *m*
cutting into two pieces division *f*
cutting knife blade lame *f* de couteau
cutting out coupe *f*; découpage *m*
cutting up débit *m*; débitage *m*; découpage
m; tronçonnage *m*
cutting-line trait *m*
cyma cimaise *f*

dado or die of pedestal dé *m*
dancing step (staircase) marche *f* balancée
daylight jour *m*
deal bois *m* blanc; madrier *m*
decay pourrissement *m*
decay (to) pourrir *v*
deepen (to) creuser *v*
defect défaut *m*
deflection débattement *m*; fléchisse-
ment *m*
depth of thread of a screw saillie *f* d'une
vis
deterioration pourrissement *m*
develop (to) aménager *v*
device dispositif *m*
diagonal brace étrésillon *m*; entretoise *f*
diagonal tie (roof) écharpe *f*
diagram plan *m* d'épure; schéma *m*
diameter diamètre *m*; calibre *m*
dimension dimension *f*
disengagement dégagement *m*
displacement débattement *m*
distance (between) écartement *m*
distance between centres entraxe *m*;
entr'axe *m*; (see also 'd'axe en axe')
distort or warp (to) déjeter *v*; déformer *v*; se
gauchir *v*
division (partition) cloison *f*
dog-spike crampon *m*
dome coupole *f*
■ small dome = petite coupole *f*
door porte *f*
door edging couvre-chant *m*; alaise *f*
rapportée
door casing dormant *m*
door cat flap chatière *f*

door frame dormant *m*
door-frame (for incorporation in concrete)
huisserie *f* banchée
door-frame (for incorporation in masonry)
huisserie *f* traditionelle
door-frame (with adjoining timbers)
huisserie *f*
door-framing huisserie *f*
door furniture (hinges, handle, lock etc)
ferrage *m;* ferrure *f* de porte
door knob bouton *m* de porte
door leaf ouvrant *m*; vantail *m*
door/leaf of double doors battant *m* de
porte
door opening ouverture *f* de porte
door or window drip jet *m* d'eau; rejet *m*
d'eau
door or window frame (wood, steel or reinforced concrete) bloc-baie *m*
door post jambage *m*
doorstep seuil *m*; pas *m* d'accès
door sill appui *m* de porte
door unit (usually comprises door, frame
and furniture) bloc-porte *m*
door unit with flush door bloc-porte *m* isoplane
doorway ouverture *f* de porte *f;* porte *f;*
seuil *m*
door, back porte *f* de derrière
door, batten porte *f* sur barres
door, double porte *f* à deux battants; porte *f*
à deux vantaux
door, fire-resistant porte *f* anti-feu
door, fireproof porte *f* à revêtment ignifuge *f*
door, fireproofed porte *f* ignifugée
door, folding porte *f* accordéon; porte *f*
extensible; porte *f* pliante
door, framed porte *f* sur chassis
door, front portail *m*; porte *f* d'entrée
door, glass panelled porte *f* vitrée
door, glazed porte *f* vitrée
door, hinged porte *f* battante
door, landing porte *f* palière
door, ledge porte *f* sur barres
door, open-lattice porte *f* à claire-voie
door, part solid, part panelled porte *f*
demi-plein *f*
door, pivoted porte *f* pivotante

door, self-closing porte *f* automatique
door, sliding porte *f* coulissante
door, solid porte *f* plein
door, swing porte *f* va-et-vient
dormer window lucarne *f* (see French-
English section for types)
double floor plancher *m* sur poutre(s)
double-glazed window double fenêtre *f*
double-sided axe bisaiguë *f*
dovetail queue-d'aronde *f*
dovetail (to) assembler *v* à queue d'aronde
dowel cheville *f;* cheville *f* en bois; tourillon
m; goujon *m*
dowelling chevillage *m*
draughtproof (to) calfeutrer *v*
draughtproofing calfeutrement *m*;
calfeutrage *m*
draw (to) tracer *v*; dessiner *v*
draw tighter (to) resserrer *v*
drawer tiroir *m*
drawing traçage *m*
drawing board planche *f* à dessin
dress (to) (wood) corroyer *v*; dresser *v*
dresser (furniture) vaisselier *m*
dressing (wood) corroyage *m*
drill (to) percer *v*; forer *v*
drill, hand porte-foret *m*; chignolle *f*
drill, electric perceuse *f;* chignolle *f*
drill bit mèche *f*
drill, twist mèche *f* bois à spirale; mèche *f*
hélicoidale; foret *m*
drilling perçage *m*
drive (to) chasser *v*
drive in a nail (to) chasser *v* un clou
driving shaft arbre *m* moteur
dry (to) sécher *v*
dry rot pourriture *f* sèche

ease a curve (to) adoucir *v* une courbe
eaves avant-toit(s) *m(pl)*; égout *m*; égout *m*
du bord du toit; queue *f* de vache
eaves overhang queue *f* de vache
eaves-board volige *f* chanlattée; coyau *m*
eaves-lath volige *f* chanlattée
edge arête *f;* chant *m*; rebord *m*; rive *f*
edge (eg of board) champ *m*
■ edgeways; edgewise = de champ
edge-plate (of a lock) têtière *f;* rebord *m*

effort effort *m*
embed (to) sceller *v*
emery cloth toile *f* d'émeri
empty vide *m*
empty space vide *m*
end bout *m*
▪ end to end = bout à bout
entrance porte *f* d'entrée
equip (to) aménager *v*
equipment outillage *m*
espagnolette bolt crémone *f*
▪ shank of espagnolette bolt = tige de crémone
establishing établissement *m*
execute (to) exécuter *v*
exposed beam poutre *f* apparente
extending roof or canopy auvent *m* en débordement
extension piece tige *f* de rallonge. rallonge *f*
extraction (of nails) arrachage *m*; arrachement *m*
extremity of piece of timber about *m*

face pan *m*; parement *m*
facia façade *f*
facia (door or drawer) for kitchen unit façade *f*
facing parement *m*
factory manufacturing screws/bolts etc visserie *f*
fanlight imposte *f*
fanlight, fixed dormant *m*
fanlight stay ferme-imposte *m*
fasten (to) sceller *v*; attacher *v*; fixer (à) *v*
fastener agrafe *f*
fastening agrafage *m*; fixation *f*; fermeture *f*; patte *f*
feather clavette *f*; languette *f*; languette *f* venue de bois
fell (to) (a tree) abattre *v*
fence post piquet *m* de clôture
fencing palissade *f*
fencing, wire grillage *m*
fibreboard panneau *m* fibres dures, panneau *m* de fibre
file lime *f*
file, flat-sided lime *f* plate à main

file, half-round lime *f* demi-ronde
file, round lime *f* ronde
file, triangular lime *f* triangulaire
file, two-tang lime *f* à deux queues
fill (to) calfeutrer *v*; reboucher *v*
filler reboucheur *m*; remplissage *m*
filler-block fourrure *f*
fillet-gutter solin *m*
filling calfeutrement *m*; calfeutrage *m*; remplissage *m*
fillister feuillure *f*
finger plate plaque *f* de propreté
finish off (to) ragréer *v*; parfaire *v*
finishing off ragrément *m*
fireproof (to) ignifuger *v*
fireproof floor plancher *m* incombustible
fireproofing agent ignifugeant *m*
first step (staircase) marche *f* de départ
fit ajustement *m*; ajustage *m*
fit out (to) aménager *v*
fitting ajustement *m*; ajustage *m*; montage *m*
fitting (together) emboîtement *m*
fix (to) sceller *v*; poser *v*; attacher *v*
fixed frame (door/window) bâti *m* dormant
fixed frame in opening (eg to take window) précadre *m*
fixed glazed sections of window châssis *mpl* fixes
fixing fixation *f*
fixing by clips etc clipsage *m*
fixing by stud gun scellement *m* au pistolet
flange collet *m*
flap trappe *f*
flap-hinge briquet *m*
flat edge strip chant *m* plat
flaw défaut *m*
flexible rule for drawing curves cerce *f*
flier (staircase) marche *f* carrée; marche *f* droite
flight (of stairs) rampe *f*; volée *f*; volée *f* d'escalier
floor plancher *m*
floor (to) planchéier *m*
floor base supporting stairs paillasse *f*
floor board planche *f*; frise *f*; frisette *f*
floor board with rounded beading frise *f*

à baguette

floor joist solive *f* de plancher; poutre *f* de plancher

floor strip lame *f*; lame *f* de parquet

floor, double plancher *m* sur poutre(s)

floor, false faux plancher *m*

floor, fireproof plancher *m* incombustible

floor, framed plancher *m* sur poutre pan de bois

floor, mezzanine mezzanine

floor, parquet parquet *m*

floor, prefabricated plancher *m* prefabriqué

floor, single plancher *m* ordinaire; plancher *m* simple

floor, raised faux plancher *m*

floor, wooden parquet *m*

flooring parquet *m*; plancher *m*; planchéiage *m*

flush affleuré,-e *adj*

flush, to make affleurer *v*

folding slatted blind or shutter jalousie *f* accordéon

footing-block semelle *f*

force (mech) effort *m*

former gabarit *m*

frame bâti *m*; cadre *m*; chambranle *m*; châssis *m*; encadrement *m*; pan *m*; ossature *f*

▪ **frame of door** = encadrement d'une porte

frame (door or window) huisserie *f*; dormant *m*

frame (of window) châssis *m*

frame of oak charpente *f* de chêne

frame(work) (eg of house) charpente *f*; ossature *f*

framed floor plancher *m* sur poutre pan de bois

framed roof-light châssis *m*

framework bâti *m*; cadre *m*; châssis *m*; dispositif *m*; ossature *f*

framing bâti *m*; cadre *m*; charpente *f*; coffrage *m*; encadrement *m*

freeing dégagement *m*

French Standards Association Association *f* Française de Normalisation; AFNOR *abb*

fret-saw (to) découper *v;* chantourner *v*

fretsaw scie *f* à chantourner; scie *f* à découper

fretwork découpage *m*

frieze frise *f*

frog (of a plane) contre-fer *m*

from centre to centre d'axe en axe; entraxe *m*

front façade *f*

front entrance portail *m*

fungicide treatment traitement *m* fongicide

furnishing fourniture *f*

furring coyau *m*

furring-piece (of a roof) coyau *m*; coyau *m* d'un comble

G-clamp serre-joint *m*

G-cramp presse *f* à coller; presse *f* à vis; serre-joint *m*

gable pignon *m*

▪ **gabled** = à pignon

gap écart *m*; intervalle *m*; vide *m*; jour *m*

gap (between) écartement *m*

garage door, overhead/tipping porte *f* de garage basculante

gate porte *f*

gate(s), wooden portail *m* en bois

gate, double portail *m*; porte *f* à deux battants

gate-hook gond *m* de porte

gauge calibre *m*; gabarit *m*

gauging calibrage *m*

gimlet vrille *f*; avant-clou *m*

girder poutre *f*; ferme *f*; solive *f*

girder (small) poutrelle *f*

girderage solivage *m*

give way (to) affaisser *v*

glass vitrerie *f*

glass-paper papier *m* de verre

glazed frame châssis *m* vitré

glazing vitrerie *f*

▪ **door with glazing** = une porte avec vitrerie

glazing bead parclose *f*

glazing fillet (eg putty) solin *m*

glue colle *f*

gluing collage *m*

going (of a step) giron *m*; largeur *f* de giron

going of the flight (staight stairs) ligne *f* de giron

gouge (carpenter's) gouge *f*
grading calibrage *m*; classement *m*
grain (of wood) fil *m*; fil *m* de bois; fibre *f*
de bois
▪ **cut against the grain** = couper dans le sens
contraire du fil
grind (to) affûter *v*
grinder (machine) affûteuse *f*
grinding affûtage *m*
gripping serrage *m*
groove entaille *f*; rainure *f*
groove (to) entailler *v*; évider *v*; rainer *v*
groove of a screw vide *m* d'une vis
grooving entaillage *m*
groundsill sablière *f* basse
guard rail garde *m* de corp; garde-corps *m*
gusset; gusset plate gousset *m*

H-hinge; lift-off hinge paumelle *f* double
hacksaw scie *f* à métaux
half-round demi-rond *m*; demi-rondin *m*
half-timbered colombage *m*
half-timbered house maison *f* à colombage
half-truss demi-ferme *f*
halved-joint entaille *f* à mi-bois
hammer marteau *m*
hammer, adze-eye marteau *m* américaine
avec arrache-clous
hammer, claw marteau *m* à dent *m*
hammer, peen- marteau *m* à panne
hand-drill porte-foret *m*; chignolle *f*
hand-rail lisse *m*
hand-saw égoïne *f*
handful (eg of sand) poignée *f*
handle béquille *f*; poignée *f*
handle (eg of saw) poignée *f*
▪ **door handle** = poignée de porte
handle (of tool) manche *m*
handrail balustrade *f*; garde *m* de corps;
garde-corps *m*; main *f* courante; rampe
handsaw égoïne *f*; scie *f* égoïne
hanging stile (of door frame etc) montant *m*
de rive
hardboard panneau *m* de fibres dures;
Isorel™ *m*
hardwood bois *m* dur
hatch trappe *f*
haunched tenon tenon *m* avec renfort carré

headroom (eg of a staircase) échappée *f*
heating of the tool échauffement *m* de
l'outil
heel talon *m*
height hauteur *f*
high line trait *m* haut (see also 'sawing
wood')
hinge charnière *f*; gond *m*; paumelle *f*;
penture *f*
hinge (ornamental) ferrure *f*
hinge, door paumelle *f*
hinge, H- paumelle *f* double
hinge, split paumelle *f*
hip arêtier *m*; croupe *f*
hip-truss ferme *f* de croupe
hit (to) taper *v*
▪ **to hit a nail** = taper sur un clou
hitched up retroussé,-e *adj*
hold up (to) appuyer *v*
holdfast patte *f* à scellement
hole trou *m*
**hole in masonry for embedding wooden
piece** empauchement *m*
hollow (out) (to) creuser *v*
hollow rod tige *f* creuse *f*
honeycomb network réseau *m* en nid
d'abeille
hood, cooker or kitchen hotte *f*
hook crochet *m*; agrafe *f*; gond *m*
hook and ride gond *m* et penture
hooking agrafage *m*
housing emboîtement *m*
housing for a sliding window, blind etc
caisson *m*; pavillon *m*

identifier repère *m*
implements outillage *m*
impost (of an arch) imposte *f*
inclination dévers *m*; inclinaison *f*
incorporated filler (timber framework)
remplissage *m*
indent adent *m*
indent (to) adenter *v*; endenter *v*
indicator repère *m*
inflate (to) gonfler *v*
inflation gonflement *m*
insulating board panneau *m* isolant
interior surface paroi *f* intérieure

intrados (of arch) intrados *m*
iron frame pan *m* de fer
iron rod tige *f* de fer
ironwork ferrure *f*

jack-hammer marteau-piqueur *m*
jalousie jalousie *f* accordéon
jamb montant *m*; jambage *m*
jamb (door or window) poteau *m* d'huisserie
jamb of a fire-place jambage *m* d'une cheminée
jamb-lining chambranle *m*
jamb-post jambage *m*
jamb-post of a doorway jambage *m* d'une baie de porte
jig-saw (to) chantourner *v*
jig-sawing chantournage *m*
joggle embrèvement *m*
joggle (to) embrever *v*
joggle-post poinçon *m*
join (to) assembler *v*
join end to end (to) assembler *v* en bout; abouter *v*
join on (to) rapporter *v*
join side by side (to) (ie in one plane) assembler *v* à plat; accoler *v*
join wood pieces unlevelly (to) désaffleurer *v*
joiner menuisier *m*
joiner's clamp serre-joint *m*
joiner's scraper racloir *m* de menuisier
joiner's workshop menuiserie *f*
joinery menuiserie *f*
joint assemblage *m;* joint *m;* jointure *f*
joint (to) assembler *v*
joint made with metal fixing pieces assemblage *m* par éléments métalliques
joint, angled halved assemblage *m* d'angle à mi-bois
joint, angled slot-mortise assemblage *m* d'angle à enfourchement
joint, bevel assemblage *m* à/en fausse coupe
joint, bolted assemblage *m* par boulons
joint, bolted joggle assemblage *m* à embrèvement boulonné
joint, box assemblage *m* à queues droites

joint, bridle joint *m* anglais; assemblage *m* à embrèvement anglais
joint, butt joint *m* en bout; joint *m* bout à bout; joint *m* plat; joint *m* à vif
joint, butting assemblage *m* en about; joint *m* plat
joint, cog joint *m* à adent
joint, cramped assemblage *m* par crampon
joint, double joggle assemblage *m* à double embrèvement
joint, diagonal assemblage *m* à/en fausse coupe
joint, double tenon assemblage *m* à double tenon
joint, double-stepped mortise and tenon assemblage *m* à tenon et mortaise à double embrèvement
joint, dovetail assemblage *m* à queue d'aronde
joint, dovetail halved- assemblage *m* à mi-bois en queue d'aronde
joint, dowel assemblage *m* à chevilles; assemblage *m* à goujon et douille
joint, glued assemblage *m* par collage
joint, half-lap assemblage *m* à mi-bois
joint, halved assemblage *m* à mi-bois
joint, hinged assemblage *m* à charnière
joint, indent assemblage *m* à endent
joint, indented assemblage *m* à dents de scie
joint, joggle assemblage *m* à embrèvement; assemblage *m* avec embrèvement
joint, joggle with U-bolt assemblage *m* à embrevement à étrier
joint, lap assemblage *m* à recouvrement; assemblage *m* à mi-bois
joint, lapped assemblage *m* à clin
joint, loose-tongue assemblage *m* à fausse languette
joint, matched joint *m* bouveté
joint, mitre assemblage *m* à/d'/en onglet
joint, mortise (between pieces of different thickness) assemblage *m* flotté
joint, mortise and tenon assemblage *m* à tenon et mortaise; tenon *m* simple
joint, multiple scarf enture *f* à sifflets multiples
joint, notch assemblage *m* à entaille
joint, notched and bolted assemblage *m* à

embrèvement avant
joint, notch-and-bridle assemblage *m* à embrèvement anglais
joint, oblique scarf enture *f* à sifflet simple
joint, overlap assemblage *m* à mi-bois
joint, pegged assemblage *m* à tourillons
joint, pinned assemblage *m* par goujons
joint, pinned tenon assemblage *m* à tenon avec cheville
joint, rabbeted assemblage *m* à feuillure
joint, rabbeted, with batten assemblage *m* à feuillure et liteau
joint, rebated assemblage *m* à feuillure
joint, reversed bevel assemblage *m* à fausse coupe renversée
joint, scarf- enture *f*; joint *m* en sifflet; joint *m* biseauté
joint, screw(ed) assemblage *m* vissé; assemblage *m* à vis; joint *m* vissé
joint, single tenon assemblage *m* à tenon simple
joint, slip-tongue assemblage *m* à fausse languette; assemblage *m* à languette rapportée
joint, slot-mortise assemblage *m* à enfourchement
joint, spiked assemblage *m* par crampon
joint, splayed assemblage *m* en sifflet; enture *f* à sifflet simple
joint, splayed indent scarf enture *f* à trait de Jupiter simple
joint, splayed scarf enture *f* en sifflet
joint, splice- enture *f*; joint *m* à recouvrement
joint, step assemblage *m* à mis-bois
joint, tenon and tusk assemblage *m* à tenon renforcé
joint, tenon, with double shoulder assemblage *m* à tenon à double épaulement
joint, tongued-and-grooved assemblage *m* à rainure et languette
joist solive *f*; poutre *f*
joist support appui *m* des solives
joisting solivage *m*
jutting out en saillie; saillant,-e *adj*

kerf trait *m* de scie

key clavette *f*
keyhole trou *m* de serrure
keying calage *m*
kind of wood essence *f* de bois
king-post poinçon *m*; aiguile *f*
king-rod (of iron/steel roof-truss) poinçon *m*
kitchen cupboard placard *m* de cuisine
knock (to) taper *v*
knock down (to) abattre *v*
knot (wood, cord) nœud *m*
knuckle (of a hinge) charnon *m*; nœud *m*

lacquer (to) laquer *v*; vernir *v*
lacquering vernissage *m*
ladder échelle *f*
laminate stratifié *m*; also *adj*
laminated lamellé,-e *adj*; laminé,-e *adj*
lamination lamellation *f*
landing (of a staircase) palier *m*; repos *m*
landing trimmer (staircase) chevêtre *m* sous la marche palière
lap over (to) chevaucher *v*
lap-joint entaille *f* à mi-bois
lapped scarf enture *f* en paume
latch fermeture *f*
latch, gate loquet *m* de porte
latch-lever béquille *f*
lath latte *f*; lame *f*; volige *f*
lath (to) voliger *v*; latter *v*
lathing lattage *m*
lathing lattis *m*
lattice-bracing charpente à croisillons
lay a wooden or parquet floor (to) parqueter *v*
lay out (to) aménager *v*; tracer *v*
layer (of wood) feuillet *m*
laying out traçage *m*
leaf (of a door/window) vantail *m*; vantaux *mpl*
lean (to) appuyer *v*
lean-to appentis *m*
leatherboard carton-cuir *m*
ledge barre *f*; saillie *f*
length longueur *f*
length of step (staircase) emmarchement *m*
length of wood with a square cross-section

carrelet *m*
length of wood with rectangular cross-section tasseau *m*
lengthen (to) rallonger *v*
lengthening rallongement *m*
lengthening-piece rallonge *f*
level niveau *m*
level (to) affleurer *v*; araser *v*; niveler *v*; recaler *v*
levelling arasement *m*; affleurage *m*
lift (to) enlever *v*
lime putty mastic *m* à la chaux
line ligne *f*; cordeau *m*; trait *m*
line of flight; walking-line (of stairs) ligne *f* de foulée; ligne *f* de giron
line (to) (a structure) blinder *v*
line trace marked with cord lignage *m*
line up (to) aligner *v*; niveler *v*
linen cupboard armoire *f* à linge
lining revêtement *m*
link rod biellette *f*; biellette *f* de liaison
link (to) liaisonner *v*; accoupler *v*; joindre *v*
lintel linteau *m*; prélinteau *m*
lip rive *f*
locate (to) situer *v*
lock serrure *f*
lock (to) fermer *v*; fermer *v* à clé
locking blocage *m*; calage *m*; condamnation *f*; fermeture *f*
locking bolt verrou *m* de fermeture
locking device condamnation *f*
loft comble *m*; grenier *m*
loose tongue languette *f* rapportée
loose/easy fit ajustage *m* lâche/facile
lorraine board (wide wooden board, at least 3 m long) planche *f* lorraine
louvre volet *m* d'aération
low line trait *m* bas; (see also 'sawing wood')
lower crossbar (of grille) sommier *m*
lower edge of timber frame of roof rive *f*

machine machine *f*
machinery (plant) outillage *m*; matériel *m*
make fabrication *f*
make (to) confectionner *v*; fabriquer *v*; produire *v*
make even (to) niveler *v*

make flush (to) affleurer *v*
make into an arch (to) cintrer *v*
make sharper (to) affûter *v*
make smoother (to) adoucir *v*
make unlevel (to) désaffleurer *v*
make up (to) confectionner *v*
make-up piece (of wood) alaise *f*
making confection *f*; fabrication *f*
making flush affleurement *m*; affleurage *m*
making up confection *f*
making wood mouldings toupillage *m*
mallet maillet *m*
mansard roof comble *m* brisé; comble *m* mansardé; mansarde *f*
mantelpiece tablette *f* de cheminée; manteau *m* de cheminée
manufacture fabrication *f*
manufacture (to) fabriquer *v*
mark repère *m*
mark out (to) repérer *v*
marking repérage *m*
marking awl traceret *m*
marking gauge trusquin *m*; troussequin *m*
marking out lignage *m*; traçage *m*
marking out mortises and tenons contre-jaugeage *m*
marking wood components for identification marquage *m* de bois
match (boards) by tongue-and-groove (to) bouveter *v*
▪ **tongued-and-grooved matched** = bouveté
match (to) bouveter *v*
material forming inner core (eg of a door) âme *f*
measure with a spirit level (to) niveler *v*
measurement dimension *f*
measuring (in metres) métrage *m*
medium milieu *m*
metal connector for Gerber™ beam system raccord *m* Gerber™
metal framework ossature *f* métallique
metal shelves unit étagère *f* acier
metre mètre *m*
metre rule mètre *m*
middle milieu *m*; centre *m*
mill (to) fraiser *v*
milling fraisage *m*
mitre onglet *m*

mitre box boîte *f* à onglet(s); boîte *f* à coupe(s)
mitre-cutting machine machine *f* à couper d'onglet
mitred angle onglet *m*
mobile glazed sections of a window châssis *mpl* mobiles
mortise mortaise *f*
mortise (to) mortaiser *v*; bédaner *v*
mortise-axe bisaiguë *f*
mortising mortaisage *m*
mortising machine mortaiseuse *f*
moulding moulure *f*
moulding, quarter or half round baguette *f*
moulding machine (wood working) moulurière *f*
mounting montage *m*
move (to) déplacer *v*; mouvoir *v*
movement déplacement *m*; mouvement *m*
mullion meneau *m*

nail clou *m*; pointe *f*
nail (to) clouer *v*
nail, flat head pointe *f* tête plate; clou *m* à tête plate
nail, finishing pointe *f* tête homme
nail, lost-head clou *m* à tête perdue; clou *m* à tête d'homme
nail, twist pointe *f* torsadée
nail, wire clou *m* de Paris
nail-extractor arrache-clou *m*
nail-punch chasse-clou *m*; chasse-pointe *m*
nail-set chasse-clou *m*; chasse-pointe *m*
nailed assembly assemblage *m* cloué
nailed construction assemblage *m* cloué
nailing clouage *m*; clouement *m*
narrow (to) resserrer (se) *v*
narrowest part of a balanced step (staircase) collet *m*
neck (of a chisel) collet *m*
needle aiguille *f*
newel (of spiral staircase) noyau *m*
nippers tenaille *f*
nose nez *m*
nosing of step nez *m* de marche
notch entaille *f*

notch (to) entailler *v*
notch (to) (edge of timber) délarder *v*
notch or cut used to lock a skewed beam repos *m*
notch to receive shoulders of a tenon épaulement *m*
notching entaillage *m*
notching in a roof post (to take ends of braces etc) dégueulement *m*
notching made in a tenon and mortise joint to reinforce it embrèvement *m*
nut écrou *m*
nuts and bolts visserie *f*; boulons *mpl* et écrous *mpl*

oak chêne *m*
oak, solid chêne massif *m*
oblique biais,-e *adj*
oeil-de-boeuf œil-de-bœuf *m*
ogee (moulding or plane) doucine *f*
open framework (timber) châssis *m* de charpente
open-lattice gate or door porte *f* à claire-voie
open staircase échelle *f* de meunier
opening ouverture *f*; baie *f*
opening in a door for a glazing panel oculus *m*
opening in a floor or roof to receive a staircase, chimney etc trémie *f*
opening section of a window ouvrant *m*
oriel window oriel *m*
out of plumb dévers,-e *adj*; hors d'aplomb
out of true dévers,-e *adj*
outer frame châssis *m* de charpente
overall length longueur *f* hors-tout
overlap (to) chevaucher *v*; recouvrir *v*

PVC frames/framework menuiseries *fpl* PVC
pack (to) garnir *v*
packing-piece cale *f*; cale *f* d'appui
pair of compasses compas *m*
pane (of glass) vitre *f*; carreau *m*
pane (eg of roof, side of nut) pan *m*
panel panneau *m*
panel (to) lambrisser *v*

panel in wood (to) boiser *v*
panel, floor, chipboard dalle *f* de particules agglomérées
panel, covering paroi *f*
panel, decorative panneau *m* décor
panel, door panneau *m* de porte
panel, faced panneau *m* décor
panel, sunk caisson *m*
panelling boiserie *f*; lambris *m*; lambrissage *m*; panneautage *m*
panelling, room-height lambris *m* de hauteur
panelling, sill-height lambris *m* d'appui
panels, framing for cimaise *f* à lambris
pare down (to) délarder *v*
parquet floor parquet *m*
parquet forming machine parqueteuse *f*
parquet strip lame *f*; lame *f* de parquet
particle board panneau *m* de particules
partition cloison *f*
partition wall cloison *f*
partition, wood cloison *f* en bois
partition-wall of a staircase échiffe *m*; échiffre *m*
partitioning cloisonnage *m*
passage coursive *f*; passage *m*
passageway passage *m*; dégagement *m*
paste colle *f*
pedestal socle *m*; support *m*
peen (of a hammer) panne *f*
peg cheville *f*
peg (to) (joinery) cheviller *v*
pegging chevillage *m*
pelmet cantonnière *f*
penthouse auvent *m*
penthouse (roof) appentis *m*
picket piquet *m*
picture rail cimaise *f*
picture window baie *f* vitrée
piece of joinery/carpentry menuiserie *f*
pierce (to) percer *v*
pile (constr) pieu *m*; pilot *m*
pin boulon *m*; cheville *f*; pivot *m*; tourillon *m*; goujon *m*
pin-drift chasse-goupille *m*
pin-punch chasse-goupille *m*
pincers tenaille *f*
pinion pignon *m*
pivot pivot *m*

plain lisse *adj*
plane (to) planer *v*; raboter *v*
plane (to) (eg flooring) replanir *v*
plane (to), rough dégrossir *v*
plane rabot *m*
plane, beading chasse-rond *m*
plane, bench rabot *m* d'établi
plane, bench rabbet guillaume *m* d'établi
plane, bench, with grooved base rabot *m* rainuré
plane-bit fer *m* de rabot
plane, cabinet maker's rabbet guillaume *m* d'ébéniste
plane, fillister feuilleret *m*
plane, grooving bouvet *m* à rainure
plane-iron fer *m* de rabot
plane, jack- demi-varlope *f*; galère *f*; riflard *m*
plane, jointing- varlope *f*
plane, nosing- nez *m* de marche
plane, ogee doucine *f*
plane, plough bouvet *m*
plane, rabbet/rebate bouvet *m*; guillaume *m*
plane, smoothing navette *f*; (with curved stock)
plane, sole of semelle *f*
plane, square rabbet guillaume *m* de bout; guillaume *m* de fil
plane, tonguing bouvet *m* à languette
plane, trying varlope *f*
planer raboteuse *f*
planing rabotage *m*
planing machine raboteuse *f*
plank planche *f*; ais *m*; bastaing *m*; madrier *m*
planking planchéiage *m*; platelage *m*
plate; head-plate sablière *f* haute
plate, roof-; wall-plate sablière *f* de comble
plinth at base of door jamb socle *m*
plot (to) tracer *v*
plug bouchon *m*; cheville *f*; tampon *m*
plugging a wood fault bouchonnage *m*
plumb (in vertical position) à plomb
plumb-bob plomb *m*; fil *m* à plomb
plumbline fil *m* à plomb
plywood bois *m* contreplaqué; contreplaqué *m*
pneumatic jack vérin *m* pneumatique

point (sharp) pointe *f*
pole poteau *m*
porch porche *f*
porch-roof auvent *m*
portable vice-stand/vice-bench établi *m*
  roulant pour étaux
portal portail *m*
post montant *m*; pieu *m*; piquet *m*; poteau *m*
post, anchor poteau *m* d'ancrage
post, boundary poteau *m* de bornage
post, corner poteau *m* cornier; poteau *m*
  d'angle
post, door poteau *m* d'huisserie
post, inertial poteau *m* d'inertie
post, jamb poteau *m* d'huisserie
post, newel poteau *m*; noyau *m* de bois
post/pole, telegraph poteau *m* télégraphique
press presse *f*
prevent (to) empêcher *v*
prick-punch pointeau *m*
proceed by stages (to) procéder *v* par
  paliers
projection saillie *f*
prop étai *m*; chandelle *f*; jambe *m* de force;
  accore *m*; étançon *m*
provision fourniture *f*
pulling out (eg nails) arrachage *m*;
  arrachement *m*
pumice ponce *f*
pumicing ponçage *m*
punch, centre pointeau *m*
purlin filière *f*; panne *f*; panne filière *f*
purlin-cleat chantignolle *f*; échantignolle *f*
put in (to) rapporter *v*
putty mastic *m*
putty, glazier's mastic *m* de vitrier

**quality certificate of the manufactured
  article** certificat *m* de suivi et marquage
quarter round beading quart *m* de rond;
  baguette *f*

rabbet feuillure *f*
rabbet (to) feuiller *v*
rachet-brace vilebrequin *m* à cliquet
rafter chevron *m*

rafter, angle chevron *m* d'arêtier; arêtier *m*
rafter, common chevron *m*; chevron *m*
  intermédiare
rafter, hip- arêtier *m*; chevron *m* d'arêtier
rafter, jack- empanon *m*; empannon *m*
rafter, main or principal arbalétrier *m*;
  chevron *m* arbalétrier
rafter, small hip- empanon *m*; empannon *m*
rafter, small valley noulet *m*
rafter, valley noue *f*; noue *f* charpente
raftering chevronnage *m*
rail barre *f*; barreau *m*; rail *m*
rail (of door frame or window sash)
  traverse *f*
railing garde *m* de corps; garde-corps *m*
raised up retroussé,-e *adj*
■ **raised tie-beam** = entrait retroussé
ramming bourrage *m*
rasp râpe *f*
ream (to) aléser *v*; fraiser *v*
reamer alésoir *m*; fraise *f*
reaming alésage *m*; fraisage *m*
rebate feuillure *f*
rebate (to) feuiller *v*
recess défonçage *m*; défoncement *m*
recess (to) défoncer *v*
recess cut in door to receive lock entaille *f*
recessing défonçage *m*; défoncement *m*
recessing-machine défonceuse *f*
recut (to) recouper *v*
reed (beading) baguette *f*
reinforce (to) renforcer *v*
reinforced armé,-e *adj*; renforcé,-e *adj*
reinforced right-angled metal bracket
  équere *f* renforcée
reinforcing piece fourrure *f*
**reinforcing piece between king-post and
  ridge beam** contreventement *m*
remove (to) enlever *v*
render rigid (to) raidir *v*
reset (to) (eg equipment) recaler *v*
rest appui *m*; repos *m*
rest (to) appuyer *v*
resting repos *m*
restore (to) restaurer *v*; ragréer *v*
reveal (archit) jouée *f*
reverse side (to face) contre-parement *m*
reverse side of partition contre-cloison *f*
ridge (of roof) faîtage *m*; faîte *m*; crête *f*

ridge beam; ridge-pole panne *f* faîtière, faîtage *m*; faîtière *f*
ridge capping; ridge tiles faîtage *m*
ridge lead faîtage *m*; faîtière *f*
ridge tile faîtière *f*
right-angled metal bracket équerre *f* simple
rim bord *m*; rebord *m*
ring anneau *m*; bague *f*; rond *m*
rip (to) refendre *v*
ripping refente *f*
rise (vertical height of step) hauteur *f* de marche
riser (of staircase) contre-marche *f*; montant *m*
rod barre *f*; tige *f*; baguette *f*
roller; runner (metal) galet *m*
roller shutter housing-box coffre *m* de volet roulant
roof toit *m*; comble *m*; toiture *f*; couverture *f*
roof beam at base of slope sablière *f*
roof covering couverture *f*
roof edge projection saillie *f* de rive
roof frame pan *m* de couverture
roof of a building comble *m* d'un bâtiment
roof truss ferme *f*; ferme *f* de comble
roof truss/trussing armature *f* à toit
roof window vélux ™ *m*
roof with a single slope appentis *m*
roof with one/two slope(s) comble *m* à une/deux pente(s)
roof with two different slopes brisé *m*
roof, flat toit *m* plat
roof, French comble *m* mansardé
roof, greatest side of long-pan *m*
roof, mansard toit *m* en mansarde
roof, sloping toit *m* en pente
roof, terraced toit *m* en terrasse
roof, trussed comble *m* sur ferme
roof, untrused comble *m* sans ferme
roof-frame charpente *f* de comble
roof-plate semelle *f*
roof-post poinçon *m*
roofing couverture *f*
rot, dry pourriture *f* sèche
rot, wet pourriture *f* humide
rot (to) pourrir *v*
rough hew (to) dégrossir *v*; blanchir *v*

rough plane (to) dégauchir *v*; dégrossir *v*;
roughing down dégrossissage *m*; dégrossissement *m*
round window œil-de-bœuf *m*
router défonceuse *f*
rub down (to) poncer *v*
rubber mallet maillet *m* caoutchouc
rubbing down ponçage *m*
rule; ruler règle *f*
rung (of ladder) barreau *m*; échelon *m*

sag (to) affaisser (s') *v*; fléchir *v*
sand down (to) poncer *v*
sand-papering ponçage *m*
sander ponceuse *f*
sander, belt ponceuse *f* à ruban abrasif; ponceuse *f* à bande
sander, disk ponceuse *f* à disque
sander, floor ponceuse *f* à parquet
sander, orbital ponceuse *f* orbitale; ponceuse *f* vibrante
sanding down ponçage *m*
sanding machine ponceuse *f*
sandpaper papier *m* de verre
sandpaper (to) poncer *v*
sash fillister feuillure *f*
saw scie *f*
saw (to) scier *v*; débiter *v*
saw blade lame *f* de scie
saw clamp entaille *f* à affûter les scies
saw into required shape (to) débillarder *v*
saw setting tool tourne-à-gauche *m*; pince *f* à avoyer
saw up (to) débiter *v*
saw, back scie *f* à dos
saw, band scie *f* à ruban; scie *f* sans fin
saw, beading scie *f* à moulure
saw, bow scie *f* à chantourner
saw, carcass scie *f* à dos
saw, chain tronçonneuse *f*
saw, circular scie *f* circulaire
saw, cleaving scie *f* à refendre
saw, cross-cut scie *f* de travers
saw, cutting-out scie *f* à débiter
saw, edge trimming déligneuse *f*
saw, endless scie *f* sans fin
saw, felling scie *f* à débiter
saw, hand scie *f* égoïne

saw, jig- scie *f* à chantourner; scie *f* sauteuse
saw, keyhole scie *f* à guichet
saw, lock- scie *f* à guichet
saw, mitre scie *f* à coupe d'onglets; scie *f* à onglet
saw, peg scie *f* à chevilles
saw, power scie *f* mécanique
saw, rip- scie *f* à refendre; scie *f* allemande
saw, tenon scie *f* à tenon; scie *f* à dos
saw, veneer scie *f* à placage
sawcut trait *m* de scie
sawing débitage *m*; sciage *m*
sawing line trait *m* de scie
sawing up débit *m*; débitage *m*
sawing wood edgeways sciage *m* par 'trait haut'
sawing wood flatways with the grain sciage *m* par 'trait bas'
sawmill scierie *f*; scie *f* mécanique
sawn piece of timber (eg plank, beam) débit *m* de bois
scaffold échafaudage *m*
scaffold board planche *f* d'échafaudage; plateau *m*
scaffolding échafaudage *m*
scale (of drawing etc) échelle *f*
scantling équarrissage *m*; équarrissement *m*
scarf; scarf joint enture *f*
Scientific and Technical Building Centre, Paris Centre Scientifique et Technique du Bâtiment, Paris; CSTB *abb*
scrape (to) racler *v*
scraper grattoir *m*; racloir *m*
scraping raclage *m*
screw vis *f*
screw (to) visser *v*
screw on (to) visser *v*
screw, coach tire *m*; tire-fond *m*
screw, cross-head vis *f* en tête cruciforme (type Phillips™); vis *f* pozidriv™ (type pozidriv™)
screw, round-headed vis *f* à tête ronde
screw, slot-head vis *f* à fente; vis *f* à tête fraisée
screw, wood vis *f* à bois
screw-clamp presse *f* à coller; presse *f* à vis
screw-jack vérin *m*

screw-spike tire *m*; tire-fond *m*
screwdriver tournevis *m*
screwdriver (type Phillips™) tournevis *m* pour vis Phillips™
screwdriver bit/tip embout *m* de tournevis
screwdriver, ratchet tournevis *m* à cliquet
screwed plug/cap bouchon *m* à vis
screwing on/down vissage *m*
screws, nails, hooks etc visserie *f*
scriber pointe *f* à tracer; traceret *m*
scribing awl traceret *m*
seal (to) sceller *v*
sealing up gaps calfeutrement *m*; calfeutrage *m*
service-hatch passe-plat(s) *m*
set (of the teeth of a saw) chasse *f*
set of beams solivage *m*
set of bench planes used by joiner affûtage *m*
set out (to) tracer *v*
set square équerre *f*; équerre *f* à dessin
set square of 45° équerre *f* à 45°
setting réglage *m*
setting up montage *m*; établissement *m*
shaft (rotating) arbre *m*
shaft (eg of axe) manche *m*
shank tige *f*
shank (of a drill) queue *f*
shank of espagnolette bolt tige *f* de crémone
sharpen (to) affûter *v*
sharpen before use (to) affiner *v* l'affûtage avant emploi
sharpening affûtage *m*
shave-hook grattoir *m* triangulaire
shaver outil *m* pour arasage
shears cisailles *fpl*
shed remise *f*; appentis *m*
sheeting (of an excavation) (wood or metal) blindage *m*
sheeting, polyethylene feuille *f* de polyéthylène
shelf étagère *f*; planche *f*; tablette *f*
shelf board with melamine surface tablette *f* mélaminée
shelf unit étagère *f*
shellac laque *f*
shellac (to) laquer *v*
shingle bardeau *m*
shoot (to) chasser *v*

shoot the bolt of a lock (to) chasser *v* le pêne d'une serrure

shoot the edge of a board (to) dresser *v* le champ d'une planche

shooting-board planche *f* à dresser

shore (up) (to) blinder *v*; étayer *v*; étançonner *v*

shrink (to) resserrer (se) *v*; rétrécir *v*

shrinkage retrait *m*; rétrécissement *m*

shutter volet *m*; contrevent *m*; fermeture *f*

shutter, barred and braced volet *m* plein barres et écharpes

shutter, louvred volet *m* persienne

shutter, roller volet *m* roulant

shuttering coffrage *m*

shutting fermeture *f*

shutting stile (of door frame etc) montant *m* de battement; montant *m* de serrure

side pan *m*; versant *m*; paroi *f*

side of a lucarne jouée *f*

sill appui *m*; sablière *f* basse

sill of door seuil *m*

single floor plancher *m* ordinaire; plancher *m* simple

size dimension *f*

skeleton châssis *m* de charpente; carcasse *f*

sketch croquis *m*

skew biais,-e *adj*

▪ **on the skew; obliquely** = en biais

skewed biais -e *adj*

skirting; skirting board plinthe *f*

skylight fenêtre *f* à tabatière; lanternau *m*; lucarne *f*; vélux™ *m*

slant biais *m*

slantwise de biais; en biais

slant assemblage of the hip-rafters with the king-post dégueulement *m*

slat (of persienne) lamelle *f*

slip-tongue languette *f* rapportée

slope pente *f*; rampe *f*; versant *m*; talus *m*

slope (of a roof or staircase) rampant *m*

slope (of roof) égout *m*; pente *f*; versant *m* d'un comble

slope, lower, of mansard roof brisis *m*

slope, upper, of mansard roof terrasson *m*

slot rainure *f*

slot (to) mortaiser *v*; rainer *v*; entailler *v*

slot-mortise enfourchement *m*

slotting entaillage *m*

small board planchette *f*

small covered vent in roof châtière *f*

small roof (covering entrance, balcony etc) auvent *m*

small shelf planchette *f*

small triangular roof truss for light loads fermette *f*

small triangular roof-light or vent outeau *m*

smooth lisse *adj*

smooth (to) lisser *v*; planer *v*; ragréer *v*; recaler *v*

smooth a surface with emery paper (to) adoucir *v* une surface avec de la toile d'émeri

smoothing lissage *m*; planage *m*

smoothing-out adoucissement *m*; adoucissage *m*

smoothness lisse *m*

snap (to) claquer *v*

snap a line (to) battre *v* une ligne; (abbreviated as 'à battre' or 'à claquer')

socket (bulb) douille *f*

socle socle *m*

soffit soffite *m*; sous face *f*; intrados *m*

soften (to) adoucir *v*

softening adoucissement *m*; adoucissage *m*

softwood bois *m* tendre

space (between) écartement *m*

space between joists, tiles etc solin *m*

space occupied by a stairway cage *f* d'escalier

span porteé *f*; travée *f*

▪ **roof span** = travée de comble

span (to) franchir *v*; chevaucher *v*

span-piece entrait *m* rétroussé; faux *m* entrait

spar chevron *m*

specification spécification *f*

spike; spike-nail broche *f*; cheville *f* (tire-fond)

spindle arbre *m*

spindle moulding machine toupie *f*

spiral stairs escargot *m*; escalier *m* en escargot; colimaçon *m*

spirit level niveau *m* à bulle (d'air)

spline clavette *f*

splinter éclat *m*

split (to) refendre *v*

splitting refente *f*

splitting/dividing in two dédoublage *m*

spokeshave wastringue *f*

spring (to) déjeter *v*
springer sommier *m*
spur contrefiche *f*; entretoise *f*
square (instrument) équerre *f*
square (to) équarrir *v*
square metre mètre *m* carré
squareness équarrissage *m*; équarrissement *m*
squaring (timber) équarrissage *m*; équarrissement *m*
staging échafaudage *m*
stair well jour *m*; jour *m* d'escalier; cage *f* d'escalier
stair well opening trémie *f*
stair, open-newel vis *f* a jour
stair, open-well vis *f* a jour
stair, solid-newel vis *f* à noyau plein
staircase escalier *m*
staircase with balanced steps escalier *m* balancé
staircase, curved escalier *m* courbe
staircase, landing of repos *m* d'escalier; palier *m*
staircase, open-tread escalier *m* de meunier *m*
staircase, private or back escalier *m* de dégagement
staircase, quarter turning escalier *m* à quartier tournant
staircase, spiral escalier *m* en colimaçon; escalier *m* helicoïdal; escalier *m* spiral; escalier *m* tournant; escargot *m*
staircase, straight escalier *m* droit
staircase, traditional escalier *m* traditionnel
stairs escalier *m*
stairway escalier *m*
stake pieu *m*; piquet *m*; jalon *m*
stand socle *m*; support *m*
staple agrafe *f*; crampon *m* à deux pointes
stapling agrafage *m*
stay arrêt *m*; tirant *m*
steel joist solive *f* en acier
stem tige *f*
step marche *f*
stick (to) adhérer *v*
sticking adhésion *f*; collage *m*
stiffen (to) raidir *v*
stile (of door frame etc) montant *m*
stone pier jambage *m*

stop arrêt *m*
stop up (to) calfeutrer *v*
stoppage arrêt *m*
stopped chamfer chanfrein *m* arrêté
stopper bouchon *m*
stopping up calfeutrement *m*; calfeutrage *m*; rebouchage *m*
storage stockage *m*
straighen (to) dégauchir *v*
straight flight (of stairs) volée *f* droite
straight-edge règle *f*
strap étrier *m*
strap (of strap hinge) penture *f*
streak trait *m*
strengthened renforcé,-e *adj*
stress effort *m*
stretcher entrait *m*; tirant *m*
string cordeau *m*
string or stringer(staircase) limon *m*
string, close limon *m* à la française; limon *m* droit
string, cut see open string
string, cut wall fausse *f* crémaillère
string, housed limon *m* droit
string, open crémaillère *f*; limon *m* à crémaillère *m*; limon *m* à l'anglaise
string, open wall fausse *f* crémaillère
string, outer limon *m* apparent
string, wall contre-limon *m*; faux limon *m*
string, wreathed (of staircase) limon *m* débillardé
string-board (staircase) limon *m*
stringer (staircase) limon *m*
strip lamelle *f*
strip of wood (cleat) languette *f* de bois
structural structurel,-elle *adj*; structural,-e *adj* -aux *mpl*
structural alterations transformations *fpl*
structure ossature *f*; structure *f*
strut barre *f* transversale; bielle *f*; cale *f*; contre-fiche *f*; entretoise *f*; étrésillon *m*; jambe *f* de force
strut (of roof-truss) jambe *f* de force; poteau *m*
stub-tenon tenon *m* invisible
stud driver; stud gun pistolet *m* de scellement
sub-frame (in opening to take door or window) précadre *m*

subside (to) affaisser *v*
supply; provision fourniture *f*
support appui *m*; console *f*; support *m*
support (to) appuyer *v*; étayer *v*
support with props accorer *v*
support piece embedded in wall corbeau *m*
supporting frame châssis *m* de charpente
supporting wall of a staircase mur *m* d'échiffre
surface crack in wood gerce *f*
surface-plane (to) dégauchir *v*
surface-planing dégauchissage *m*; dégauchissement *m*
surface-planing machine dégauchisseuse *f*
sway (to) balancer *v*
swell (to) gonfler *v*
swelling gonflement *m*
swing (to) balancer *v*
system système *m*

T-square double équerre *f*; équerre *f* en T
table table *f*
table (of a girder) table *f*; semelle *f*
tail trimmer enchevêtrure *f*; solive *f* d'enchevêtrure
taking up play rattrapage *m* de jeu
talon talon *m*
tamping bourrage *m*
tang (of a file) queue *f*
template gabarit *m*; calibre *m*
temporary protective support for a door frame cadre *m* d'attent
tenon tenon *m*
tenon (to); make a tenon (to) tennoner *v*
tenon cutting machine tenonneuse *f*
thickness épaisseur *f*
thickness (of a board) rive *f* d'une planche
thin (to) (eg a board) affiner *v*
thin sheet feuillet *m*; lamelle *f*
thread fil *m*
threshold seuil *m*
tie-brace blochet *m*
tie-rod tirant *m*; entrait *m*
tighten (up) (to) resserrer *v*
tightening serrage *m*
timber bois *m*; bois *m* de menuiserie
timber (to) (eg excavation) blinder *v*
timber frame charpente *f* en bois

timber frame panel pan *m* de bois
timber framing ossature *f* en bois
timber, bar of rondin *m*
timber, builder's bois *m* de construction
timber, building bois *m* de charpente
timber, constructional bois *m* de construction
timber, cut-end of bout *m* rejeté
timber, round rondin *m*
timber, sawn bois *m* de sciage
timber, side- filière *f*; panne *f*
timber, square-sawn bois *m* carré
timber, unhewn/uncut bois *m* rond
timber, waney bois *m* flache
timber, warped bois *m* déjeté; bois *m* déversé
timbering boisage *m*
timbers, roof comble *m*; ferme *f*
timberwork boisage *m*
tongs tenaille(s) *f*
tongue languette *f*; languette *f* venue de bois
tongued-and-grooved chipboard aggloméré *m* bouveté
tool outil *m*
tools outillage *m*
trace (to) tracer *v*
trace a line with a cord (to) battre *v* une ligne; (abbreviated as 'à battre')
trace of raised perpendicular on a straight line trait *m* carré
trace out line using string (to) cingler *v*
tracing traçage *m*
tracing iron rénette *f* (de charpentier)
transfer (to) (eg measurements) reporter *v*
transom traverse *f*
transom (horizontal) meneau *m*
transom (of window, door) sommier *m*
transom (window) imposte *f*
trap door trappe *f*
trap door access to attic/loft trappe *f* accès combles
traverse traverse *f*
tread (of a girder) table *f*
tread (of step) marche *f*; largeur *f* de marche
tree arbre *m*
treenail tourillon *m*; trenail *m*
trim habillage *m*
trim (to) (wood) corroyer *v*; dresser *v*; blanchir *v*

trim joists (to) enchevêtrer *v* des solives
trimmer chevêtre *m*; linçoir *m*
trimming corroyage *m*; dressage *m*;
trimming joist chevêtre *m*; chevêtrier *m*
true (up) (to) dégauchir *v*
truing dégauchissage *m*; dégauchissement *m*
truing up dégauchissage *m*; dégauchissement *m*
trunking (elect) moulure *f*
truss ferme *f*
truss post poinçon *m*
truss-rod tirant *m*
trussed armé,-e *adj*; renforcé,-e *adj*
trussing armature *f*; renforcement *m*
try (to) varloper *v*
try up (to) varloper *v*
trying varlopage *m*
trying up varlopage *m*
turn (to) tourner *v*
turret tourelle *f*
tusk tenon tenon *m* renforcé
twist nail pointe *f* torsadée
two metre wooden rule double métre bois *m*

U-bolt étrier *m*
U-strap étrier *m*
under ridge-board sous-faîte *m*
underfloor space vide *m* sanitaire
underside sous-face *f*
unscrew (to) dévisser *v*
up-and-over garage door porte *f* de garage basculante
upper slope of a mansard roof terrasson *m*
upright montant *m*

vacuum vide *m*
valley (roof) noue *f*
valley flashing noue *f* métallique
valley-gutter (eg curved tiles, lead sheet) noue *f*
valley rafter noue *f*
valley rafter (small) noulet *m*
varnish (to) vernir *v*
varnishing vernissage *m*
vault (to) cintrer *v*
velux™ vélux™ *m*; châssis *m*

veneer placage *m*
veneer, peeled bois *m* déroulé
veneer (to) plaquer *v*
veneering placage *m*
ventilate (to) aérer *v*
veranda véranda *f*
vernier callipers pied *m* à coulisse
vertical cheek of an opening (reveal) tableau *m*
vertical height (base to top) of a staircase montée *f* de l'escalier
vice étau *m*; étaux *mpl*
vice, swivel étau *m* à rotule
vice with parallel jaws étau *m* à mors paralleles
void (archit) vide *m*

wainscot (to) lambrisser *v*; boiser *v*
wainscoting lambris *m*; lambrissage *m*; boiserie *f*
walking-line; line of flight (of stairs) ligne *f* de foulée; ligne *f* de giron
walkway coursive *f*
wall mur *m*; paroi *f*
wall rail cimaise *f*
wall supporting treads of a staircase échiffe *m*; échiffre *m*
wall-plate plate-forme *f*; lambourde *f*; semelle *f*; solive *f* de ferme; sablière *f*
wall-plug cheville *f*
waney; waney edged flache *adj*; flacheux,-euse *adj*
ward (of lock) arrêt *m*
wardrobe armoire *f*; placard *m*
warp (to) déjeter *v*; voiler *v*; déverser *v*; se gauchir *v*
warped board planche *f* voilée
warping gauchissement *m*
washer rondelle *f*
waterproofing (treatment) hydrofuge *m*; also *adj*
waterproofing solution or paint hydrofuge *m*; also *adj*
waterproofness étanchéité *f*
weatherboard (on door, window) jet *m* d'eau; rejet *m* d'eau
wedge cale *f*; coin *m*
wedge (to) caler *v*

wedge for splitting wood coin *m* à fendre le bois
wedging calage *m*
wet rot pourriture *f* humide
whitewood bois *m* blanc
widening piece (wood) alaise *f*
width largeur *f*
width of stair tread emmarchement *m*
width of stairwell jour *m*
wind-brace contrevent *m*
wind-bracing contreventement *m*
winder (stair) marche *f* dansante
window fenêtre *f*; croisée *f*; fermeture *f*
window frame châssis *m* de fenêtre
window ledge or sill appui *m* de fenêtre; pièce *f* d'appui; rebord *m* de la fenêtre
window opener, mechanical ferme-imposte *m*
window opening baie *f* de fenêtre
window security stay compas *m* de sécurité
window stay arrêt *m* de chassis
window, arched fenêtre *f* cintrée
window, bay fenêtre *f* en saillie
window, bow fenêtre *f* en saillie
window, casement fenêtre *f* à battants, fenêtre *f* ordinaire; croisée *f*
window, casement, inward-opening fenêtre *f* à la française
window, casement, outward-opening fenêtre *f* à l'anglaise
window, centre-hung (horizontal pivot) fenêtre *f* à bascule; fenêtre *f* basculante
window, centre-hung (vertical pivot) fenêtre *f* à pivot; fenêtre *f* pivotante
window, circular oculus *m*
window, dormer fenêtre *f* mansardée; lucarne *f*
window, double-glazed double fenêtre *f*
window, French fenêtre *f* à la française; fenêtre *f* ordinaire; porte-fenêtre *f*
window, inward opening (pivoted at base) fenêtre *f* à soufflet
window, lattice fenêtre *f* à croisillons; fenêtre *f* treillissée; fenêtre *f* treillagée
window, mullioned fenêtre *f* à meneaux
window, sash fenêtre *f* à coulisses; fenêtre *f* à guillotine
window, single-glazed fenêtre *f* à vitrage simple

window, sliding fenêtre *f* coulissante
window-fastener crampon *m* de fermeture
window-ledge rebord *m* de la fenêtre
window-lock crampon *m* de fermeture
windowsill rebord *m* de la fenêtre
wire fil *m*
wood bois *m*
wood across the grain, to cut couper *v* bois contre le fil
wood along the grain, to cut couper *v* bois dans le fil
wood cut along the grain bois *m* de fil
wood beading petit bois *m*
wood carver sculpteur *m* sur bois
wood drill foret *m* à bois
wood edge strip chant *m* plat
wood fibre (for packing) fibre *f* de bois
wood length, square cross-section carrelet *m*
wood length, square edge tasseau *m*
wood or metal piece reinforcing a tie-beam aiguille *f*
wood piece joined to edge of a door couvre-chant *m*; alaise *f* rapportée
wood plug cheville *f*; trenail *m*
wood preservation treatment traitement *f* de préservation du bois
wood profiling toupillage *m*
wood reinforcement piece aisselier *m*
wood strip petit bois *m*
wood strip (often tongued-and-grooved for panelling) frise *f*
wood strip (section approx 25x75 mm) lambourde *f*.
wood strip flooring parquet *m*
wood support strip (eg for flooring) lambourde *f*; lambourdette *f*
wood, close-grained bois *m* compact
wood, exotic bois *m* des îles; bois exotique *m*
wood, green bois *m* vert; bois *m* vif
wood, laminated bois *m* lamellé
wood, planed bois *m* raboté
wood, rose bois *m* de rose
wood, rotten bois *m* carié
wood, solid bois *m* massif
wood, species of essence *f* de bois
wood, square-sawn unplaned bois *m* avivé *m*
wood, unseasoned bois *m* vert

wood, varnished bois *m* verni
wood, worm-eaten bois *m* vermoulu
wood-framed house maison *f* à ossature bois
wood-turning lathe tour *m* à bois
wooden board frise *f*
wooden floor parquet *m*
wooden piece in core of door to receive door furniture fourrure *f*
wooden piece on outer side of window for attachment of shutter tapée *f*
wooden rod, round rond *m*
wooden strip lame *f*
woodland bois *m*; pays *m* boisé

woodwork boiserie *f*
woodworm ver *m* à/du bois
▪ **worm holes** = vermoulures *fpl*
woodworm traces vermoulure *f*
work ouvrage *m*; travail *m*
workbench établi *m*
working drawing plan *m* d'épure; épure *m*
working-plan épure *m*
workshop atelier *m*; menuiserie *f*
worm hole trou *m* de vers
worm-eaten vermoulu,-e *adj*
wreath (to) débillarder *v*

5. WOODS AND VENEERS

acacia acacia *m*
afara, black framiré *m*
alder auine *m*; aune *m*
ash frêne *m*

beech hêtre *m*
beechwood hêtre *m*
box tree; boxwood buis *m*

cedar cèdre *m*
cherry wood merisier *m*
chestnut, horse marronnier *m*; marronnier *m* d'inde
chestnut, sweet châtaignier *m*
common maple érable *m* champêtre
cork-oak chêne-liège *m*
Corsican pine pin *m* laricio de Corse
cypress cyprès *m*

deal bois *m* blanc; bois *m* de sapin; madrier *m*
douglas fir sapin *m* de douglas

ebony ébène *f*; ébénier *m*
ebony wood bois *m* d'ébène
elm orme *m*
European walnut noyer *m* d'Europe
exotic wood bois *m* des îles; bois *m* exotique

false acacia robinier *m*; acacia *m*
field maple érable *m* champêtre
fir sapin *m*
fir (grown at high altitude) sapin *m* d'altitude

gaboon (mahogany) okoumé *m*
green wood bois *m* vert

hornbeam charme *m*
horse chestnut marronnier *m*; marronnier *m* d'Inde

indigbo framiré *m*
iroko iroko *m*

larch mélèze *m*
lime (tree) tilleul *m*
locust tree robinier *m*

mahogany acajou *m*; also *adj.*
■ **made of mahogany** = en acajou
maple érable *m*
maritime pine pin *m* des Landes; pin *m* maritime
maritime/umbrella pine pin *m* parasol/pignon
meranti méranti *m*
mountain pine pin *m* de montagne

niangon niangon *m*
northen pine sapin *m* du Nord

oak chêne *m*
oak, fumed chêne *m* fumé
oak, holm chêne *m* vert
oak, medium chêne *m* moyen
oak, country chêne *m* campagne
oak, red American chêne *m* rouge d'Amérique
oak, solid chêne *m* massif
oak, white chêne *m* blanc
Oregon pine pin *m* d'Oregon

Panama pine pin *m* de panama
pine pin *m*
pine (from the Landes region of France) pin *m* des Landes
pitch pine pitchpin *m*
plane (tree) platane *m*
plane-tree maple érable *m* plane; érable *m* sycomore
plywood contreplaqué *m*
poplar peuplier *m*

ramin ramin *m*
redwood séquoia *m*
rosewood bois *m* de rose; palissandre *m*

sapele sapelli *m*
scotch fir pin *m* sylvestre
scots pine pin *m* sylvestre
sequoia séquoia *m*
silver birch bouleau *m*
sipo (mahogany) sipo *m*
Sitka spruce épicéa *m* de Sitka
species of wood essence *f* de bois
spruce épicéa *m*
sweet chestnut châtaignier *m*
sycamore sycomore *m*
sycamore maple érable *m* sycomore

teak teck *m*
thuja thuya *m*
timber bois *m* de menuiserie
timber, unhewn/uncut bois *m* rond

unseasoned wood bois *m* vert

veneer placage *m*; bois *m* déroulé

walnut noyer *m*
walnut, European noyer *m* d'Europe
weeping willow saule *m* pleureur
western red cedar thuya *m*
whitewood bois *m* blanc
willow saule *m*
wood sheet, faced bois *m* contreplaqué

yew if *m*

air air *m*
air tight roofing couverture *f* étanche à l'air
air-vent chatière *f*
air-vent at roof ridge level lanternau *m*.
air-ventilation enclosure below eaves
  caisson *m*
airtightness étanchéité *f*.
aloe rope corde *f* en aloès
alter (to) remanier *v*
alterable remaniable *adj*
alteration; altering remaniage *m*;
  remaniement *m*
aluminium aluminium *m*
anvil enclume *f*
area superficie *f*
asbestos cement amiante-ciment *m*
asphalted sheet (usually corrugated) plaque
  f asphaltée
assembly assemblage *m*; habillage *m*
attic grenier *m*; combles *mpl*; mansarde *f*
attic with lining comble *m* aménagé *m*
attic without lining comble non aménagé *m*

backing strip lambourde *f*
band bande *f*
barrier écran *m*
batten liteau *m*; volige *f*; latte *f*
batten (to) voliger *v*
battening voligeage *m*; liteaunage *m*
belt with pocket for carrying tools tablier *m*
bevelled en biseau *adj*; biseauté *adj*
bib bavette *f*
bituminous coating chape *f* bitumineuse
bitumised roofing felt feutre *m* bitumé
bitumised roofing sheet film *m* bitumeux
bitumised shingle bardeau *m* bitumé
block cale *f*; taquet *m*
block for corrugated sheet cale *f* d'onde
border débord *m*; rive *f*
boring perçage *m*
brad pointe *f*

caisson caisson *m*
calipers compas *m*
cast iron fonte *f*
cast iron downpipe chute *f* en fonte

cat ladder échelle *f* plate
ceiling plafond *m*; plafonnage *m*
ceiling material plafonnage *m*
cement fillet solin-ciment *m*
cement/mortar filling calfeutrement *m* en
  ciment
cement sheet (usually corrugated) plaque *f*
  ciment
chip épaufrure *f*
chop (to) hacher *v*
clean (to) nettoyer *v*
cleaning nettoyage *m*
clearance of debris/rubble déblayage *m* des
  gravats
cleat taquet *m*; tasseau *m*
cleave (to) fendre *v*
coach screw tire-fond *m*
coat with zinc (to) galvaniser *v*
coating revêtement *m*
coating (mortar, cement); screed chape *f*
collar-beam roof comble *m* retroussé
collar-tie roof comble *m* retroussé
comb crête *f*
compass compas *m*
concrete roofing (tiles or sheet) couverture *f*
  béton
construct a ceiling (to) plafonner *v*
converted roof space comble *m* aménagé
coping (archit) chaperon *m*
copper cuivre *m*
copper hook crochet *m* en cuivre
copper nail clou *m* de cuivre; clou *m* de
  cuivre rouge
copper sheet tôle *f* de cuivre
cord corde *f*
cordage cordage *m*
corrugated iron/steel sheet tôle *f* ondulée
corrugated sheet plaque *f* ondulée
counter lath contre-latte *f*
couple roof comble *m* à deux long pans sans
  fermes
cover couverture *f*
cover a roof with zinc (to) zinguer *v*
covered part of tile or slate recouvrement *m*
covering piece; cover strip couvre-joint *m*
covering revêtement *m*
covering over bâchage *m*
crack fente *f*

crane grue *f*
crest (of roof) faîtage *m*; faîte *m*; crête *f*
cupola coupole *f*
curb roof comble *m* à la française; comble *m* à la mansarde; comble *m* brisé; comble *m* en mansarde; toit *m* en mansarde
curved metal cover piece boudin *m*
cut (to) couper *v*; découper *v*; hacher *v*
cut up (to) débiter *v*; découper *v*
cutting découpage *m*
cutting up débitage *m*; découpage *m*
cutting-hammer décintroir *m*

deaden (to) hourder *v*
deafen (to) hourder *v*
dome coupole *f*; dôme *m*
double row of tiles/slates forming eaves doublis *m*
downpipe tuyau *m* de descente
dress (to) dresser *v*
dressing (eg stone) dressage *m*
dressing iron enclume *f*
drilling perçage *m*
drip larmier *m*
drop chute *f*

ear oreille *f*; mentonnet *m*
eaves avant-toit *m*; égout *m*; égout *m* du bord du toit
eaves; eaves overhang queue *f* de vache
eaves board or lath volige *f* chanlattée; chanlatte *f*; chanlate *f*
edge bord *m*; débord *m*; rebord *m*; rive *f*
edge batten liteau *m* de rive
edge rafter chevron *m* de rive
embed (to) sceller *v*
equipment outillage *m*; appareil *m*; agrés *mpl*
erect a scaffold (to) échafauder *v*
erecting (scaffolding) échafaudage *m*; dressage *m*
expanded cork liège *m* expansé
expanded polyurethane polyuréthane *m* expansé
exposed edge (of roof) rive *f* exposée

face pan *m*

face-down side (eg of slate) envers *m*
face-up side (eg of slate) endroit *m*
facing parement *m*; revêtement *m*
facing in mortar parement *m* en mortier
fasten (up) (to) agrafer *v*
fastener agrafe *f*
fastening (up) agrafage *m*
felt feutre *m*
felting feutrage *m*; feutre *m*
fibrocement fibrociment *m*
fill (to) remplir *v*
fill up (to) remplir *v*
fillet filet *m*; solin *m*
filling remplissage *m*
filling of cement calfeutrement *m* en ciment
filling up remplissage *m*
fired-clay tile tuile *f* en terre cuite
fissure fente *f*
fitting emboîtement *m*
fixing tiles by wiring to underlying batten pannetonnage *m*
flange rebord *m*; collet *m*
flashing noquet *m*; chaperon *m*; bavette *f*; alaise *f*; couvre-joint *m*; noquet *m*; engravure *f*
flashing of mortar (between roof and wall) ruellée *f*
flashing, oblique-cut noquet *m* biais
flashing, right-angled noquet *m* droit
flat or slightly inclined section of roof terrasson *m*
flat stone (for roofs) pierre *f* plate; lauze *f*
flat-top vent in roof outeau *m* plat
flexible (waterproof) barrier écran *m* souple *m*
flexible rule règle *f* souple
foam glass; cellular glass verre *m* expansé
foam polystyrene panel panneau *m* de mousse de polystyrène
foam rubber joint/gasket joint *m* mousse
format; size format *m*
format (tiles) moule *m* (see grand moule; petit moule)
forming façonnage *m*; façonnement *m*

gable pignon *m*
gable roof comble *m* sur pignon(s)

galvanize (to) galvaniser *v*
galvanized corrugated sheet tôle *f* galvanisée ondulée
galvanized iron/steel sheet tôle *f* zinguée
galvanized steel acier *m* galvanisé
gauging échantillonnage *m*
glass roof couverture *f* en verre
glass tile tuile *f* en verre
glass wool laine *f* de verre
glass wool insulant/insulator isolant *m* laine de verre
glass, cellular verre *m* expansé; verre *m* moussé
glass, foamed verre *m* expansé
glass granules, foamed verniculite *f*
grating (of vent pipe) crapaudine *f*
grilled inlet/opening orifice *m* grillagé
gutter gouttière *f*
gutter (roof) chéneau *m*
gutter band bande *f* d'egout
gutter bracket crochet *m* de gouttière
gutter, bracket supported gouttière *f* pendante
gutter, eaves gouttière *f* pendante
gutter, English gouttière *f* à l'anglaise
gutter, Laval gouttière *f* de Laval
gutter, parallel chéneau *m* encaissé
gutter, parapet cheneau *m* à l'anglaise; gouttière *f* en dessus
gutter, triangular section (roof) gouttière *f* havraise/nantaise
gutter, trough chéneau *m* encaissé
gutter, valley noue *f*; noulet *m*
gutter, zinc chéneau *m* en zinc
gutter-fillet solin *m*

half-lath demi-latte *f*
half-length demi-longueur *f*
half-slate demi-ardoise *f*; demie *f*
half-truss demi-ferme *f*
hammer marteau *m*
hammer, cutting- décintroir *m*
hammer, slater's essette *f*; assette *f*; tille *f* de couvreur
hand-drill chignole *f*
handling manutention *f*
handrail lisse *f*; appui *m*; main *f* courante
handsaw scie *f* égoïne

hangable accrochable *adj*
hanging scaffold échafaud(age) *m* volant
hatchet hachette *f*
heel talon *m*
hemp rope corde *f* en chanvre
hip arêtier *m*; chevron *m* arêtier; chevron *m* d'arêtier; croupe *f*
hip covering arêtier *m*
hip edge rive *f* en arêtier
hoisting levage *m*
hoisting tackle agrès *mpl*
hook crochet *m*; agrafe *f*
hook (up) (to) accrocher *v*; agrafer *v*
hook with pointed end crochet *m* à pointe
hook with undulated shank crochet *m* à tige ondulée
hook, clip on crochet *m* à agrafe
hook, copper crochet *m* en cuivre
hook, nail-on crochet *m* à pointe
hook, S crochet *m* en S
hook, stainless steel crochet *m* en acier inoxydable; crochet *m* inox
hook, tile crochet *m*
hook, uncorrodable crochet *m* inoxydable
hookable accrochable *adj*
hooking (up) agrafage *m*
hopper-head (of downpipe) cuvette *f*

imbrex (imbrices pl) (Roman curved overtile) imbrex *m*
insulation isolation *f*; isolement *m*
insulation layer couche *f* d'isolant
insulation under the slope of roof isolation *f* sous rampant
interlocking emboîtement *m*
interlocking ridge tiling faîtage *m* à emboîtement
intersection edge (of roof with wall) rive *f* de penetration
isolation isolement *m*

jut out (to) déborder *v*
jute cloth reinforcement armature *f* en tissus de jute
jutting out débordement *m*

knotted rope corde *f* à nœuds

ladder échelle *f*
ladder, cat échelle *f* plate
ladder hook crochet *m* d'échelle
ladder, roof échelle *f* plate; échelle *f* de couvreur
ladder, standard échelle *f* courante
lagging habillage *m*
lap recouvrement *m*
lap (of tiles); overlap chevauchement *m*
lath latte *f*; volige *f*
lath (to) latter *v*; voliger *v*
lathing voligeage *m*
lathing; lathwork lattis *m*
lead coping engravure *f*
lead roofing sheet engravure *f*
lead sheet plomb *m* en feuille
leading plombage *m*
lean-to appentis *m*
leg strap jambière *f*
length lé *m*
length of bitumised felt lé *m* de feutre bitumé *m*
lift (to) lever *v*
lift up (to) soulever *v*
lifting levage *m*
lifting by block and pulley levage *m* à la poulie
lifting by crane levage *m* à la grue
line corde *f*; cordeau *m*
line (to) ligner *v*
lining up lignage *m*
loft grenier *m*; comble *m*
loose (waterproof) barrier écran *m* non tendu
lug oreille *f*; mentonnet *m*
lug, wiring (on underside of tile) panneton *m*

make out (to) (eg estimate, report) dresser *v*
making roofing complete raccord *m* de couverture
margin visible (of slate, tile) pureau *m*
mark the line (to) ligner *v*
marking the line lignage *m*
metal roofing strip bande *f*
mineral insulator isolant *m* minéral
mortar filling between rafters remplissage

m mortier entre chevrons
mortared edge of tiled roof parement *m* en mortier
mould moule *m*

nail clou *m*; pointe *f*
nail, copper clou *m* de cuivre; clou *m* de cuivre rouge; pointe *f* cuivre rouge
nail, felt clou *m* à tête large
nail, French clou *m* de Paris
nail, galvanized clou *m* galvanisé; pointe *f* galvanisée *f*; clou *m* galva
nail, galvanized, flat-headed clou *m* galva tête plate
nail, lath clou *m* à latter
nail, lead clou *m* de plomb
nail, slate clou *m* à ardoise
nail-draw; nail puller tire-clou(s) *m*
nib mentonnet *m*
number of tiles per square metre moule *m*; grand moule (12 à 15); petit moule (21 à 23)

oblique-cut soaker noquet *m* biais
open tiling (reduced overlap) couverture *f* à claire-voie
over-tile tuile *f* de dessus
overflow débord *m*
overflow (to) déborder *v*
overflowing débordement *m*
overhang débordement *m*
overhang (to) déborder *v*
overlap recouvrement *m*; chevauchement *m*
overlapping (of tiles) imbrication *f*
overlapping tiles tuiles *fpl* imbriquées

packing piece cale *f*
pair of compasses compas *m*
pane pan *m*
pantile tuile *f* en S
paring-chisel riflard *m*
pattern gabarit *m*
penetration pénétration *f*
penthouse auvent *m*
pitch chute *f*
pitch of roof pente *f*; chute *f* de comble;

rampe *f* de chevrons
plain tile tuile *f* plate
plaster plâtre *m*
plasterer plâtrier *m*
plastering trowel riflard *m*
plastic sheeting film *m* plastique
plumbing plombage *m*
point pointe *f*
pointing of a ridge (mortar, plaster)
   embarrure *f*
pole plate sablière *f* de comble
polycarbonate sheet (usually corrugated)
   plaque *f* polycarbonate
polyester sheet (usually corrugated)
   plaque *f* polyester
polyethylene sheet (waterproof) barrier
   écran *m* en polyéthylène
polystyrene granules billes *fpl* de
   polystyrène
polyvinyl chloride; PVC chlorure *m* de
   polyvinyl; PVC *abb.*
prevent (to) empêcher *v*
principal rafter chevron *m* principal;
   arbalétrier *m*
process of marking rafters for lathing
   échantillonnage *m*
prop support *m*
proportion rapport *m*
pug (to) hourder *v*
pulley poulie *f*
pulley-block poulie *f*
purlin panne *f*; filière *f*
PVC sheet (usually corrugated) plaque *f*
   PVC

rafter chevron *m*
rafter, angle arêtier *m*; chevron *m* arêtier;
   chevron *m* d'arêtier
rafter, common chevron *m* intermédiaire
rafter, common (of hip roof) chevron *m* de
   long pan
rafter, edge chevron *m* de rive
rafter, hip arêtier *m*; chevron *m* arêtier;
   chevron *m* d'arêtier; chevron *m* d'arête
rafter, principal chevron *m* principal;
   arbalétrier *m*
rafter, valley noue *f*; chevron *m* de noue
raftering chevronnage *m*

rail lisse *f*
rain-water eaux *fpl* pluviale
raise (to) soulever *v*
raising to the roof montée *f* sur le toit
ratio rapport *m*
rebattening remaniage *m*; remaniement *m*
recut (to) recouper *v*
redo (to) remanier *v*
redoing remaniage *m*; remaniement *m*
refill (to) remplir *v* de nouveau
relay slates (to) reposer *v* des ardoises
removal of roofing material démolition *f* de
   couverture
renailed batten liteau *m* recloué
repair réparation *f*
repair (to) remanier *v*; réparer *v*
repair of roof/roofing réparation *f* de
   toiture
repairing remaniage *m*; remaniement *m*;
   réparation *f*
repairing the roof remaniage *m* de toiture
repairing the roofing/tiling remaniage *m* de
   couverture; raccord *m* de couverture
report rapport *m*
reverse side envers *m*
rib nervure *f*
ribbed nervuré,-e *adj*
ridge faîtage *m*; faîte *m*; crête *f*
ridge beam panne *f* faîtière
ridge course lignolet *m*
ridge course of ordinary slates lignolet *m*
   simple
ridge course with pointed slates lignolet *m*
   décoré
ridge pole panne *f* faîtière; faîtage *m*
ridge tile faîtière *f*
ridge tiles; ridge tiling faîtage *m*
ridge-beam faîtage *m*
ridge-capping faîtage *m*
ridge-lead faîtage *m*
right side endroit *m*
right-angled edge rive *f* droite
rigid (waterproof) barrier écran *m* rigide
rim rebord *m*
rise rampe *f*
rock wool; mineral wool laine *f* de roche
rock wool insulant/insulator isolant *m* laine
   de roche
rod tige *f*

roll-tile tuile *f* de couvert
rolled steel sheet tôle *f* laminée
Roman tile tuile *f* romaine
roof couverture *f*; toit *m*; toiture *f*
roof of building comble *m* d'un bâtiment
roof board; batten volige *f*
roof drainage évacuation *f* des eaux du toit
roof ladder échelle *f* plate; échelle *f* de couvreur
roof plate sablière *f* de comble
roof shape forme *f* d'une comble
roof sheeting with double-lock seams couverture *f* à double agrafure
roof sheeting with lap joints couverture *f* à recouvrement
roof sheeting with single seams couverture *f* à agrafure simple
roof space comble *m*
roof terrace toiture-terrasse *f*
roof timbers comble *m*
roof truss/trussing armature *f* à toit
roof trussing comble *m*
roof ventilator chatière *f*
roof, collar-beam comble *m* retroussé
roof, couple comble *m* à deux long pans sans fermes
roof, curb comble *m* à la française; comble *m* à la mansarde; comble *m* brisé; comble *m* en mansarde; toit *m* en mansarde; comble *m* mansardé; comble *m* brisé
roof, dome comble *m* en dôme
roof, double-pitched comble *m* à deux long pans; comble *m* à deux pentes; comble *m* à deux rampes; comble *m* à deux versants; comble *m* à deux égouts
roof, double-pitched, with asymmetric sides comble *m* à deux pentes asymétriques
roof, flat toiture-terrasse *f*
roof, French see 'curb roof'
roof, gable comble *m* sur pignon(s)
roof, glass couverture *f* en verre
roof, hip or hipped comble *m* en croupe
roof, hipped ridge comble *m* à deux longs pans avec croupes; comble *m* à croupe et deux longs pans
roof, mansard see ' curb roof'
roof, multiple-pitched comble *m* à plusieurs pentes
roof, pavilion comble *m* en pavillon; comble *m* pyramidal; comble *m* à autant de versants que de côtes
roof, penthouse appentis *m*
roof, pitch of chute *f* de comble
roof, projecting avant-toit *m*
roof, pyramidal same as 'pavilion roof'
roof, ridge same as 'double-pitched roof'
roof, saw-tooth comble *m* en dent de scie; comble-shed *m*
roof, shed same as 'saw-tooth roof'
roof, single slope appentis *m*
roof, single-pitch comble *m* à un versant; comble *m* à une pente; comble *m* à une seule pente
roof, span same as 'double-pitched roof'
roof, square-to same as 'saw-tooth roof'
roof, trussed comble *m* sur fermes
roof, umbrella comble *m* avec avant-toit
roof-pitch rampe *f* de chevrons
roofed with slates couverte en ardoises
roofer couvreur *m*
roofing couverture *f*; toiture *f*
roofing felt carton *m* bitumé; feutre-toiture *m*; film *m* bitumeux; feutre *m* bitumé
roofing materils matériaux *mpl* de couverture
roofing, sheet metal couverture *f* métallique
roofing shingle essente *f*
roofing support support *m* de couverture
roofing with slates of variable size couverture *f* en ardoises 'brouillées'
roofing work travaux *mpl* de couverture
rope cordage *m*; corde *f*
rough-wall (to) hourder *v*
row rang *m*; rangée *f*
row of slates protecting edge rafter bardeli *m*
row of slates protecting outermost rafter ardoises *fpl* en bardeli
row of trimmed slates protecting edge rafter bardeli *m* décor
rubble gravats *mpl*
rust rouille *f*

S hook *m* crochet en S
safety hook crochet *m* de sécurité
sampling échantillonnage *m*

saw up (to) débiter *v*
saw-timber sciage *m*
sawing sciage *m*
sawing up débitage *m*
scaffold (to) échafauder *v*
scaffold; scaffolding échafaud *m*; échafaudage *m*
screen écran *m*
screw-spike tire-fond *m*
seal (to) sceller *v*
sealant enduit *m* étanche
sealing scellement *m*
security rope défense *f*
shank tige *f*
shank of slate-hook tige *f* du crochet
shaping façonnage *m*; façonnement *m*
sheet tôle *f*
sheet iron coated with lead tôle *f* plombée
sheet lead feuille *f* de plomb; plomb *m* en feuille
sheet, copper tôle *f* de cuivre
sheet, corrugated iron tôle *f* ondulée
sheet, galvanized iron tôle *f* zinguée
sheet metal roofing couverture *f* métallique
sheet, rolled steel tôle *f* laminée
sheet, zinc feuille *f* de zinc
sheeting bâchage *m*
shingle bardeau *m*
shingle, American shingle *m*
shingle, terra cotta brique *f* de couvert
shoulder épaulement *m*
side côté *m*; pan *m*
side edge rive *f* latérale; rive *f* de débord
side-timber panne *f*
size (tiles) format *m*
sized slates ardoises *fpl* d'échantillon
skewed top edge (of roof) rive *f* de tête biasie
skylight tabatière *f*; vélux ™
slant pente *f*
slate (roof) ardoise *f*
slate (to) ardoiser *v*
slate, stone (variable in shape) lauze *f*
slate a roof (to) couvrir *v* un toit d'ardoises
slate splitting quernage *m*
slate tile ardoise *f*
slate trimmer (person) rondisseur *m*
slate trimming machine rondisseuse *f*
slate, asbestos-cement ardoise *f* en amiante-ciment
slate, bevelled ardoise *f* taillée en biseau
slate, edge ardoise *f* de rive
slate, types of (by size and weight) modèles *mpl* d'ardoise

viz:

standard/ordinary	ordinaire
English	Anglais
square	carré
historic (H1, H2)	historique

slate, half- demi-ardoise *f*; demie *f*
slate, Spanish ardoise *f* d'Espagne; ardoise *f* naturelle d'Espagne
slate-coloured ardoisé, -e *adj*
slater couvreur *m*
slater's anvil enclume *f*
slater's hammer essette *f*; assette *f*; tille *f* de couvreur
slater's/roofer's tools outils *mpl* du couvreur
slope pente *f*; chute *f*; rampe *f*
■ **sloping** = en pente
slope, lower, of mansard roof brisis *m*
slope, upper, of mansard roof terrasson *m*
slope (of a roof) rampant *m*; égout *m*; versant *m*
small covered vent in roof outeau *m*
small cradle sellette *f*
small plate or board plaquette *f*
small roof vent chapeau *m* de gendarme
small tower tourelle *f*
soaker noquet *m*
soldering soudage *m*; soudure *f*
spalling épaufrure *f*
splinter épaufrure *f*
split fente *f*
split (to) fendre *v*
split (to) (slate) querner *v*
split up (to) débiter *v*
splitter (of slates) fendeur *m*; fendeuse *f*
splitting slates refente *f* d'ardoises
splitting up débitage *m*
spur talon *m*
square tiles set with one diagonal horizontal couverture *f* en modèles carrés
square washer plaquette *f*
stackpipe tuyau *m* de descente
staging échafaud *m*; échafaudage *m*
standard ladder échelle *f* courante
staple agrafe *f*
staple (to) agrafer *v*

stapler agrafeuse *f*
stapling agrafage *m*
stem tige *f*
stop taquet *m*
stop (to); prevent (to) empêcher *v*
storage stockage *m*
storm damage dégâts *mpl* tempête
straightening (eg rod, bar) dressage *m*
stretch (to) tendre *v*
stretched (waterproof) barrier écran *m* tendu
string cordeau *m*
strip lé *m*
strip of bitumised felt lé *m* de feutre bitumé
strip of wood tasseau *m*
strip, metal roofing bande *f*
support support *m*
surface surface *f*; superficie *f*
surface area surface *f*

tackle agrès *mpl*
taking down démontage *m*
taking to pieces démontage *m*
talon talon *m*
tegula (Roman flat under-tile) tegula *f*
templet; template gabarit *m*
tension (to) tendre *v*
terra cotta terre *f* cuite
terra cotta ridge tiling faîtage *m* terre cuite
terra cotta shingle brique *f* de couvert
terra cotta tile tuile *f* en terre cuite
thatch chaume *m*
thatch (to) couvrir *v* de chaume
thatched cottage chaumière *f*; maison *f* à toit de chaume
thatched roofing couverture *f* de chaume
thaw water eau *f* de fonte
thermal insulation isolation *f* thermique
thick rope défense *f*
thickness of a board rive *f* d'une planche
threaded rod tige *f* filetée
tighten (to) tendre *v*
tile ; roof tile tuile *f*
tile hook crochet *m*
tile piece; part tile tuileau *m*
tile, angle tuile *f* de rive
tile, angled ridge faîtière *f* angulaire
tile, arched tuile *f* canal

tile, channel tuile *f* de courant
tile, clay tuile *f* en terre cuite
tile, combined channel and roll tuile *f* panne
tile, concrete (interlocking) tuile *f* en béton mécanique
tile, corner tuile *f* cornière
tile, corner hip (truncated pyramid shape) arêtier *m* cornier
tile, cover tuile *f* de couvert; tuile *f* de dessus; brique *f* de couvert
tile, curved tuile *f* canal; *f* tuile creuse; tuile *f* romaine; tuile *f* ronde
tile, cut tuile *f* tranchée
tile, edge tuile *f* de rive
tile, end hip about *m* d'arêtier
tile, end ridge about *m* faîtière
tile, fired clay tuile *f* en terre cuite
tile, flange tuile *f* à rebord
tile, flat tuile *f* plate
tile, glass tuile *f* en verre
tile, hip arêtier *m*; arêtière *f*; tuile *f* arêtière; arêtier *m* fermé
tile, interlocking tuile *f* mécanique; tuile *f* à emboîtement
tile, inerlocking, with lateral ribs only tuile *f* à glissement
tile, lozenge-shaped ridge faîtière *f* losangée
tile, over tuile *f* de dessus
tile, plain tuile *f* plate
tile, plain with rounded end tuile *f* plate écaille
tile, ridge tuile *f* faîtière; faîtière *f*
tile, ridge, with collar faîtière *f* à bourrelet
tile, roll tuile *f* de couvert
tile, rectangular which is concave across the width tuile *f* gambardière
tile, rectangular which is convex across width tuile *f* coffine
tile, rectangular which is half curved tuile *f* gauche
tile, ridge tuile *f* faîtière; faîtière *f*
tile, ridge (spigot-and socket type) faîtière *f* à bourrelet
tile, roll- tuile *f* de couvert
tile, Roman tuile *f* romaine
tile, saddle tuile *f* en dos d'âne
tile, single-lap tuile *f* à emboîtement
tile, Spanish tuile *f* canal
tile, terra cotta tuile *f* en terre cuite

tile, terra cotta (interlocking) tuile *f* en terre cuite mécanique

tile, terra cotta, valley noue *f* préfabriquée en terre cuite

tile, under tuile *f* de courant; tuile *f* de dessous

tile, undulated hip arêtier *m* ondulé

tile, valley noue *f*

tile, ventilation chatière *f*; tuile *f* de ventilation

tile, waterway tuile *f* de courant

tile with socket and cowl vent tuile *f* à douille et chapeau

tile, wooden bardeau *m*

tile-cutting machine machine *f* à tailler

tiled roofing couverture *f* en tuiles

tiler couvreur *m*; tuilier *m*

tiles per square metre (12 to 15) grand moule *m*

tiles per square metre (21 to 23) petit moule *m*

tile pieces rough-set in mortar tuileaux *fpl* hourdés au mortier

tiling, Bardeli (form of slate tiling) couverture *f* en bardeli

tiling, terra cotta ridge faîtage *m* terre cuite

tiling with enlarged area of uncovered tile couverture *f* à pureau développé

tilted row of edge tiles basculement *m*

timber bois *m*

tingle patte *f* à tasseau

tools outillage *m*

top or upper edge (of roof) rive *f* de tête

topmost two rows of slates/tiles next to ridge lignolet *m*

travelling cradle échafaud(age) *m* volant

tray, mixing (eg for mortar) auge *f*

treated deal batten liteau *m* sapin traité

triangular-shaped air vent in roof outeau *m* triangulaire

trim (to) (timber) dresser *v*

trimming of slates rondissage *m*

trough auge *f*

trowel truelle *f*

trowel, toothed truelle *f* berthelet mixte; truelle *f* bretellée

truss ferme *f*

trussed roof comble *m* sur fermes

turret tourelle *f*

unconverted roof space comble *m* non aménagé

uncorrodable hook crochet *m* inoxydable

uncovered or visible part of tile or slate pureau *m*

under ridge-board sous-faîte *m*

under roof covering or cladding sous-toiture *f*

under-roof sheeting film *m* sous toiture

under-tile tuile *f* de courant

underface sous-face *f*

unstretched barrier écran *m* non tendu

untrussed roof comble *m* sans ferme

valley (roof) noue *f*; noulet *m*

valley flashing noquet *m*

valley gutter noue *f*; noulet *m*

valley-lead noue *f*

valley-piece noue *f*

valley-rafter noue *f*

vapour barrier pare-vapeur *m*

ventilation ventilation *f*

ventilation hole chatière *f*

ventilation tile chatière *f*; tuile *f* de ventilation

verge rive *f* latérale droite

wall plate lambourde *f*; sablière *f* de comble

washer plaquette *f*; rondelle *f*

washer, watertight rondelle *f* étanche

water tight under-roof sheeting complément *m* étanche à l'eau

waterproof étanche *adj*

waterproof barrier écran *m* étanche

waterproofness étanchéité *f*

watertight étanche *adj*

watertightness étanchéité *f*

waterway tile tuile *f* de courant

wedge cale *f*

welding soudage *m*; soudure *f*

wing (of wing nut) oreille *f*

wiring lug on underside of tile panneton *m*

wood bois *m*

wood strip lisse *f*

wooden peg cheville *f* en bois

wooden rule règle *f* en bois
wooden tile bardeau *m*
work-lead plomb *m* d'œuvre
wrong side (opp. l'endroit) envers *m*
zinc zinc *m*

zinc flashing bavette *f* zinc
zinc gutter cheneau *m* en zinc
zinc sheet feuille *f* de zinc
zinc soaker noquet *m* zinc
zinc work zinguerie *f*

7. IRONMONGER

alloy alliage *m*
anchor ancre *f*
anchor in form of an S ancre *f* en forme d'un S
angle clamp; angle cramp presse *f* d'angle
angle iron fer *m* cornière; fer *m* d'angle; équerre *f*
angle-piece; angle-iron cornière *f*
angle-plate équerre *f* d'angle
axle arbre *m*

ballcock robinet *m* à flotteur
bearing coquille *f*
bell push bouton *m* de sonnerie
bichromated (anticorrosion) zingué jaune *adj*; bichromaté *adj*
bit fer *m*
blade lame *f*
body corps *m*
bolt boulon *m*; cheville *f*; verrou *m*
bolt, anchor boulon *m* d'ancrage
bolt, assembling boulon *m* d'assemblage
bolt, barrel- verrou *m* à coquille
bolt, cotter boulon *m* à clavette
bolt, countersunk-head boulon *m* à tête fraisée
bolt, door verrou *m* de porte
bolt, foundation boulon *m* de fondation
bolt, hexagonal-headed boulon *m* tête hexagonal
bolt, holding-down boulon *m* de fixation
bolt, hook boulon *m* à croc; boulon *m* à crochet
bolt, locking- verrou *m* de fermeture
bolt, retaining boulon *m* de retenue

bolt, round-head with square collar boulon *m* tête ronde collet carré
bolt, round-head, slotted boulon *m* à tête ronde fendue
bolt, screw boulon *m* à écrou
bolt, spring- verrou *m* à ressort
bolt, stove boulon *m* poêliers
bolt, square-head boulon *m* à tête carrée
brace bretelle *f*
bracket console *f*; support *m*; tasseau *m*
bracket for fixing wood to concrete équerre *f* pour fixation sur béton
bracket, metal console *f* métallique
bracket, wall console *f* murale
brad pointe *f*; clou *m* sans tête
bush coquille *f*
butt-hinge charnière *f*
butt strip couvre-joint *m*
button bouton *m*

C-clamp presse *f* de mécanicien
casement-fastener agrafe *f*
castor roulette *f*
castor shoe patin *m*
catch arrêt *m*
catch (eg for window, door) loqueteau *m*
catch, magnetic loqueteau *m* magnétique
catch, mechanical loqueteau *m* mécanique
check plate plaque *f* d'arrêt
cheek joue *f*
clamp bride *f*; bride *f* à capote; collier *m* de fixation; valet *m* d'établi
clamp, mason's serre-joint *m* de maçon
clamp; cramp agrafe *f*
clamping bridage *m*

clip virole *f*; clip *m*
clip (for conduits) patte *f* d'attache
collar bride *f*; collier *m*; collet *m*
connecting piece raccord *m*
connection raccord *m*
contact (elect) plot *m*
corner coin *m*
corner-plate équerre *f* d'angle
cover plate plaque *f* de protection
cover strip bande *f* de recouvrement; couvre-joint *m*
covering plate bande *f* de recouvrement
cramp bride *f*; patte *f*; patte *f* à scellement
cramp; cramp-iron crampon *m*
cutter lame *f*
cylinder cylindre *m*
cylinder lock cylindre *m*

dognail crampon *m*
door furniture (hinges, handle, lock etc) ferrage *m*
door hinge paumelle *f*
dowel cheville *f*
downfall pipe chute *f*
drain-cock robinet *m* purgeur
drawer runner coulisse *f* de tiroir
drawing pin punaise *f*

edge-plate (of a lock) têtière *f*; rebord *m*
equipment appareillage *m*
espagnolette bolt crémone *f*; espagnolette *f*
expanding plug for hollow partitions cheville *f* à expansion pour parois creuses
eyelet œillet *m*

fastener attache *f*
fastening armature *f*
fastening together bridage *m*
fastening; fastener fermeture *f*
fence post piquet *m* de clôture
ferrule virole *f*
finger plate plaque *f* de propreté
fitments équipement *m*; garniture *f*
fitting équipement *m*
fittings appareillage *m*; garniture *f*
fixing anchor ancre *f* de maintien

fixing clip attache *f* de fixation
fixing collar collier *m* de fixation
flange bride *f*; joue *f*
french window locking bolt espagnolette *f*; crémone *f*
funnel entonnoir *m*
furniture shoe patin *m*

G-clamp bride *f* à capote; presse *f* de mecanicien
G-clamp; G-cramp serre-joint *m*
G-clamp, masons serre-joint *m* de maçon
gate latch loquet *m* de porte
gate-hook gond *m* de porte

hacksaw blade lame *f* de scie à métaux
handle béquille *f*; poignée *f*
handle, door poignée *f* de porte
head (of a hammer) corps *m*
hinge charnière *f*; paumelle *f*
hinge reinforcement renfort *m* de paumelle
hinge with knobbed pin fiche *f* à bouton
hinge, cabinet fiche *f*
hinge, English penture *f* anglaise
hinge, H- paumelle *f* double
hinge, split paumelle *f*
holder, bulb porte-ampoule *m*
holdfast clou *m* à patte; patte *f*; patte *f* à scellement
hook agrafe *f*; esse *f*; gond *m*; crochet *m*
hook and hinge (eg of gate, shutter) gond *m* et penture *f*
hook and ride gond *m* et penture *f*
hook, cupboard crochet *m* d'armoire
hook, picture crochet *m* à tableau
hooks and eyes pitonnerie *f*

iron fer *m*
iron fittings ferrure *f*

joiners' clamp serre-joint *m*
joint cover couvre-joint *m*

key coin *m*
keyhole guard cache-entrée *m*
knob bouton *m*
knob, door bouton *m* de porte

knob, milled bouton *m* moleté
knob, oval bouton *m* à olive
knuckle (of a hinge) charnon *m*

L iron fer *m* cornière; fer *m* d'angle; cornière
f; équerre *f*
L-plate joining bracket with unequal plates
équerre *f* inégale d'assemblage
latch loquet *m*; verrou *m* à ressort
latch, door, high-security verrou *m* haute
securité
letter box boîte *f* aux lettres
lift-latch loquet *m* à bouton
lock fermeture *f*; serrure *f*
lock for espagnolette bolt serrure *f* de
crémone
lock, box/chest serrure *f* de coffre
lock, dead serrure *f* à pêne dormant
lock, flush serrure *f* entaillée
lock, latch serrure *f* à ressort
lock, mortise serrure *f* à encastrer; serrure *f* à
larder; serrure *f* à mortaise; serrure *f* entaillée
lock, rim serrure *f* en applique; serrure *f*
encloisonnée
lock, spring serrure *f* à ressort
lock, surface serrure *f* en applique
lock-staple gâche *f*
locking bolt verrou *m* de fermeture
locking hardware (eg bolts, locks) quincaillerie *f* de condamnation
locking; locking device condamnation *f*

mesh screen tamis *m* à mailles
metal connector for Gerber ™ beam system
raccord *m* Gerber ™
metal coupling piece raccord *m*
metal items; metal grilles etc métallerie *f*
metal wall tie patte *f* métallique
metalwork métallerie *f*
mountings ferrure *f*

nail clou *m*; pointe *f*
nail, barbed-wire clou *m* barbelé
nail, cast clou *m* fondu
nail, copper pointe *f* cuivre rouge
nail, cut clou *m* decoupé

nail, flat-headed clou *m* à tête plate; pointe *f*
tête plate
nail, flooring clou *m* à parquet
nail, for plasterboard pointe *f* pour plaque
de plâtre
nail, French clou *m* de Paris
nail, galvanized pointe *f* galva; pointe *f*
galvanisée
nail, glazier's pointe *f* de vitrier
nail, headless pointe *f* à éclats
nail, insulation pointe *f* d'isolation
nail, lath clou *m* à latter
nail, finishing pointe *f* tête homme
nail, ridged, countersunk head, masonry
pointe *f* striée tête fraisée maçonnerie
nail, roundheaded pointe *f* à tête ronde
nail, twist pointe *f* torsadée
nail, upholstery clou *m* tapissier
nail, veneer pointe *f* à placage
nail, wire clou *m* de Paris
nail, zinc clou *m* en zinc
nut écrou *m*
nut, blank écrou *m* borgne
nut, blind écrou *m* borgne
nut, box écrou *m* à chapeau
nut, hexagonal écrou *m* à six pans
nut, irremovable écrou *m* indesserrable
nut, lock écrou *m* indesserrable
nut, locking écrou *m* de blocage; écrou *m*
frein
nut, slotted écrou *m* à entailles; écrou *m* à
rainures
nut, square écrou *m* carré
nut, standard écrou *m* ordinaire
nut, wing écrou *m* à oreilles
nuts and bolts boulonnerie *f*; visserie *f*

padlock cadenas *m*
padlock, combination cadenas *m* à combinaisons
peg cheville *f*; chevillette *f*; fiche *f*
pin cheville *f*; chevillette *f*; fiche *f*; pivot *m*;
plot *m*
pin, upholstery clou *m* tapissier
pin, veneer pointe *f* à placage
pipe clip collier *m* d'attache
pipe support support *m* de tuyau
pipe, threaded tube *m* filetée

pipe-strap patte *f* à crochet
pitch (screw thread) pas *m*
pivot pivot *m*
plug bouchon *m*; fiche *f*
plug for brittle materials cheville *f* pour matériaux friables
plug for hollow materials cheville *f* pour matériaux creux
plug for solid materials cheville *f* pour matériaux pleins
plug, wall cheville *f*
plumbing plomberie *f*
plumbing (taps) robinetterie *f*
post piquet *m*; poteau *m*
protective grill grille *f* de défense
pump pompe *f*

reinforced right-angled metal bracket équerre *f* renforcée
reinforcing plate plaque *f* de renfort
ride penture *f*
right-angled metal bracket équerre *f* simple
ring bague *f*
ring, split anneau *m* brisé; rondelle *f* grower
rivet rivet *m*; clou *m* à river
rivet, round-headed rivet *m* à tête ronde
rod tige *f*
rod, threaded tige *f* filetée
roller rouleau *m*; roulette *f*
runner coulisse *f*; galet *m*

S-plate ancre *f* en forme d'un S
S-shaped pipe connector esse *f*
saddle patte *f* d'attache
screw vis *f*
screw cup cuvette *f* pour vis
screw hook piton *m* à crochet
screw, adjusting vis *f* de reglage
screw, butterfly vis *f* à oreilles; vis *f* ailée
screw, clamp(ing) vis *f* d'arrêt; vis *f* de blocage; vis *f* de serrage
screw, coach tire-fond *m*; tire *m*
screw, coach, square-headed vis *f* à bois à tête carrée
screw, countersunk-head vis *f* à tête fraisée
screw, countersunk-head, slotted vis *f* à tête fraisée fendue

screw, countersunk, rounded head vis *f* à tête fraisée bombée
screw, cylindrical-head vis *f* à tête cylindrique
screw, double threaded vis *f* double filet; vis *f* à deux filets
screw, earthing vis *f* de mise à terre
screw, flat-headed vis *f* à tête plate
screw, for plasterboard vis *f* pour plaques de plâtre
screw, grub vis *f* sans tête
screw, grub, pointed vis *f* à pointeau sans tête
screw, hexagonal-head vis *f* à tête à six pans; tirefond *m*
screw, irremovable vis *f* indesserable
screw, metal (for metals) vis *f* à métaux
screw, metal sheet vis *f* à tôle
screw, round-head vis *f* à tête ronde
screw, securing vis *f* de fixation
screw, security (smooth head) vis *f* de securité
screw, self-tapping vis *f* autotaraudeuse
screw, self-drilling vis *f* auto-foreuse
screw, square-head vis *f* à tête carrée
screw, strap-hinge vis *f* de penture
screw, threaded both ends vis *f* double filet
screw, trumpet-head vis *f* tête trompette
screw, wing vis *f* à oreilles; vis *f* ailée
screw, wood vis *f* à bois
screw, wood, brass, round-head vis *f* à bois en laiton à tête ronde
screw, wood, iron, countersunk vis *f* à bois en fer à tête plate
screw-eye piton *m*; piton *m* à anneau; piton *m* à vis
screw-eye, white plastic covered piton *m* plastifié blanc
screw-spike tire-fond *m*
screwed cap bouchon *m* à vis
screwed plug bouchon *m* à vis
screws etc; nails etc; hooks etc visserie *f*
seal rondelle *f* d'étanchéité
security bar for garage door barre *f* de securité pour porte de garage
security grating grille *f* de securité
security grill grille *f* de securité
set of shelves étagère *f*
set square équerre *f*

shaft (driving) arbre *m*
shank tige *f*
sheet iron cover plaque *f* en tôle
sheet lame *f*; feuille *f*; plaque *f*
shelf étagère *f*
shell coquille *f*
shutter mountings ferrure *f* de volets
shutter retaining hook crémaillère *f*
slide-block coulisseau *m*
slide; slider coulisse *f*
sliding stay with adjustable stop coulisseau *m* à frein réglable
small slide coulisseau *m*
special design type *m* special
spike broche *f*; cheville *f*; crampon *m*; tire *m*; cheville *f* (tire-fond)
spike-nail broche *f*
spindle arbre *m*
spiral spring ressort *m* à boudin
spring ressort *m*
spring clip collier *m* à ressort
spring hinge charnière *f* à ressort
square équerre *f*
stake piquet *m*; tasseau *m*
staple crampon *m* à deux pointes
staple conduit *m*; crampillon *m*; clou *f* à deux pointes; agrafe *f*
stay compas *m*
stay with adjustable stop compas *m* à frein reglable
stay, jointed compas *m* genouillère
steel wool laine *f* d'acier
stem tige *f*
stiffener pièce *f* de renfort
stiffening plate plaque *f* de renfort
stop arrêt *m*
stopper bouchon *m*
strap armature *f*; bretelle *f*; feuillard *m*
strap hinge (eg of gate, shutter) penture *f*
striking-plate gâche *f*
strip (eg of iron, steel) feuillard *m*
support support *m*

support bracket patte *f* de maintien; patte *f* de support
surveyor's tape roulette *f* d'arpenteur
suspender bretelle *f*

T clamp agrafe *f* à T
T-iron équerre *f*; profilé *m* en T
tack semence *f*
tack, carpet semence *f* tapissier
tack, carpet, copper semence *f* tapissier cuivre
tack, countersunk semence *f* fraisée
tack, upholstery semence *f* tapissier
tap robinet *m*
tap trade robinetterie *f*
taps and fitting robinetterie *f*
thimble virole *f*
thread pas *m*
threaded flange bride *f* filetée
thumb-latch loquet *m* à poucier
trowel, plasterer's gâche *f*

valve soupape *f*; valve *f*; vanne *f*

wall tie patte *f* de liason
wall-hook gâche *f*
wallplug cheville *f*
washer rondelle *f*; rondelle *f* d'étanchéité
washer, large rondelle *f* carrossier
washer, flat rondelle *f* plate
washer, serrated rondelle *f* à denture
washer, split rondelle *f* Grower
wedge coin *m*
wire brush brosse *f* métallique; brosse *f* en fil de fer
wire gauge filière *f*

Z-shaped metal connector raccord *m* en Z
zinc plated and coated with black epoxy paint zingué époxy noir *adj*

alloy alliage *m*
alloying alliage *m*
aluminium aluminium *m*
aluminium brass laiton *m* d'aluminium
aluminium foil feuille *m* d'aluminium
aluminium-bronze bronze *m* d'aluminium
annealed copper cuivre *m* recuit
anodise (to) anodiser *v*
antimony antimoine *m*

brass cuivre *m* jaune; laiton *m*
brass (to) laitonner *v*
brass tubing tube *m* en laiton
brass, cast laiton *m* fondu
brassing laitonnage *m*
Britannia metal métal *m* anglais
bronze bronze *m*
bronze (to) bronzer *v*

case-harden (to) cémenter *v*; aciérer *v*
chromium chrome *m*
chromium plate (to) chromer *v*
chromium plated chromé,-e *adj*
chromium plating chromage *m*
cobalt cobalt *m*
cock-brass bronze *m* pour robinetterie
cold-rolled copper cuivre *m* écroui
copper cuivre *m*
copper (to) cuivrer *v*
copper pipe tuyau *m* en cuivre
copper sheet tôle *f* de cuivre; feuille *f* de cuivre
cover with zinc (to) zinguer *v*

ferro-alloy ferro-alliage *m*
ferrochromium fonte *f* chromée
ferrous metals métaux *mpl* ferreux
filament fil *m*

galvanize (to) galvaniser *v*
galvanized corrugated iron sheet tôle *f* galvanisée ondulée
galvanized iron sheet tôle *f* zinguée
gold or *m*

gold foil feuille *f* d'or
gold leaf feuille *f* d'or
gun metal métal *m* à canon; bronze *m* à canon; bronze *m* industriel

iron fer *m*
iron, black fer *m* noir
iron, cast fer *m* de fonte; fonte *f*; fonte *f* de fer
iron, galvanized fer *m* galvanisé
iron, hammered fer *m* battu
iron, hard fer *m* dur
iron, malleable fer *m* affiné; fer *m* ductile
iron, malleable cast fonte *f* malléable
iron, pig fonte *f*; fonte *f* brute
iron, rolled fer *m* laminé
iron, sheet fer *m* en lame(s)
iron, soft fer *m* doux
iron, structural fer *m* de construction
iron, wrought fer *m* forgé

lead plomb *m*
lead flashing (roof) revêtement *m* de plomb
lead sheet feuille *f* de plomb; plomb *m* en feuilles
leading plombage *m*

magnesium magnésium *m*
manganese manganèse *m*
manganese-bronze bronze *m* au manganèse
manganese-copper bronze *m* au manganèse
mercury mercure *m*
metal métal *m*
molybdenum molybdène *m*

nickel nickel *m*
nickel-plate (to) nickeler *v*
nickel-plating nickelage *m*

osmium osmium *m*

phosphor-bronze bronze *m* phosphoreux
plate metal fonte *f* mazée
platinum platine *m*

rolled steel sheet tôle *f* laminée

scrap iron fer *m* de masse
sheet feuille *f*
sheet iron tôle *f*; tôle *f* de fer; fer *m* en lame(s)
silver argent *m*
silver (to) argenter *v*
silver-plate (to) argenter *v*
soft metal métal *m* tendre
stainless; non-corrodable inoxydable *adj*; inox *abb*
steel acier *m*
steel (to) aciérer *v*
steel pipe tuyau *m* d'acier
steel wool laine *f* d'acier
steel, annealed acier *m* adouci
steel, black acier *m* noir
steel, carbon acier *m* au carbone
steel, case-hardened acier *m* cémenté
steel, cast acier *m* coulé; acier *m* fondu; acier *m* moulé; fonte *f* d'acier
steel, chrome acier *m* au chrome; acier *m* chromé
steel, chrome-vanadium acier *m* au chrome-vanadium
steel, galvanized acier *m* galvanisé
steel, hard acier *m* dur
steel, hardened acier *m* trempé
steel, high-tensile acier *m* à haute résistance; acier *m* de haute tension
steel, mild acier *m* doux
steel, nickel acier *m* au nickel
steel, rolled acier *m* marchand
steel, stainless acier *m* inoxydable

steel, structural acier *m* de construction; acier *m* pour la construction
steel, tool acier *m* à outils
strip-iron feuillard *m* de fer
strip-steel feuillard *m* d'acier

tap-metal bronze *m* pour robinetterie
tin étain *m*
tin solder étain *m*; étain *m* à braser
tin-foil feuille *f* d'étain
tin-plate fer-blanc *m*
tin-plate working ferblanterie *f*
titanium titane *m*
tungsten tungstène *m*

vanadium vanadium *m*

wire fil *m*
work-lead plomb *m* d'œuvre

zinc zinc *m*
zinc, cover with (to) zinguer *v*
zinc covering or flashing (roof) revêtement *m* de zinc
zinc coated iron sheet tôle *f* zinguée
zinc sheet feuille *f* de zinc
zinc work zinguerie *f*
zinc-bronze bronze *m* au zinc
zincing zincage *m*

9. PLUMBER

ABS (plastic) ABS (plastique)
access port regard *m*
adhesive strip (of insulating material) band *f* adhesive
adjustable spanner clé *f* à molette
air bubble bulle *f* d'air
air pocket poche *f* d'air
airlock (in pipe) bouchon *m*; bulle *f* d'air
align (to) aligner *v*
aluminium aluminium *v*
angle; angle-piece angle *m*
anodic corrosion corrosion *f* anodique
anti-knocking device antibélier *m*
antivibration antivibratile *adj*
antivibration support bloc *m* antivibratile
aperture orifice *m*
appliance appareil *m*
arc welder unit poste *f* de soudage à l'arc
arc welding soudure *f* à l'arc
artesian well puits *m* artésian
asbestos amiante *m*
asbestos cement amiante *m* ciment
asbestos packing garniture *f* d'amiante
asbestos sheet plaque *f* d'amiante
asbestos thread; asbestos string fil *m* d'amiante
assemble (to) assembler *v*
auger-gimlet queue *f* de cochon

background noise level intensité *f* de bruit de fond
bacteriological analysis analyse *f* bactériologique
BAG coupling (collar-type coupling) raccord *m* type bague
ball valve soupape *f* à flotteur; robinet *m* à flotteur sphérique; clapet *m* sphérique
ball-joint joint *m* à rotule
ball-socket cuvette *f* rotule
band bande *f*
base of down-pipe pied *m* de chute
basin vasque *f*; bassin *m*; cuvette *f*
bath bain *m*; baignoire *f*
bath, angled baignoire *f* d'angle
bath drain bouche *f* d'évacuation de bagnoire
bath, hip- baignoire *f* sabot

bathroom salle *f* de bain
bathroom appliance appareil *m* sanitaire
bathroom installations les sanitaires *mpl*
bathroom plumbing installation *f* sanitaire
be protected from frost (to) être *v* à l'abri du gel
beater; bat batte *f*; batte-plate *f*; boursault *m*; bourseau *m*
bellmouth (to) évaser *v*
bellmouth évasement *m*
belt bande *f*
bend (to) cintrer *v*
bend, copper-iron union coude *m* union cuivre-fer
bend, expansion coude *m* compensateur
bend, pipe coude *m* de tube
bend, return; U-bend coude *m* en U
bend, double; S-bend coude *m* de renvoi; raccord *m* courbe double
bending cintrage *m*; pliage *m*
bending machine machine *f* à cintrer
bending radius rayon *m* de cintrage; rayon *m* de courbure
bibcock robinet *m*
bidet bidet *m*
bidet basin bassin *m* de bidet
bidet, fixed bidet *m* fixé
bidet, pivoted bidet *m* pivotant
bidet trap siphon *m* de bidet
bidet valve soupape *m* de bidet
bleed-tap (of radiator) purgeur *m*
block bloc *m*
blow-lamp lampe *f* à souder; chalumeau *m*
boiler chaudière *f*
boiler chemical descaler détartreur *m* de chaudière
boiler, combination chaudière *f* mixte
boiler, cylindrical chaudière *f* cylindrique
boiler feed alimentation *f* de chaudière
boiler fittings raccorderie *f* de chaudière
boiler flue carneau *m* de chaudière
boiler, hot-water chaudière *f* à eau chaude
bore of pipe alésage *m* de tuyau
bottled gas gaz *m* en bouteille
bowl cuvette *f*; bassin *m*
bowl (of sink unit) cuve *f*; bac *m*
bracket (eg for pipe) gâche *f*
branch embranchement *m*

branch connection (in existing pipe) piquage *m*
branch connector raccord *m* de branchement
branch off point point *f* de dérivation
branch, outlet branchement *m* de sortie
branch piece raccord *m* de branchement
branch pipe embranchement *m*; branchement *m*
branch, Y- culotte *f*
branching branchement *m*
brass laiton *m*; cuivre *m* jaune
brass solder brasure *f* au cuivre
brass, cast laiton *m* fondu
braze (to) braser *v*
brazed flange bourrelet *m* en laiton
brazed joint joint *m* brasé
brazing brasage *m*; brasure *f*
brazing, capillary brasage *m* capillaire
brazing, hard brasage *m* fort
brazing, soft brasage *m* tendre
brazing solder brasure *f*
brazing solder stick baguette *f* de brasure
brazing torch torche *f* à braser
breeches pipe culotte *f*
bucket seau *m*
burner brûleur *m*
burner giving fine pointed flame brûleur *m* à pointe fine et flamme dard
burner head (of blow-lamp) brûleur *m*
burner, plumber's brûleur *m* plombier
bush douille *f*
butane butane *m*
butane/propane gas gaz *m* butane/propane
butt coupling manchon *m* buté
butt joint joint *m* abouté; nœud *m* de jonction
butt weld soudure *f* bout à bout
by-pass tube *m* de dérivation

cable clamp serre-câbles *m*
calipers compas *m*
colorie calorie *f*
canalisation canalisation *f*
casing enveloppe *f*
cast coupling raccord *m* moulé
cast in one piece monobloc *adj*
cast iron fonte *f*

cast iron pipe tuyau *m* en fonte
cast iron sleeve manchon *m* en fonte
caulk (to) calfater *v*
caulking calfatage *m*
caulking chisel/iron calfait *m*
ceramic disk disque *m* céramique
cesspool fosse *f* d'aisances; puits *m* perdu
chain pipe-cutter coupe-tuyaux *m* à chaîne
chamfer (to) chanfreiner *v*; chanfreindre *v*
chamfer; bevelled edge chanfrein *m*
chamfered joint joint *m* en biseau
changeover device inverseur *m*
channel canalisation *f*
chased pipework canalisation *f* engravée
chemical analysis analyse *f* chimique
chisel; cold chisel burin *m*
chromium chrome *m*
chromium plate (to) chromer *v*
chromium plating chromage *m*
chuck mandrin *m*
cistern réservoir *m* d'eau; citerne *f*; cuve *f*
cistern, high-level flushing réservoir *m* de chasse haute
cistern, low-level flushing réservoir *m* de chasse bas
clean (to) nettoyer *v*; décaper *v*
cleaning nettoiement *m*; nettoyage *m*
cleaning aperture plug tampon *m* de visite
cleaning flux flux *m* décapant
cleaning opening (at base of downpipe) té *m* hermétique
cleaning rod baguette *f* de nettoyage
cleansing assainissement *m*
clear (to) (empty) vider *v*
clip clip *m*
clip (to) découper *v*
clogging material matières *f* colmatantes
cloth toile *f*
coating pellicule *f*
cock robinet *m* à boisseau
cock, drain robinet *m* de vidange; robinet *m* purgeur; robinet *m* de purge
cock, gas robinet *m* de gaz
cock, main robinet *m* principal
cock, outlet robinet *m* d'écoulement
cock, stop- robinet *m* d'arrêt; robinet *m* de fermeture
cock, test robinet *m* d'essai

cock, three-way robinet *m* à trois voies
cock, water robinet *m* de prise d'eau
coil serpentin *m*
coil, expansion serpentin *m* de dilatation
coil of pipe batterie *m* de serpentins
coiled piping tube *m* en couronne
cold chisel burin *m*; burin *m* à froid
cold water eau *f* froide
collar collier *m*; collet *m*
collar support, two halves demi-collier *m*
collector plate (solar) absorbeur *m*
combined unit monobloc *adj*
comfort confort *m*
compass, drawing compas *m*
compression coupling raccord *m* à compression *m*
compression coupling with olive raccord *m* olive; raccord *m* bicône; montage *m* bicône
compression coupling with ring seal montage *m* américain
compression joint, american type (with ring seal) raccord *m* américain
compression joint, double-cone type raccord *m* bicône
condensation condensation *f*
condensation, surface condensation *f* par surface
conduit conduit *m*; tuyau *m*
connecting raccordement *m*
connecting piece raccord *m*
connecting to the drains raccordement *m* aux égouts
connection branchement *m*
connection, flexible raccord *m* flexible
control handle manette *f* de commande
control tap manette *f* de commande
controller régulateur *m*
convection convection *f*
cooker, gas cuisinière *f* à gaz
copper cuivre *m*
copper, annealed cuivre *m* recuit
copper, cold-rolled cuivre *m* écroui
copper pipe/piping tuyau *m* en cuivre
cork liège *m*
cork slab plaque *m* de liège
corrode to corroder *v*
corrosion corrosion *f*
corrosion inhibitor inhibiteur *m* de corrosion

corrosion, soil corrosion *f* par l'influence du sol
counter compteur *m*
counterflow contre-courant *m*
countersink bit fraise *f*
coupling manchon *m*; raccord *m* union; raccord *m*
coupling, BAG (compression with plastic ring or sleeve) raccord *m* type bague
coupling, butt manchon *m* buté
coupling, flat-collar type raccord *m* à collet battu
coupling, female, threaded on inside raccord *m* femelle filetage intérieur
coupling, male, threaded on outside raccord *m* mâle filetage extérieur
coupling, moulded or cast raccord *m* moulé
coupling, reducer manchon réduit
coupling, slide manchon *m* coulissant
coupling, T-; T-piece pied-de-biche *m*
coupling, taper-joint type raccord *m* à collet repoussé
cover couvercle *m*; enveloppe *f*
cowl capot *m*
cross té double *m*
crossbranch raccord *m* en té double
crusher broyeur *m*
curve (to) cintrer *v*
cut rainure *f*
cut a thread on (to) fileter *v*
cut off (to) découper *v*
cylinder cylindre *m*; fourrau *m*
cylinder-jacket enveloppe *f* de cylindre
cylinder, storage hot water ballon *m* de stockage
cylinder, water, of solar heated system ballon *m* solaire
cylindrical boiler chaudière *f* cylindrique

daily flow débit *m* journalier
daily water consumption consommation *f* d'eau journalière
damp humide *adj*
damp; dampness humidité *f*
deep sink bac *m* à laver
deep well puits *m* profond

defect (due to poor workmanship) malfaçon *f*
defective joint joint *m* défectueux
defrost (to) dégeler *v*; déglacer *v*
degree of hardness degré *m* de dureté
de-ice (to) déglacer *v*
deionise to déioniser *v*
demineralisation déminéralisation *f*
demineralise to déminéraliser *v*
demountable démontable *adj*
deposit sédiment *m*; dépôt *m*
descale (to) détartrer *v*
descaler, boiler chemical détartreur *m* de chaudière
descaling détartrage *m*
dewatering (of a pump) désamorçage *m*
dial cadran *m*
diameter diamètre *m*
dip-pipe siphon *m* renversé
direct bonding (of tubes) façonnage *m* direct
direction of circulation sens *m* de circulation
discharge décharge *f*; vidange *f*; vidage *m*
discharge, automatic (lever type) vidage *m* automatique
discharge, plug and chain water discharge vidage *m* à chainette; vidage *m* à bouchon
discharge of waste water décharge *f* des eaux usées
disconnect débrancher *v*
disinfection désinfection *f*
displace (to) déplacer *v*
dome (of tap) boisseau *m*
domestic appliance appareil *m* ménager
domestic water softener adoucisseur *m* domestique
double sink unit évier *m* avec deux bacs
double wash basin lavabo *m* double
downpipe chute *f*; tuyau *m* de descente; tube *m* de descente; descente *f*
drain puisard *m*; collecteur *m*; égout *m*; évacuation *f*; bouche *f* d'égout; écoulement *m*; drain *m*
drain, bath bouche *f* d'évacuation de bagnoire
drain, common vertical outlet chute *f* unique
drain, main (sewage) collecteur *m* à l'égout

drain, storm conduite *f* des eaux pluviales; égout *m* pluvial
drain, street caniveau *m*
drain, waste and storm water collecteur *m* EU, EP (eaux usées, eaux pluviales)
drain, bottom outlet bouche *f* d'égout
drain, discharge évacuation *f*
drain (to) vider *v*; drainer *v*; égoutter *v*
drain hole (of washbasin etc) bonde *f*
drain off (to) vidanger *v*
drain trap valve *f* d'égout
drainage écoulement *m*; assainissement *m*; évacuation *f* des eaux usées
drainage (eg of a pump) désamorçage *m*
drainage, communal network of réseau *m* communal d'assainissement
drainage ditch fossé *m* d'écoulement
drainage, house assainissement *m* d'habitation
drainage, natural écoulement *m* naturel
drainage system système *m* de drainage; système *m* d'écoulement des eaux
drainage, waste water évacuation *f* des eaux usées
drainage well puisard *m*
draining asséchement *m*
draining board (sink unit) égouttoir *m*
drainpipe tuyau *m* de drainage; tuyau *m* d'écoulement
drainpipe, earthenware conduit *m* en grés
drainpipe, subsurface tuyau *m* de drainage souterrain
dresser see 'lead dresser'
drift broche *f*; mandrin *m*
drift, taper broche *f* conique
drinking water eau *f* buvable/potable
drip (to) égoutter *v*
drive (to); cause (to) entraîner *v*
driving device entraîneur *m*
dry (to) essuyer *v*
duct conduite *f*
ducted piping canalisation *f* encastrée
duo filter filtre *m* duplex

edge trimmer (tool) débordoir *m*
elbow coude *m*
elbow connection conduit *m* coudé
elbow connector, with wall bracket

applique *f*
electric pump pompe *f* électrique
electrode électrode *f*
electrode, welding electrode *f* de soudure
emery cloth toile *f* émeri
empty vide *m*
empty (to) vidanger *v*; vider *v*
empty out (to) vidanger *v*
emptying vidage *m*; vidange *f*
enlarge (to) agrandir *v*
exchange (to) échanger *v*
expand (to) dilater *v*
expansion dilatation *f*; expansion *f*
expansion bend coude *m* compensateur
expansion coefficient coefficient *m* de dilatation
expansion coil serpentin *m* de dilatation
expansion tank or vessel vase *m* d'expansion
expansion joint joint *m* de dilatation
expansion, thermal dilatation *f* thermique

fall descente *f*
fault malfaçon *f*
fibre washer joint *m* de fibre
file lime *f*
file (to) limer *v*
filler metal for welding/soldering métal *m* d'apport de brasage
filter pit puits *m* filtrant; puits *m* de filtrage
filter, purification filtre *m* épurateur
filter, sand filtre *m* à sable
filter, sand and gravel filtre *m* à gravier
filter unit (attached to septic tank) décolloïdeur *m*
filtration bank (for septic tank drainage) tertre *m* d'infiltration
filtration mound tertre *m* d'infiltration
fit into (to) emboîter *v*
fit pipes into each other (to) emboîter *v* des tuyaux
fixing; fixation fixation *m*
flame guard; flame shield pareflamme(s)
flange collet *m*
flange (of a tube) collerette *f*
flange joint raccord *m* par brides; joint *m* à bride
flange, blind rondelle *f* obturatrice

flange, brazed bourrelet *m* de brasure
flange, flared collet *m* repoussé
flange, formed (on metal pipe) collet *m* battu
flange-forming tool appareil *m* à battre les collets
flange, mating contrebride *f*
flanging façonnage *m* de brides
flare (to) évaser *v*
flaring évasement *m*
flexible flexible *adj*
flexible connection raccord *m* flexible
flow velocity meter compteur *m* de vitesse
flow écoulement *m*
flue conduit *m* de cheminée; carneau *m*; conduit *m*; conduit *m* de fumée
flue, boiler carneau *m* de chaudière
flushing cistern of WC chasse *f* d'eau
flushing device appareil *m* de chasse d'eau
flux (soldering) flux *m* décapant; flux *m*
flux (to) décaper *v*
folding pliage *m*
form flanges (to) battre *v* les collets
form of embedding pipes below floor boards ravoirage *m*
freezing congélation *f*
French Gas Board Gaz *m* de France; G.D.F *abb*

galvanize (to) galvaniser *v*
galvanized pipe tuyau *m* galvanisé
gap vide *m*
gas gaz *m*
gas bottle/cylinder bouteille *f* de gaz
gas, bottled gaz *m* en bouteille
gas, butane/propane gaz *m* butane/propane
gas cock/tap robinet *m* de gaz
gas, compressed gaz *m* comprimé
gas cooker cuisinière *f* à gaz
gas governer régulateur *m* de gaz
gas, mains; town gas gaz *m* de ville
gas, natural gaz *m* naturel
gas pipe line canalisation *f* de gaz; gazoduc *m*
gas pressure regulator écrêteur *m*
gasket joint *m* d'étanchéité
gasket ring anneau *f* de joint

gasket, rubber joint *m* en caoutchouc
gauge indicateur *m*; jauge *f*
geyser chauffe-bain *m*
glass-wool laine *f* de verre
glue colle *f*
glue (to) coller *v*
gluing collage *m*
grating (on ventpipe) crapaudine *f*
grease trap bac *m* à graisse; séparateur *m* à graisse; bac *m* dégraisseur
grid réseau *m*
groove rainure *f*
ground water level niveau *m* de la nappe phréatique
ground water table nappe *f* phréatique
gutter gouttière *f*
gutter clip crochet *m*
gutter outlet moignon *m*; naissance *f*

hack-saw scie *f* à métaux
hacksaw blade lame *f* de scie à métaux
hacksaw blade holder porte-lame *m* de scie à métaux
hammer, club or lump massette *f*
hammer, dressing marteau *m* à garnir
hammer, fitter's marteau *m* d'ajusteur
hammer, heavy massette *f* angle abattus
hammer, pin marteau *m* à garnir
hammer (to); beat (to) battre *v*
hand basin lave-main *m*
hand basin, corner lave-main *m* d'angle
hand-saw scie *f* égoïne
hard brazing-solder brasure *f* dure
hard brazing brasage *m* fort; brasage *m* dur
hardness dureté *f*
hardness of water dureté *f* de l'eau
hardness, residual dureté *f* résiduelle
hardness, temporary dureté *f* temporaire
head of water chute *f* d'eau
heat (to) chauffer *v*
heat exhanger échangeur *m* de chaleur
heat loss perte *f* de chaleur
heat pump pompe *f* à chaleur
heat shield bouclier *m* thermique
heating appliance radiateur *m*
heating system système *m* de chauffage
hook crochet *m*
hopper (rainwater) jambonneau *m*

hosepipe tube *m* flexible; tuyau *m* d'arrosage
hot water eau *f* chaude
hot water boiler chaudière *f* à eau chaude
hot water heater calorifère *m* d'eau chaude
hot-water tank ballon *m* d'eau chaude
hot-water tank with immersion heater cumulus *m* électrique
house (to) emboîter *v*
hydrant prise *f* d'eau

immersion heater chauffe-eau *m* à élément chauffant; chauffe-eau *m* électrique; thermo-plongeur *m*
immersion thermostat thermostat *m* à immersion
impermeable imperméable *adj*
in one piece monobloc *adj*
inhibitor inhibiteur *m*
inlet admission *f*; entrée *f*
inlet pipe tuyau *m* d'entrée
inspection chamber, prefabricated concrete regard *m* en béton préfabriqué
inspection chamber (small) regard *m* de visite
inspection hole/port trou *m* de regard; regard *m*
inspection/access door regard *m* de visite
install (to) installer *v*
instrument appareil *m*
insulate (to) isoler *v*
insulation isolation *f*; isolement *m*
insulator (heat) calorifuge *m*; also adj
iron fer *m*
iron, cast fonte *f*
iron, galvanised fer *m* galvanisé

jacket enveloppe *f*
jacket, cylinder enveloppe *f* de cylindre
jacket (to) garnir *v*
join (to) assembler *v*
joining raccordement *m*; assemblage *m*; jonction *f*
joint assemblage *m*; nœud *m*; raccord *m*; joint *m*
joint (to) assembler *v*; emboîter *v*
joint, ball- joint *m* à rotule

joint, brazed joint *m* brasé
joint, butt joint *m* abouté; nœud *m* de jonction
joint, chamfered joint *m* en biseau
joint, compressed joint *f* comprimé
joint, defective joint *m* défectueux
joint, expansion joint *m* de dilatation
joint, flange raccord *m* par brides; joint *m* à bride
joint, free; loose joint joint *m* libre
joint, glued joint *m* collé
joint, lap(ped) assemblage *m* à clin
joint, lead(ed) joint *m* coulé (à plomb); joint *m* de plomb
joint, overlapping joint *m* par recouvrement
joint, rammed joint *m* bourré
joint, spigot and socket raccord *m* à emboîtement
joint, brazed T-; oblique joint nœud *m* d'empattement
joint, welded; soldered joint joint *m* soudé
joint, wiped nœud *m* de soudure
joint, wiped solder brasage *m* à la louche
jointing by gluing assemblage *m* par collage
jointing compound mastic *m* pour joints
jointing paste lut *m*
junction jonction *f*

key clé *f*; clef *f*
kitchen unit bloc-cuisine *m*
knot nœud *m*

label étiquette *f*; label *m*
lag (to) garnir *v*; calorifuger *v*; envelopper *v*
lag/jacket a cylinder (to) garnir *v* un cylindre
lagging enveloppe *f*; calorifugeage *m*
lap joint assemblage *m* à clin
lap-weld; lap-welding soudure *f* à recouvrement
lapping tool rodoir *m*
lapping tool for taps rodoir *m* de robinet
laying out traçage *m*
layout tracé *m*
layout of the pipes tracé *m* des tuyauteries

lead plomb *m*
lead (to) plomber *v*
lead dresser batte *f*; batte-plate *f*; boursault *m*; bourseau *m*; batte à dresser *m*
lead joint joint *m* de plomb; joint *m* coulé
lead lap rodoir *m* en plomb
leading; sealing with lead plombage *m*
leadwork plomberie *f*
leak; leakage (eg water) fuite *f*
leakage (eg of gas) déperdition *f*
left-hand thread filet *m* à gauche
lift (to) relever *v*
lifting relevage *m*
location emplacement *m*
locking nut écrou *m* de blocage
locking wrench pince-étau *f*
loss (eg of heat, gas) déperdition *f*
loudness level niveau *m* d'intensité sonore
low-level flushing cistern réservoir *m* de chasse bas

macerator broyeur *m*
main cock robinet *m* principal
main drain (sewage) collecteur *m* à l'égout
main sewer collecteur *m* à l'égout; tout-à-l'égout *m*; collecteur *m* principal; égout *m* collecteur
mains drainage tout-à-l'égout *m*
mains gas gaz *m* de ville
maintaining maintien *m*
make-up piece/pipe tube *m* de rallonge
mallet maillet *m*; batte *f*; batte-plate *f*
mallet, rubber maillet *m* caoutchouc
manhole regard *m*; trou *m* d'homme
manhole cover couvercle *m* de trou d'homme; plaque *m* d'égout
marble marbre *m*
mass masse *f*; bloc *m*
mastic mastic *m*
measuring instrument appareil *m* de mesure
mechanical joining (eg screw-joint) assemblage *m* mécanique
meter compteur *m*
meter, flow velocity compteur *m* de vitesse
meter, volume compteur *m* volumétrique; compteur *m* de volume
meter, water compteur *m* à eau; compteur *m*

d'eau
method méthode *f*
microbiological purification unit (for domestic sewage) micro-station *f* d'épuration
mild steel acier *m* doux
milling-cutter fraise *f*
mixing tray (eg for mortar) bac *m* gâcher
mouth of chute vidoir *m*
move (to) déplacer *v*

neoprene néoprène *m*
neoprene glue colle *m* au néoprène
neoprene joint joint *m* néoprène
network réseau *m*
node nœud *m*
noise bruit *m*
noise level niveau *m* de bruit
noise level, background intensité *f* de bruit de fond
noise rating pondération *f* des bruits
noise reduction réduction *f* de bruit
non-conductor (of heat) calorifuge *m*; also *adj*
noxious effluent eaux *fpl* nocives
nozzle buse *f*
nut écrou *m*
nut, hexagonal écrou *m* à six pans
nut, lock(ing) contre-écrou *m*; écrou *m* de blocage

O-ring joint *m* torique
olive olive *f*
opening orifice *m*
operating conditions mode *m* opératoire
orifice orifice *m*
outlet décharge *f*; évacuation *f*; orifice *m* de sortie; départ *m*
outlet branch branchement *m* de sortie
outlet, waste water décharge *f* des eaux usées
overflow débordement *m*
overflow pipe trop-plein *m*; conduit *m* de trop-plein; tuyau *m* de trop-plein

packed joint joint *m* bourré
packing gland chapeau *m* de presse-étoupe

pail seau *m*
pedestal (hand basin) colonne *f*
pedestal wash basin lavabo *m* sur colonne
permeable perméable *adj*
pH value valeur *f* du pH
pH-meter pH-mètre *m*
pickle (to) décaper *v*
pipe/piping tuyau *m*; tube *m*; conduit *m*
pipe bend coude *m* de tube
pipe bending cintrage *m* des tubes
pipe bending machine cintreuse *f* de tube
pipe bending spring ressort *m* à cintrer
pipe blockage remover, compressed air operated déboucheur *m* à air comprimé
pipe blockage remover, flexible rod déboucheur *m* flexible
pipe blockage remover, water-pressure operated déboucheur *m* à pression d'eau
pipe bracket gâche *f*
pipe clip or collar collier *m* (d'attache)
pipe collar, fixed collier *m* serré
pipe collar support (demountable half-collar type) demi-collier *m*
pipe coupling manchon *m* de tuyau; manchon *m* pour tuyaux
pipe coupling with bend chapeau *m* de gendarme
pipe cutter coupe-tube *m*; coupe-tuyau *m*
pipe cutter and pipe wrench combined coupe-tubes *m* avec pince
pipe cutter, copper coupe-tube *m* cuivre
pipe fitter poseur *m* de tuyaux; tuyauteur *m*
pipe hanger étrier *m* de suspension des tubes
pipe hook gâche *f*
pipe line, gas canalisation *f* de gaz
pipe positioning clamp positionneur *m* de tubes
pipe socket manchon *m* de tuyau; manchon *m* pour tuyaux
pipe system, hidden/concealed canalisation *f* cachée
pipe system, overhead canalisation *f* aerienne
pipe system, visible (surface mounted) canalisation *f* apparente
pipe threader (die) filière *f*
pipe threading filetage *m* de tubes
pipe threading machine machine *f* à fileter

les tubes
pipe union raccord *m* union
pipe vice étau *m*
pipe wrench serre-tubes *m*
pipe wrench, stillson clé *f* serre-tubes type stillson
pipe, by-pass tube *m* de dérivation
pipe, bore of alésage *m* de tuyau
pipe, branch tuyau *m* de branchement
pipe, cast iron tuyau *m* en fonte
pipe, circulation tuyau *m* de circulation
pipe, communication antenne *f*
pipe, connecting tuyau *m* de raccordement
pipe, copper tuyau *m* en cuivre
pipe, down- chute *f*; tube *m* de descente
pipe, drainage tuyau *m* d'écoulement; tube *m* de drainage
pipe. drip tube *m* de purge; pipette *f*
pipe, earthenware tuyau *m* en terre; tuyau *m* en grès
pipe, extension tube *m* de rallonge
pipe, feed tuyau *m* d'alimentation
pipe, galvanized tuyau *m* galvanisé
pipe, hose tube *m* flexible; tuyau *m* d'arrosage
pipe, inlet tuyau *m* d'entrée
pipe, leaking fuite *m* de tuyau
pipe, make-up tube *m* de rallonge
pipe, overflow tuyau *m* de trop-plein; conduit *m* de trop-plein
pipe, plastic tuyau *m* en plastique
pipe, return conduite *f* de retour
pipe, riser conduite *f* montant
pipe, run of section *f* de tuyau
pipe, seamless tube *m* sans soudure
pipe, service conduite *f* de raccordement
pipe, soil tube *m* d'égout; tuyau *m* d'égout
pipe, spreader tube *m* d'épandage
pipe, stand tuyau *m* de prise d'eau
pipe, supply tuyau *m* d'alimentation
pipe, threaded tube *m* fileté; tube *m* taraudé
pipe, vent tuyau *m* d'évent
pipe, WC vertical outlet chute *f* WC
pipe-bender pince *f* à cintrer
pipe-cutter, chain coupe-tuyaux *m* à chaîne
pipe-slick lissoir *m* à tuyau
pipe-smoother lissoir *m* à tuyau
pipes and fittings; pipework tuyauterie *f*
pipework installation tuyauterie *f*

pipework, buried tuyauterie *f* enterrée
pipework, chased canalisation *f* engravée
pipework, encased (eg within concrete) canalisation *f* enrobée
pipework, prefabricated tuyau *m* préfabiqué
piping; pipes tuyauterie *f*; canalisation *f*
piping, buried canalisations *fpl* enterrées
piping, coiled tube *m* en couronne
piping, concealed; ducted piping canalisation *f* dissimulée
piping, copper tuyau *m* en cuivre
piping, embedded; below surface piping canalisation *f* encastrée
piping, waste water tuyauterie *f* des eaux usées
pit puits *m*
plug bonde *f*
plug, access bouchon *m* de visite; tampon *m* de visite
plug and chain waste discharge vidage *m* à bouchon; vidage *m* à chainette
plug, drain bouchon *m* de vidange
plug, reducing tampon *m* de réduction
plug, rubber bouchon *m* de caoutchouc
plug, screwed bouchon *m* à vis
plug, sealing- tampon *m* obturateur
plug, shower bonde *f* de douche
plug seal nœud *m* de tamponnage
plug (to) tamponner *v*
plughole; outlet bonde *f*
plumb (to) plomber *v*
plumber plombier *m*
plumber's burner (large flame) brûleur *m* plombier
plumber's workshop plomberie *f*
plumbing plomberie *f*; robinetterie *f*; plombage *m*
plumbline plomb *m*
polyethylene polyéthylène *m*
polyethylene tubing tube *m* polyéthylène
polypropylene polypropylène *m*
polyvinyl chloride; PVC polychlorure *m* de vinyle; PVC *abb*
position emplacement *m*
power puissance *f*
prefilter préfiltre *m*
pressure pression *f*
pressure reducer réducteur *m* de pression

pressure reducing valve détendeur *m*
pressure regulator écrêteur *m*
propane propane *m*
protection protection *f*
protection against freezing protection *f* contre le gel
protection against heat loss protection *f* contre déperdition de chaleur
protective sheathing (of pipes) gaînage *m*
pump, circulating pompe *f* de circulation
pump, electric pompe *f* électrique
pump, heat pompe *f* à chaleur
pump operated WC WC *m* compact
pumping station, waterworks station *f* de pompage
purification purification *f*; épuration *m*
purification filter filtre *m* épurateur
purify (to) épurer *v*
putty mastic *m*

radiator radiateur *m*
radiator regulating valve valve *f* de radiateur
radiator tap robinet *m* de radiateur
rainwater eaux *fpl* pluviales; EP *abb*
rainwater drainage canalisation *f* des eaux de pluie
rainwater head/hopper jambonneau *m*
rainwater shoe dauphin *m* coudé
raise (to) (eg by pumping) relever *v*
raising (eg by pumping) relevage *m*
rasp râpe *f*
receiver (tank) collecteur *m*
reduction piece réduction *f*
regulate (to) régler
regulation(s) règlement *m*; réglementation *f*
regulator régulateur *m*
regulator, two-position régulateur *m* à deux positions
reservoir réservoir *m*
residual hardness dureté *f* résiduelle
ring bague *f*
ring, split bague *f* fendue
rise in temperature élévation *f* de temperature
riser pipe conduite *f* montant; colonne *f* montante

rising-main colonne *f* montante
rockwool laine *f* de roche
room heating chauffage *m* des locaux
room temperature température *f* ambiante
rubber caoutchouc *m*
rubber gasket joint *m* en caoutchouc
rubber hose tuyau *m* en caoutchouc
rubber ring anneau *m* en caoutchouc
rubber tubing tuyau *m* en caoutchouc
rubber, vulcanised caoutchouc *m* vulcanisé
run (to); flow (to) couler *v*
run of pipe section *f* de tuyau
rust rouille *f*
rust protection protection *f* antirouille

S-bend coude *m* de renvoi; raccord *m* courbe double
S-hook esse *f*
S-shaped esse *f*
S-trap siphon *m* en S
safety valve soupape *f* de sûreté
sanitary sanitaire *adj*
sanitary engineer ingénieur *m* sanitaire
sanitary engineering génie *m* sanitaire
sanitary installation installation *f* sanitaire
sanitation assainissement *m*
saw, hand- scie *f* égoine
saw, metal-; hacksaw scie *f* à metauax
saw, metal- (small) scie *f* midget
scale (boiler) incrustations *fpl*; tartre *m* des chaudières
scale deposit encroûtement *m*
scale formation formation *f* d'incrustation; entartrage *m*
scour (to) décrasser *v*; décaper *v*
screw up (to) (a nut) serrer *v*
screw with notched head vis *f* à tête crantée
screw-cutting filetage *m*
screwed socket (for hose) manchon *m* vissé
screwing die filière *f*
scriber pointe *f* à tracer
seal joint *m*; bourrage *m*; joint *m* d'étanchéité
seal, fibre joint *m* de fibre
sael, gasket joint *m* d'étanchéité
seal, leather joint *m* de cuir
seal, plug nœud *m* de tamponnage

seal off (to) colmater *v*
sealing off colmatage *m*
sealing with lead plombage *m*
sealing-plug tampon *m* obturateur
seat siège *m*
sediment sédiment *m*
separate sewage system système *m* séparatif d'assainissement
separator séparateur *m*
septic tank fosse *f* septique
septic tank, all domestic wastes fosse *f* septique toutes eaux
sewage eaux *fpl* vannes; EV *abb*; eaux *fpl* résiduaires
sewage disposal assainissement *m*; évacuation *f* des eaux d'égouts
sewage system système *m* du tout à l'égout
sewage system, separate système *m* séparatif d'assainissement
sewage, raw eaux *fpl* d'égout brutes
sewer collecteur *m*; égout *m*
sewer, main égout *m* collecteur
sewerage system système *m* d'égouts; rè-seau *m* d'égouts
shaping façonnage *m*; façonnement *m*
shears cisailles *fpl*
shears, metal cisailles *fpl* à métaux; cisailles *fpl* à tôles
shift (to) déplacer *v*
shoe (rainwater) dauphin *m* coudé
shower douche *f*
shower cabinet cabine *f* de douche
shower fittings robinetterie *f* de douche
shower plug bonde *f* de douche
shower tray bac *f* de douche
shower unit bloc-douche *m*
shower; shower closet cabinet *m* de douche
shower; shower-room salle *f* de douches
shutting off; cutting off obturation *f*
sink bac *m*
sink unit bloc *m* évier
sink, deep bac *m* à laver
sink, kitchen évier *m*
sink, single/double évier *m* simple/double; évier *m* à un bac/deux bacs
siphon siphon *m*
siphon-type inspection box regard *m* siphoïde
site emplacement *m*

sleeve fourreau *m*; manchon *m*
sleeving, continuous (containing pipes) gaînage *m*
slot rainure *f*
sludge boue *f*; les boues *fpl*
soakaway puits *m* d'infiltration; puits *m* perdu
soaking douche *f*
socket douille *f*; manchon *m*
socket, connecting manchon *m* de raccordement
socket end embout *m* femelle
socket forming tool évaseur *m*
socket forming universal tool appareil *m* à emboiture universel
socket, pipe manchon *m* de tuyau; manchon *m* pour tuyaux
socket pipes (to) emboîter *v* des tuyaux
socket with spigot tail manchette *f*
socket-forming universal tool appareil *m* à emboîture universel
soft brazing-solder brasure *f* tendre
soft brazing brasage *m* tendre
soft metal métal *m* tendre
soft solder soudure *f* étain; métal *m* d'apport de brasage
soft-solder (to) braser *v* à l'étain
soften (to) (water) adoucir *v*
soil eaux *fpl* vannes, EV *abb*
solar collector capteur *m* solaire
solar energy énergie *f* solaire
solder soudure *f*
solder, copper brazing solder brasure *f* au cuivre
solder, hard brasure *f*
solder, hard brazing solder brasure *f* dure
solder, soft brazing solder brasure *f* tendre
solder, stick of baton *m* de soudure
solder, tin; soft solder soudure *f* étain; étain *m* à braser
solder (to) braser *v*; souder *v*
solder (to); soft-solder (to) braser *v* à l'étain
solder electrode électrode *f* de soudure
solder stick baguette *f* de soudage
solder wire fil *m* de soudure
solder with flux core soudure *f* autodécapante; soudure *f* avec âme décapante
soldered joint joint *m* brasé; joint *m* de

plomb
solderer; welder soudeur *m*
soldering; welding soudage *m*; soudure *f*
soldering flux pâte *f* décapante
soldering iron fer *m* à souder; fer *m* à braser
soldering iron, electric fer *m* à souder électrique
soldering lamp lampe *f* à souder
soldering pistol, electric pistolet *m* à souder électrique
sound intensity level niveau *m* d'intensité sonore
sound level niveau *m* sonore
spanner clé *f*; clef *f*
spanner, adjustable clé *f* à molette
spanner for wash basins clé *f* de lavabo
spirit level niveau *m* à bulle
split ring bague *f* fendue
spokeshave wastringue *f*
spreader pipe (septic tank) tube *m* d'épandage
spreading épandage *m*
stagnant water eau *f* stagnante; eaux *fpl* mortes
stainless inoxydable *adj*; inox *abb*
stand pipe tuyau *m* de prise d'eau
state état *m*
steel wool laine *f* d'acier
steel, black acier *m* noir
steel, galvanized acier *m* galvanisé
steel, mild acier *m* doux
stillson pipe wrench clé *f* stillson
stop (to) tamponner *v*
stop pin ergot *m* de butée
stopcock arrêt *m*; robinet *m* d'arrêt; robinet *m* de fermeture
stopcock, double-male union arrêt *m* double-mâle
stopcock, female union arrêt *m* femelle
stopcock, male union arrêt *m* mâle
stoppage arrêt *m*; désamorçage *m*; engorgement *m*
stoppage (obstruction) obstruction *f*
stopper tampon *m*; obturateur *m*; bouchon *m*
stopping up (a conduit) obturation *f*
storm drain conduite *f* des eaux pluviales; égout *m* pluvial
strap wrench serre-tubes *m* à sangle; clé *f* à sangle

street drain caniveau *m*
street gulley bouche *f* d'égout
strip bande *f*
sullage eaux *fpl* usées; EU *abb*
supply alimentation *f*
supply pipe tuyau *m* d'alimentation
supply system réseau *m* d'alimentation
support bracket patte *f* de support; gâche *f*
system réseau *m*

T-coupling pied-de-biche *m*
T-joint nœud *m* d'empattement
T-piece té *m*
T-piece, branch or end reduced té *m* réduit
T-piece, ends and branch equal té *m* égal
tamping bar batte *f* à bourre
tank réservoir *m*; citerne *f*
tank, hot-water ballon *m* d'eau chaude
tank, water ballon *m*; citerne *f*
tap robinet *m*
tap, mixer mélangeur *m*; mitigeur *m*; robinet *m* mélangeur/mitigeur
tap, mixer tap with ceramic discs mélangeur *m* à disques céramiques
tap, radiator robinet *m* de radiateur
tap trade robinetterie *f*
tap washer rondelle *f* de robinet; clapet *m*
taper drift broche *f* conique
tapping branchement *m*
taps and fittings robinetterie *f*
tee té *m*
temperature, ambient température *f* ambiante
temperature regulator thermorégulateur *m*
temperature, rise in élévation *f* de temperature
temporary hardness dureté *f* temporaire
thermal expansion dilatation *f* thermique
thread (to) fileter *v*
thread, left-hand filet *m* à gauche
thread, right-hand filet *m* à droite
threading filetage *m* **threading die** filière *f*
three-way fitting tuyau *m* trois voies
tighten (to) serrer *v*
tin étain *m*
tin solder étain *m*; étain *m* à braser; soudure

f étain
toilet cabinets *mpl*
toilet seat siège *m* de cabinet
toilet seat and cover abattant *m* de WC
tool outil *m*
town gas gaz *m* de ville
tracing traçage *m*
trap valve *f*; purgeur *m*
trap (U-bend) siphon *m*
tray bac *m*
treatment traitement *m*
tremor trépidation *f*
trench tranchée *f*
trough bac *m*
tube; tubing tube *m*; tuyau *m*
tube, end of bout *m* de tube
tubing, polythene tube *m* polyéthylène
tubing, rubber tuyau *m* en caoutchouc
turn-pin, jointed (plumber's) toupie *f* articulée
turn-pin, plumber's toupie *f*

union union *f*
unit bloc *m*

valve clapet *m*; soupape *f*; valve *f*
valve, balancing; overflow-valve; relief valve soupape *f* de trop-plein
valve, ball clapet *m* sphérique
valve, bidet soupape *m* de bidet
valve, changeover soupape *f* directionnelle
valve, check; non-return valve clapet *m* anti-retour; clapet *m* de retenue; clapet *m* de non-retour
valve, cut-off clapet *m* d'obturation
valve, dump clapet *m* de décharge
valve, expansion soupape *m* d'expansion; soupape *f* de détente
valve, float soupape *f* à flotteur
valve, inlet soupape *f* d'admission; clapet *m* d'admission
valve, overflow clapet *m* de trop-plein
valve, pressure reducing détendeur *m*
valve, relief vanne *f* de sûretè
valve, safety soupape *f* de sûreté
valve; shut-off; gate vanne *f*
valve, stop soupape *f* d'arrêt

valve, suction clapet *m* d'aspiration
valve, thermostatic control soupape *f* de contrôle thermostatique
valve, three-way soupape *m* à trois voies
valve, water regulating robinet *m* de réglage, vanne *f* régulatrice
valve, water shut-off vanne *f* d'arrêt de l'eau
velocity of flow vitesse *f* d'écoulement
velocity of outflow vitesse *f* de décharge
vent hood chapeau *m* d'évent
vent pipe tuyau *m* d'évent
ventilation ventilation *f*
ventilation, mechanically controlled ventilation *f* mécanique contrôlée; VMC *abb*
ventilator cowl chapeau *m* de ventilation
venting ventilation *f*
venting, primary/secondary venting (of drains) ventilation *f* primaire/secondaire
vertical outlet pipe from WC chute *m* WC
vibrate (to) vibrer *v*
vibratile; vibration vibratile *adj*
vibration vibration *f*; trépidation *f*
vice étau *m*

wash basin lavabo *m*; cuvette *f*; vasque *f*
wash basin, corner lavabo *m* d'angle
wash basin, double lavabo *m* double
wash basin, pedestal lavabo *m* sur colonne
washer rondelle *f*
washer, blind rondelle *f* obturatrice
washer, leather rondelle *f* de cuir
washer, rubber rondelle *f* caoutchouc
washer; seal rondelle *f* d'échanchéité
washer, tap rondelle *f* de robinet; clapet *m*
waste pipe trop-plein *m*
waste water outlet/discharge décharge *f* des eaux usées
waste water piping/pipework tuyauterie *f* des eaux usées
waste water (domestic) eaux *fpl* usées; EU *abb*
water eau *f*
water butt réservoir *m* d'eau
water closet; WC WC *m*
water closet, siphonic flush WC *m* à action siphonique

water cock robinet *m* de prise d'eau

water consumption consommation *f* d'eau

water consumption, daily consommation *f* d'eau journalière

water cylinder ballon *m*

water cylinder of solar heated system ballon *m* solaire

water hammer coup *m* de bélier; choc *m* de l'eau

water heater, electric chauffe-eau *m* électrique

water leg; gutter outlet naissance *f*

water level niveau *m* de l'eau

water level, ground niveau *m* de la nappe phréatique

water meter compteur *m* à eau; compteur *m* d'eau

water quality qualité *f* de l'eau

water softener adoucisseur *m* d'eau

water softener, domestic adoucisseur *m* domestique

water softener (ion-exchange filter) filtre *m* permutite™

water supply alimentation *f* en eau; approvisionnement *m* d'eau

water supply (company) service *m* des eaux

water tank réservoir *m* d'eau

water tower château *m* d'eau

water works station *f* de pompage; station *f* hydraulique

water, cold eau *f* froide

water, drinking eau *f* buvable/potable

water, foul eaux *fpl* vannes; EV *abb*

water, fresh eau *f* fraîche; eau *f* douce

water, hard eau *f* dure

water, head of chute *f* d'eau

water, hot eau *f* chaude

water, household waste eaux *fpl* ménagères

water, noxious waste; noxious effluent eaux *fpl* nocives

water, rain; storm water eaux *fpl* pluviales; EP *abb*

water, soft eau *f* douce

water, stagnant eaux *fpl* mortes; eau *f* stagnante

water, subsoil; underground water eaux *fpl* souterraines

water, surface eaux *fpl* superficielles

water, tap eau *f* de distribution; eau *f* de ville

water, waste eaux *fpl* usées ; EU *abb*

water-sump puisard *m*

waterfall chute *f* d'eau

waterproofness étanchéité *f*

WC WC *m*; cabinets *mpl*

WC basin cuvette *f* de WC

WC cistern réservoir *m*

WC, direct flush WC *m* à chasse direct

WC flushing box chasse *f* d'eau

WC, pump operated WC *m* compact

WC, siphonic flush WC *m* à action siphonique

weld (to) souder *v*

welder soudeur *m*

welding soudure *f*; soudage *m*

welding, arc soudure *f* à l'arc

welding, gas; oxyacetylene welding soudage *m* autogène

well puits *m*

well, artesian puits *m* artésian

well, deep puits *m* profond

widen at the mouth (to) évaser *v*

wipe (to) essuyer *v*

wrench, chain pipe clé *f* à chaine

wrench, locking; lever-jaw wrench pince-étau *f*

wrench, monkey clé *f* anglaise

wrench, pipe; stillson pipe wrench clé *f* serre-tubes type stillson

wrench, stillson pipe clé *f* stillson

Y-branch culotte

zeolite zéolite *m*

zinc zinc *m*

blocking calage *m*
butt-strip couvre-joint *m*

cement mastic *m*
cement (to) mastiquer *v.*
cheek contre-feuillure *f*; joue *f*
conservatory jardin *m* d'hiver; serre *f*
counter putty contre-mastic *m*; contre-masticage *m*
counter puttying contre-masticage *m*
cover-strip couvre-joint *m*
covering piece couvre-joint *m*
cut (to); cut off (to) couper *v*; découper *v*

distance piece cale *f*
door opening baie *f* de porte
door, glass panelled porte *f* vitrée
door, glazed porte *f* vitrée
dormer window; lucarne lucarne *f*
double-glazed window double fenêtre *f*
double glazing double vitrage *m*
drained glazing rebate feuillure *f* drainée
dry (puttyless) glazing vitrage *m* sans mastic

fanlight imposte *f*; vasistas *m*
filler mastic *m*
filling masticage *m*
fillister feuillure *f*
fixed glazed sections of window châssis *mpl* fixes
furnished with glass vitré,-e *adj*

glass verre *m*; vitrerie *f*;
glass vitré,-e *adj*
glass adhesive mastic mastic *m* colle verre
glass cleaner nettoyant *m* vitre
glass cutter (tool) coupe-verre *m*
glass cutter, wheel coupe-verre *m* à molette
glass door vitrage *m*
glass drill foret *m* pour le verre
glass industry verrerie *f*
glass items vitrerie *f*
glass partition cloison *f* vitrée; vitrage *m*
glass roof toit *m* vitré; verrière *f*
glass trade verrerie *f*
glass wall paroi *f* vitrée; verrière *f*

glass, cast verre *m* coulé
glass, clear verre *m* clair
glass, coloured verre *m* de couleur
glass, corrugated verre *m* cannelé; verre *m* strié
glass, drawn verre *m* étiré
glass, frosted verre *m* dépoli
glass, laminated verre *m* feuilleté
glass, pane of carreau *m* de verre; vitre *f*
glass, plate verre *m* à glaces; glace *f*
glass, reeded verre *m* strié
glass, reinforced verre *m* armé
glass, safety verre *m* de securité
glass, sheet of feuille *f* de verre; plaque *f* de verre
glass, sheet of (plate) glace *f*
glass, silvered verre *m* argenté
glass, smoked verre *m* fumé
glass, stained verre *m* de couleur
glass, synthetic verre *m* synthétique
glass, toughened verre *m* trempé; verre *m* durci
glass, transparent plastic sheet verre *m* synthetique
glass, unbreakable verre *m* incassable
glass, window verre *f* à vitre
glass, wire verre *m* armé
glasshouse serre *f*
glaze (to) vitrer *v*
glazed vitré,-e *adj*
glazed door porte *f* vitré
glazed frame châssis *m*
glazier vitrier *m*
glazier's knife couteau *m* de vitrier
glazier's point pointe *f* vitrier
glazier's putty mastic *m* de vitrier
glazing vitrage *m*; vitrerie *f*
glazing bar fer *m* à vitrage
glazing bead parclose *f*
glazing block cale *f*
glazing brad pointe *f* vitrier
glazing fillet parclose *f*
glazing fillet (eg of putty) solin *m*
glazing sprig pointe *f* vitrier
glazing, dry (puttyless) vitrage *m* sans mastic
glazing, patent vitrage *m* sans mastic
glazing, secondary survitrage *m*
greenhouse serre *f*

inner layer of glazing putty contre-mastic *m*
inner side of rebate contre-feuillure *f*
inserting distance or packing pieces
calage *m*

knife, glazier's couteau *m* de vitrier
knife, hacking couteau *m* à démastiquer
knife, putty couteau *m* à mastiquer; couteau
m de vitrier
knife, stopping couteau *m* à mastiquer

mastic mastic *m*
mastic for glazing aquaria, etc mastic *m*
auto marine
mastic, silicone mastic *m* silicone
mobile glazed sections of a window châssis
mpl mobiles
mounted glazing bead parclose *f* en applique

opening baie *f*
opening roof-light vasistas *m*

packing piece cale *f*
packing piece, base cale *f* d'assise
packing piece, edge cale *f* périphérique
packing piece, rubber cale *f* en caoutchouc
packing piece, side cale *f* latéral
packing piece, wood cale *f* en bois
pane of glass vitre *f*; carreau *m* de verre
patent glazing vitrage *m* sans mastic
picture window baie *f* vitrée
plate glass glace *f*
plug of metal or wood used to retain glass
in metal frame cheville *f*
put glass in (to) vitrer *v*
put in a window pane (to) poser *v* une vitre
put windows in (to) vitrer *v*
putty mastic *m*; mastic *m* de vitrier
putty (to) mastiquer *v*
putty, counter contre-masticage *m*;
contre-mastic *m*
putty, filling mastic *m* de bourrage
putty, glazier's mastic *m* de vitrier
putty, iron mastic *m* de fer
putty, linseed oil based mastic *m* à l'huile de
lin
putty, silicone mastic *m* silicone

putty, stopping mastic *m* obturateur
puttying masticage *m*
puttying, counter- contre-masticage *m*

rabbet; rebate feuillure *f*
roof light vélux™ *m*; vasistas *m*

seating piece cale *f* d'assise
sheet of glass plaque *f* de verre; feuille *f* de
verre
sheet of (plate) glass glace *f*
sheet glass verre *m* plat
shim cale *f*
side of rebate flanc *m* de feuillure
silicone mastic mastic *m* silicone
skylight claire-voie *f*; claires-voies *fpl*;
fenêtre *f* à tabatière; vélux™ *m*; vasistas *m*
small metal lozenge used as glazing sprig
losange *m* de vitrier
small metal triangle used as glazing sprig
triangle *m* de vitrier
stained glass window vitrail m
stop up with putty (to) mastiquer *v*

translucent translucide *adj*
transom (window) imposte *f*
transparent transparent,-e *adj*
transparent plastic sheet verre *m* synthetique

velux™ vélux™ *m*

wedge cale *f*
wedging calage *m*
window fenêtre *f*; baie *f*
window (eg of a church) verrière *f*
window cleaner (fluid) nettoyant *m* vitre
window opening baie *f* de fenêtre
window pane vitre *f*
window scraper gratte *f* vitres
window, arched fenêtre *f* cintrée
window, bay fenêtre *f* en saillie; baie *f* vitrée
window, bow fenêtre *f* en saillie
window, casement fenêtre *f* à battants,
fenêtre *f* ordinaire
window, casement, inward-opening fenêtre
f à la française
window, centre-hung (horizontal pivot)

fenêtre *f* à bascule; fenêtre *f* basculante
window, centre-hung (vertical pivot) fenêtre *f* à pivot; fenêtre *f* pivotante
window, dormer fenêtre *f* mansardée; lucarne *f*
window, double-glazed double fenêtre *f*
window, French fenêtre *f* à la français; fenêtre *f* ordinaire
window, inward opening (pivoted at base) fenêtre *f* à soufflet
window, lattice fenêtre *f* à croisillons; fenêtre *f* treillisée

window, mullioned fenêtre *f* à meneaux
window, outward-opening casement fenêtre *f* à l'anglaise
window, picture baie *f* vitrée
window, sash fenêtre *f* à coulisses; fenêtre *f* à guillotine
window, single-glazed fenêtre *f* à vitrage simple
window, sliding fenêtre *f* coulissante
window, stained glass vitrail *m*
windows (pl) vitrage *m*

11. ELECTRICIAN

accessory accessoire *m*
accumulator accumulateur *m*; accu *m*
act as earth (to) faire *v* masse
activate a circuit (to) enclencher *v* un circuit
adaptor adaptateur *m*; prise *f* multiple
adhesive colle *f*; adhésif *m*
adjustment réglage *m*
aerial antenne *f*
alarm bell sonnerie *f* d'alarme
all poles omnipolaire *adj*
alternating alternatif, -ive *adj*
alternating current (a.c.) courant *m* alternatif
alternator alternateur *m*
ambiance ambiance *f*
ammeter ampèremètre *m*
amperage ampèrage *m*
ampere ampère *m*
antenna antenne *f*
anti-interference antiparasite *adj*
anti-shock handle (eg for masonry chisel) poignée *f* pare-coups
appliance appareil *m*
arrangement dispositif *m*
artificial light lumière *f* artificielle
as one proceeds au fur et à mesure *adv phr*
assembly montage *m*

auto-locking plug cheville *f* autobloquante
automatic lighting éclairage *m* automatique
automatic wire-stripper pince *f* à dénuder automatique
autotransformer autotransformateur *m*
auxiliary auxiliaire *m*

bar barre *f*
bare (not insulated) nu, -e *adj*
bare wire fil *m* nu
base of a lamp socle *m*
bathroom lighting appliques *f* de sdb (salle de bain)
battery batterie *f*; pile *f*
battery charger chargeur *m*
battery, rechargeable accu *m* rechargeable
battery-operated à piles
battery-operated lighting éclairage *m* autonome
bayonet bulb socket douille *f* à baïonnette
bayonet cap (of bulb) culot *m* à baïonnette
beacons balisage *m*
below surface installation encastrement *m*
benchmark repère *m*
bend (to) cintrer *v*
berthelet trowel (toothed edge) truelle *f* berthelet

bipolar bipolaire *adj*
bipolar socket with earth socle *m* bipolaire avec terre (2P+T)
blank flange obturateur *m*
blanking plate obturateur *m*
blow (to) (a fuse) griller *v*; fondre *v* un fusible
blowing (of a fuse) jeu *m*
board tableau *m*
bolt cheville *f*
boosted survolté, -e *adj*
boosting survoltage *m*
box coffret *m*; boîte *f*
branch (wire, conductor) branchement *m*
branch box boîte *f* de branchement; boîte *f* de distribution; boîte *f* de connexion
branching branchement *m*
break a circuit (to) déclencher *v* un circuit
break-down défaillance *f*
breaking or opening (a circuit) ouverture *f*
bulb ampoule *f*; lampe *f*
bulb holder douille *f*
bulwark light hublot *m*
buried cable câble *m* enterré
burn out (to) (a fuse, electric motor) griller *v*
busbar barre *f* omnibus; barre *f* collectrice

cable câble *m*
cable channel conduite *f* de câbles
cable connecting clamp pince *f* de raccordement
cable connector connecteur *m*
cable cutter coupe-câble *m*
cable distribution box boîte *f* de raccordement
cable drum bobine *f* de câble
cable duct conduit *m*
cable fittings accessoires *mpl* pour câbles
cable guide guide-fil *m*
cable hanger porte-câble *m*
cable protection sleeve/sheath gaine *f* de câble
cable socket/terminal borne *f* de câble
cable staple cavalier *m*
cable terminal/termination embout *m* de câble
cable with PVC sheath câble *f* gaine PVC

cable, electric câble *m* électrique
cable, flexible câble *m* souple
cable, mains câble *m* de distribution
cable, multi-wire câble *m* multifilaire
cable, rigid câble *m* rigide
cable, earthing câble *m* de mise à la terre
cable, multi-wire câble *m* multifilaire
cables canalisation *f*
cabling canalisation *f*
canalisation canalisation *f*
candela candela *f*
cap obturateur *m*
cap (of electric light bulb) culot *m*
capacitor condensateur *m*
cartridge fuse cartouche *f* fusible; fusible *m* à cartouche
case boîtier *m*
casing (for wires, etc) moulure *f*
category of installation catégorie *f* d'installation
ceiling light plafonnier *m*
certificate of conformity certificat *m* de conformité (see also 'CONSUEL attestation/certificate')
change-over wires (commutator) fils *mpl* navettes
channel conduite *f*
channel (cut in plaster etc) saignée *f*
charge charge *f*
chase (to) ciseler *v*
check vérification *f*
check (to) vérifier *v*
chisel (to) ciseler *v*
chisel ciseau *m*
chisel, cold burin *m*
circuit circuit *m*
circuit breaker coupe-circuit *m*; brise-circuit *m*; disjoncteur *m*; interrupteur *m*
circuit closer commutateur *m* conjoncteur
circuit connection connecteur *m* de circuit
circuit control commande *f* de circuit
circuit protection protection *f*; protection des circuits *f*
circuit scheme or diagram montage *m* électrique
circuit wiring câblage *m* de circuit
class classe *f*
class of insulation (0 to 3) classe *f* d'isolation

clip attache *f*; pince *f* de fixation
clip, crocodile pince *f* crocodile
clip (to) clipser *v*
clip-in bridging strip barre *f* de pontage enclipsable
close (to) fermer *v*
close a circuit (to) enclencher *v* un circuit; fermer *v* un circuit
close coupling couplage *m* fermé
closed circuit circuit *m* fermé
collar collier *m*
collector plate absorbeur *m*
colour couleur *f*
colour of wires couleur *f* des conducteurs

live:	red	phase:	rouge
	brown		marron
	black		noir
neutral:	blue	neutre:	bleu
earth:	green+	terre:	vert +
	yellow		jaune

coloured bulb lampe *f* couleur
comb distributor (of current) peigne *m* de répartition
commutator commutateur *m*
compass compas *m*
component élément *m*
condenser condensateur *m*
conduction conduction *f*
conductor conducteur *m*
conduit conduit *m*; conduite *f*; gaine *f*
conduit (wiring/cable) canalisation *f*
conduit coupling couplage *m*
conduit type codes conduit (nature) *m* (see French-English section for list)
conduit, bendable conduit *m* cintrable
conduit, flexible conduit *m* souple
conduit, rigid conduit *m* rigide
connect (to) connecter *v* ; coupler *v*; raccorder *v*; accoupler *v*
connect in parallel (to) coupler *v* en parallèle
connect in series (to) coupler *v* en série
connect up (to) brancher *v*; mettre *v* en circuit; raccorder *v*
connect wrongly (to) coupler *v* mal
connecting montage *m*; raccordement *m*
connecting strip barrette *f* de raccordement
connecting-up branchement *m*
connection accouplement *m*; branchement *m*; connexion *f*; contact *m*; montage *m*; raccordement *m*; couplage *m*
connection in parallel/in series montage *m* en parallèle/en série
connection to local electricity supply branchement *m* sur le secteur
connection to the mains branchement *m* sur le secteur
connector connecteur *m*; cosse *f*
connector between earth and earth wire (permitting resistance to be measured) barrette *f* de terre
connector plug fiche *f* de connexion
connector strip barrette *f* de connexion
CONSUEL attestation/certificate attestation *f* CONSUEL; certificat *m* CONSUEL
consumption (eg of electricity) dépense *f*; consommation *f*
contact contact *m*; plot *m*
contactor contacteur *m*
continuous continu, -e *adj*
control device (eg switch) appareil *m* de commande
control switch interrupteur *m* de contrôle
control(s) commande *f*
controlling commande *f*
convector convecteur *m*
cooker cuisinière *f*
cooker, electric cuisinière *f* électrique
cooking appliance appareil *m* de cuisson
copper cuivre *m*
copper core âme *f* en cuivre
cord (of electric appliance) fil *m*
cord (lead) cordon *m*
cordless sans fil
core âme *f*
counter compteur *m*
counting comptage *m*
couple (to) raccorder *v*
coupling accouplement *m*
coupling couplage *m*; montage *m*
cover capot *m*; couvercle *m*; gaine *f*
crimper pince *f* à sertir les cosses
cross-section section *f*
current courant *m*
current consumption consommation *f* de courant
current limiter limiteur *m* de courant
current-sensitive circuit-breaker disjonc-

teur *m* différentiel
curve (to) cintrer *v*
cut (to) couper *v*
cut off power from (to) delester *v*
cut off the power (to) couper *v* le courant
cut out (to) interrompre *v*
cut-off (to) couper *v*
cut-out coupe-circuit *m*
cut (power) coupure *f*
cutout box coffret *m* de coupe-circuit
cutting coupure *f*
cylinder fourreau *m*

dead wire fil *m* hors courant
dead (no current) hors *adj* courant
delaying temporisation *f*
dependability fiabilité *f*
dephasing déphasage *m*
device appareil *m*; dispositif *m*
diagram schéma *m*
diagram, wiring schéma *m* de montage
differential circuit-breaker disjoncteur *m*
differentiel; différentiel *m*
differential device différentiel *m*
differential switch interrupteur *m* différentiel
dimmer variateur *m* (de lumière)
direct coupling accouplement *m* direct
direct current (d.c.) courant *m* continu
direct current generator génératrice *f*
direct lighting éclairage *m* direct
disconnect (to) déconnecter *v*
disconnecting (a circuit) ouverture *f*
disconnection coupure *f*
disengage (to) déclencher *v*
disengagement déclanchement *m*; déclanchement *m*
dishwasher lave-vaisselle *m*
distribute (to) répartir *v*
distribution répartition *f*
distribution board tableau *m* (de) répartition; tableau *m* de distribution
distribution box coffret *m* de distribution; boîte *f* de connexion; boîte *f* de branchement; coffret *m* de répartition
divert (to) dériver *v*
dividers compas *m* à pointe sèche
division (into sections) sectionnement *m*

double wall socket prise *f* double
double-pole switch commutateur *m* bipolaire
down-stream (from) en aval (de); à l'aval
drill perceuse *f*
drum bobine *f*
dry battery pile *f* sèche
duct conduite *f*; gaine *f*; buse *f*
ducting goulotte *f*
dynamo dynamo *f*

earth (elect) masse *f*; prise *f* de terre; sol *m*; terre *f*
earth (soil) terre *f*
earth (to) mettre *v* à la masse; mettre *v* à terre
earth leakage circuit breaker disjoncteur *m* de perte à la terre
earth stake piquet *m* de terre
earth terminal borne *f* de terre
earthed (elect) au sol
earthing mise *f* à la terre
earthing cable/wire câble *m* de mise à la terre
earthing line (equipotential line) ligne *f* équipotentielle
earthing link (to water pipes, etc) liaison *f* équipotentielle
earthing rod piquet *m* de terre
earthing spike piquet *m* de terre
eclipse (safety guard in electric socket) éclipse *f*
EDF meter (for power requirements up to 9 kW) compteur *m* bleu
electric cable câble *m* électrique
electric charge charge *f*
electric circuit circuit *m* électrique
electric convection heater convecteur *m*
electric drill perceuse *f*
electric current generating set groupe *m* électrogène; groupe *m* générateur
electric immersion heater thermoplongeur *m*
electric light socket douille *f*
electric plug fiche *f* électrique
electric plug/socket prise *f* de courant mâle/femelle
electric power puissance *f*
electric shock choc *m* électrique

electric spark étincelle *f* électrique
electric switch (pear-shaped) poire *f* électrique
electric; electrical électrique *adj*
electrical accessories accessoires *mpl* électriques
electrical equipment appareillage *m* électrique
electrical fittings équipement *m* électrique
electrical installation appareillage *m*; installation *f* électrique
electrical network/system réseau *m* électrique
electrician électricien *m*
electricity électricité *f*
electricity supply alimentation *f* en électricité
electricity supply meter compteur *m* électrique
electrification électrification *f*
electrode électrode *f*
electromagnetic électromagnétique *adj*
electron électron *m*
electrostatic électrostatique *adj*
element élément *m*
embed (to) encastrer *v*
embedded conduit system montage *m* encastré
end-piece embout *m*
engage (to) (mechanism) enclencher *v*
entangled connections (wires) raccordements *mpl* enchevêtrés
equipment appareillage *m*
equipotential équipotentiel, -elle *adj*
equipotential connection liaison *f* équipotentielle
equipotential line ligne *f* équipotentielle
extension cable reel enrouleur *m* de câble
exterior box holding meter coffret *m* de comptage
exterior fittings équipement *m* extérieur
eyelet cosse *f*

failure défaillance *f*
farad farad *m*
fastener attache *f*
fault défaillance *f*; défaut *m*
filament (of electric bulb) fil *m*

fit a suppressor (to) antiparasiter *v*
fit flush (to) encastrer *v*
fitments équipement *m*
fitting accessoire *m*
fitting a suppressor to antiparasitage *m*
fitting out équipement *m*
fittings appareillage *m*; équipement *m*
fixing appareillage *m*
fixing (a cable) with clips or collars fixation *f* par collier
fixing collar (for electric cable) collier *m* de fixation
flat-nose pliers pince *f* plates
flex, heavy-duty câble *m*
flow of electricity écoulement *m* d'électricité
flow; flowing écoulement *m*
fluorescent lamp lampe *f* à fluorescence
fluorescent tube fluo *f*; un tube *m* fluo
flush fitting encastrement *m*
flush-fitted switch interrupteur *m* encastré
four-pole tétrapolaire *adj*
free-standing autonome *adj*
French electricity supply company EDF; Électricité de France
frequency fréquence *f*
frost stat thermostat *m* à gel
fuse fusible *m*; coupe-circuit *m*
fuse board tableau *m* de fusibles
fuse box boîte *f* à fusibles
fuse-holder fusible *m* tabatière
fuse of known rating fusible *m* calibré
fuse, intact/burnt out fusible *m* bon/grillé
fuse, main fusible *m* principal
fused circuit-breaker coupe-circuit *m* à fusible

gauge appareil *m* de mesure
generating générateur, -trice *adj*
generator dynamo *f*; générateur *m*; génératrice *f*
glue colle *f*
gluing collage *m*
grid réseau *m*
grid (electricity) réseau *m* électrique; grille *f*
grille grille *f*
grommet passe-fil *m*
groove saignée *f*
groove-cutting machine rainureuse *f*

ground masse *f*; sol *m*; terre *f*

halogen lamp lampe *f* halogène
hammer, electrician's marteau *m* d'électricien
hammer, club massette *f*
hanging lamp baladeuse *f*
heater appareil *m* de chauffage
henry henry *m*
hertz hertz *m*
high tension; HT haute tension *f*; HT
high voltage haute tension *f*; HT; haut voltage *m*
high voltage supply substation poste *m* de livraison H.T.
hold prise *f*
holding/fixing collar collier *m* de serrage
hot water cylinder with immersion heater cumulus *m* électrique
hot water heater circuit circuit *m* chauffe-eau
house wiring câblage *m* électrique intérieur
housing boîtier *m*; coffret *m*
housing for electrical fitment (eg switch) boîtier *m*
humidity-proof étanche *adj*

identification of conductors (by colour codes) identification *f* des conducteurs
illumination éclairage *m*
immersion heater thermoplongeur *m*
impedance impédance *f*
incandescent lamp lampe *f* à incandescence
independent autonome *adj*
indicator light lampe *f* témoin
indirect lighting éclairage *m* d'ambiance
induced current courant *m* induit
inductance inductance *f*
induction coil bobine *f* d'induction/inductrice
inductive current courant *m* inducteur
inspection lamp baladeuse *f*
installation, electrical installation *f* électrique; branchement *m*
installation diagram (wiring) schéma *m* d'implantation
insulating isolant,-e *adj*; isolateur,

isolatrice *adj*
insulating adhesive tape ruban *m* adhésif, isolant *m* électrique
insulating sheath (of wire or cable) enveloppe *f* isolante
insulating tape ruban *m* isolant; ruban isolateur *m*
insulating, flexible, deformable (conduit) ICD *abb*; isolant, cintrable, déformable
insulating, flexible, ordinary (conduit) ICO *abb*; isolant, cintrable, ordinaire
insulating, flexible, transversally elastic (conduit) ICT *abb*; isolant, cintrable, transversalement élastique
insulating, rigid, ordinary (conduit) IRO *abb*; isolant, rigide, ordinaire
insulation isolation *f*; isolement *m*
insulator isolant *m*; isolateur *m*
intensity intensité *f*
interconnect (to) interconnecter *v*
interconnection interconnexion *f*
interconnection substation poste *m* d'interconnexion
interference (radio,TV) bruits *mpl* parasites; parasites *mpl*; interférence *f*
interference suppression antiparasitage *m*
interrupt (to) interrompre *v*
ion ion *m*
isolation preventing electric shock séparation *f*
isolating switch sectionneur *m*

join (to) raccorder *v*
joining raccordement *m*
joule joule *m*
junction branchement *m*; dérivation *f*
junction box boîte *f* de dérivation; boîte *f* de jonction

knife, electrician's couteau *m* électricien

lamp lampe *f*; luminaire *m*
land terre *f*
lead cordon *m*
lead (metal) plomb *m*
lead accumulator accumulateur *m* au plomb

lead, extension cordon *m* prolongateur
lead, flexible cordon *m* souple
leakage écoulement *m*
lid capot *m*; couvercle *m*
light lampe *f*; luminaire *m*; lumière *f*
light bulb ampoule *f*
light bulb, 60W ampoule *f* en 60 W
light fitting point *m* lumineux
light point point *m* lumineux
light track glissière *f* des lumières
light up (to) allumer *v*
light switch and point allumage *m* simple
lighting éclairage *m*
lighting fitment luminaire *m*
lighting system réseau *m* d'éclairage
lightning foudre *f*
lightning protector déchargeur *m*; para-foudre *m*
lightning voltage surge protector protection *f* anti-foudre
lightning-arrester déchargeur *m*; para-foudre *m*
limited or selective lighting éclairage *m* ponctuel
limiter limiteur *m*
line ligne *f*
link up (to) brancher *v*
live actif, active *adj*
live (wire) phase *f*; fil *m* de phase; fil *m* sous tension
load-shedding délestage *m*
local electricity supply area secteur *m*
locate (to) repérer *v*
locating repérage *m*
low tension basse *f* tension
low voltage basse *f* tension; bas *m* voltage
low voltage current courant *m* basse ten-sion
lumen lumen *m*

magnetic permeability perméabilité *f* mag-nétique
main fuse fusible *m* principal
main switch board tableau *m* de commande principal
mains cable câble *m* de distribution
mains voltage tension *f* du secteur
mark repère *m*
mark (to) repérer *v*

mark out (to) repérer *v*
marker repère *m*
marker lights balisage *m*
marker staple cavalier *m* de repérage
marking repérage *m*
marking out repérage *m*
mass masse *f*
maximum voltage tension *f* maximale
measure (to) mesurer *v*
measurement mesure *f*
measuring device appareil *m* de mesure
medium voltage supply substation poste *m* de livraison MT (tension *f* moyenne)
meter compteur *m*
meter box (holding meter on exterior wall of house) coffret *m* de comptage.
metering comptage *m*
microfarad microfarad *m*
minus pole pôle *m* moins
module élément *m* modulaire
moulded casing (for wires, etc) moulure *f*
multi-cable housing goulotte *f*
multiple circuit accouplement *m* en quant-ité; couplage *m* en batterie
multiple connection couplage *m* en batterie; couplage *m* en parallèlle; couplage *m* en quantité
multiple socket block bloc *m* de prise de courant; bloc *m* multiprise
multiple wire connector bornier *m*

negative pole pôle *m* négatif
network réseau *m*
network with multiple supply lines réseau *m* interconnecté
neutral neutre *adj*
neutral wire fil *m* neutre
nippers pince *f*
no current hors *adj* courant
nominal nominal,-e, -aux *adj*
nominal current courant *m* nominal
non-insulated (bare) nu,-e *adj*
normal current courant *m* de regime

ohm ohm *m*
ohmmeter ohmmètre *m*
opening ouverture *f*

operational duration of battery-powered device autonomie *f*
out-of-service en repos *m*
outflow écoulement *m*
outside lamp/light luminaire *m* extérieur
overcurrent; excess current surintensité *f* de courant
overhead line ligne *f* aérienne
overload (to) surcharger *v*
overload device interrupteur *m* de surcharge
overload; overloading surcharge *f*
override switch interrupteur *m* de dérogation
overvoltage surtension *f*

panel panneau *m*
pass (to) parcourir *v*
pass wire through (to) enfiler *v*
peak current courant *m* de crête
peg cheville *f*; fiche *f*
period période *f*
permanent wiring câblage *m* permanent
permitivity permitivité *f*
phase phase *f*
picture lighting éclairage *m* des tableaux
pilot light lampe *f* témoin
pin broche *f*; cheville *f*; fiche *f*
pipe conduit *m*; fourreau *m*; tube *m*
plan (diagram) schéma *m*
plastic cable clip pontet *m* plastique
plastic conduit clip pontet *m* plastique
pliers pince *f*
pliers with adjustable head pince *f* multiprise
pliers, crimping, for terminal connectors pince *f* à sertir les cosses; pince *f* de sertissage
pliers, cutting pince *f* coupante
pliers, diagonal cut pince *f* coupante diagonale
pliers, flat-nose pince *f* à becs plats
pliers, round-nose pince *f* à becs ronds; pinces *f* rondes
pliers, universal pince *f* universelle
pliers, wire-cutting pince *f* coupante en bout
plug (elect) fiche *f*
plug in (to) brancher *v*
plug-in fuse fusible *m* à broche

plugging-in branchement *m*
plumb line fil *m* à plomb
plus pole pôle *m* plus
point point *m*; prise *f*
polarity polarité *f*
pole pôle *m*
▪ **2 poles (pins) and earth** = 2 pôles et terre (2P + T)
portable torch/lantern light éclairage *m* autonome
positive pole pôle *m* positif
potential potentiel *m*
power courant *m*; puissance *f*
power breaker strip barrette *f* de coupure
power consumption puissance *f* absorbée
power cut coupure *f*; coupure *f* de courant/ d'électricité; délestage *m*
power economiser délesteur *m*
power point prise *f*; prise *f* de courant
power rationer délesteur *m*
power supply alimentation *f* en énergie; courant *m* de secteur
primary/secondary coil bobine *f* primaire/ secondaire
primary/secondary voltage voltage *m* primaire/secondaire
programmable thermostat thermostat *m* électronique
programmable time-switch programmateur, -trice *m/f*
programming programmation *f*
programming in 2 hour intervals programmation *f* par tranche de 2 heures
projection saillie *f*
PROMOTOLEC *abb* Association pour le Promotion de la Qualité des Installations Électriques (see French entry)
protected (safety) socket socle *m* à éclipses
protection protection *f*
protective sheath (of wire or cable) enveloppe *f* protectrice; gaine *f* de protection
pull-through (for cables) tire-fil *m*
pumice block cale *f* à poncer
push button bouton *m* poussoir
push-button switch interrupteur *m* à poussoir
put (to) mettre *v*
put in place (to) poser *v*

put power back on again (to) rétablir _v_ le courant

radiant heating panel panneau _m_ radiant
radio-command switch interrupteur _m_ radio
razor point prise _f_ pour résoir électrique
receiver récepteur _m_
rechargeable battery accu _m_ rechargeable
rectifier redresseur _m_
reel bobine _f_
reel, extension cable enrouleur _m_ de câble
reestablish rétablir _v_
regulation réglage _m_
relay relais _m_
release déclanchement _m_; déclenchement
release (to) déclencher _v_
reliability fiabilité _f_
remote-control switch interrupteur _m_ à distance
remote control switching device télérupteur _m_
remotely operated appliance contacteur _m_
removable amovible _adj_
removable appliance appareil _m_ amovible
resistance résistance _f_
resistivity résistivité _f_
resting en repos _m_
restore rétablir _v_
rheostat rhéostat _m_
rigid cable câble _m_ rigide
ring-main réseau _m_ primaire en boucle
rod barre _f_
roll bobine _f_

safety shutter in electric socket éclipse _f_
sander ponceuse _f_
sanding block cale _f_ à poncer
scheme projet _m_; plan _m_
scissors, electricians' ciseaux _mpl_ d'électricien
scraper, triangular grattoire _m_ triangulaire
screen (to) (elect) blinder _v_
screening (elect) blindage _m_
screw bulb socket douille _f_ à vis
screwdriver tournevis _m_
screwdriver, cross-point tip tournevis _m_ pour vis cruciforme

screwdriver, Phillips™ tournevis _m_ pour vis phillips™
screwdriver, tester tournevis _m_ testeur
screwed cap culot _m_ à vis; culot _m_ taraudé
sealant enduit _m_ étanche
section élément _m_; section _f_
section circuit-breaker disjoncteur _m_ divisionnaire
sector secteur _m_
selectivity sélectivité _f_
self-contained autonome _adj_
self-contained source (eg torch battery) source _f_ autonome
sensitivity sensibilité _f_
sensor operated lighting éclairage _m_ automatique
separation séparation _f_
separator sectionneur _m_
series connection couplage _m_ en série; couplage _m_ en cascade
setting réglage _m_
severance sectionnement _m_
shears cisaille _f_; cisailles _fpl_
sheath gaine _f_; fourreau _m_
sheathing material (of cable) gaine _f_ de bourrage
short-circuit court-circuit _m_
short-circuit (to) court-circuiter _v_
shunt (to) dériver _v_
shunt dérivation _f_
shuttle wires; change-over wires fils _mpl_ navettes
shutter obturateur _m_
shuttered socket socle _m_ à éclipses
single conductor conducteur _m_ unique
single phase monophasé,-e _adj_; uniphasé,-e _adj_
single-pole unipolaire _adj_
single pole switch interrupteur _m_ unipolaire
single principal supply line antenne _f_
single wire unifilaire _adj_
single-phase current courant _m_ monophasé
sleeve fourreau _m_; buse _f_
slot-drilling machine rainureuse _f_
small bar or strip barrette _f_
socket prise _f_; prise _f_ de courant; socle _m_
socket (20A) with earth prise _f_ 20A+ T(erre)
socket cover cache-prise _m_

socket end embout *m* femelle

socket with 2 holes without/with earth prise *f* à 2 alvéoles sans/avec contact de terre

socket with safety shields socle *m* à éclipses

soil sol *m*; terre *f*

solar panel absorbeur *m*

solid metal strip conductor barre *f*

solid wire core âme *f* massive

source source *f*

source of energy source *f* d'énergie

spanner; key clé *f*; clef *f*

spanner, open-end clé *f* à fourche; clef *f* à fourche

spanner, ring clé *f* fermée; clef *f* fermée

spare terminal borne *f* de réserve

specific resistance résistivité *f*

spirit-level niveau *m* à bulle

splice épissure *f*

spool bobine *f*

spot light applique *f* électrique; spot *m*

spotlight projecteur *m*

stand socle *m*

standard lamp lampadaire *m*

standard specification norme *f*

staple cavalier *m*

star; Y (connected) étoile *f*

star- or Y- connection montage *m* en étoile; étoile *f*

star-connection couplage *m* en étoile

star-delta connection montage *m* en étoile-triangle

start (up) (to) démarrer *v*

step-down transformer transformateur *m* reducteur de tension

step-up transformer transformateur *m* élévateur de tension

stepped up survolté,-e *adj*

sticking collage *m*

storage battery accumulateur *m*

strand (of wire) brin *m*

stranded wire cable câble *m* métallique

strap attache *f*

strip of 12 (wire) connectors barrette *f* de 12 dominos

strip-light applique *f* électrique

supply (to) alimenter *v*

supply; supply system alimentation *f*

suppressor dispositif *m* anti-parasite; anti-parasite *m*

surface-mounted apparent,-e *adj*; saillie *f*

surface-mounted installation installation *f* apparente

surge protector, lightning voltage protection *f* anti-foudre

surroundings ambiance *f*

switch interrupteur *m*; bouton *m*

switch (pear-shaped) poire *f*

switch and light point; switch and socket allumage *m* simple

switch box coffret *m* d'interrupteur

switch, control interrupteur *m* de contrôle

switch, changeover commutateur *m*

switch, delayed-action interrupteur *m* à action retardée

switch, differential interrupteur *m* différentiel

switch, electronic interrupteur *m* électronique

switch, flush-fitted interrupteur *m* encastré

switch, override interrupteur *m* de dérogation

switch, push-button interrupteur *m* à poussoir

switch, radio-command interrupteur *m* radio

switch, remote-control interrupteur *m* à distance

switch, residual current interrupteur *m* différentiel

switch, selector commutateur *m*

switch, single-pole interrupteur *m* unipolaire

switch, time interrupteur *m* horaire; interrupteur *m* à minuterie; minuterie *f*; programmeur *m*

switch, time-delay interrupteur *m* à relais temporisé

switch, touch sensitive interrupteur *m* électronique

switch, trip disjoncteur *m*

switch, tumbler interrupteur *m* à bascule

switch, two-pole interrupteur *m* bipolaire

switch, two-way interrupteur *m* de va-et-vient; commutateur *m* va-et-vient

switch off (to) couper *v*

switch on (to) (light) allumer *v*

switch on (to) (electrical appliance) démarrer *v*; enclencher *v*

switch-board tableau *m* de commutateurs

switching on lighting allumage *m*

system réseau *m*

tap (wire, conductor) branchement *m*
tapping branchement *m*
temperature controller thermostat *m*
d'ambiance
tension tension *f*
terminal borne *f*
terminal connector (spade, fork or ring type) cosse *f* électrique
terminal cover cache-fils *m*
tester screwdriver tournevis *m* testeur
thermostat thermostat *m*
thread fil *m*
thread (to) enfiler *v*
three-phase triphasé,-e *adj*
three-phase current courant *m* triphasé
three-phase current, mesh/delta/triangle connected courant *m* triphasé, montage *m* en triangle
three-phase current, star connected courant *m* triphasé, montage *m* en étoile
three-pole tripolaire *adj*
threshold seuil *m*
threshold of action sensibilité *f*
tie attache *f*
time progamme programmation *f*
time programmable thermostat thermostat *m* à horloge
time-delay device temporisation *f*
time-delay switch interrupteur *m* à relais temporisé
time-switch interrupteur *m* horaire; minuterie *f*; programmeur *m*
timer temporisateur *m*; temporisation *f*
tongs pince *f*
top couvercle *m*
transformer transformateur *m*
transformer substation poste *m* de transformation
transmission transmission *f*
traverse (to) parcourir *v*
triggering off déclanchement *m*; déclenchement *m*
trip déclencheur *m*; déclancheur *m*
trip (to) déclencher *v*
trip-switch disjoncteur *m*
triple pole; tripolar tripolaire *adj*

tripping déclanchement *m*; déclenchement *m*
trowel truelle *f*
trunking goulotte *f*
tube tube *m*
tube (flourescent) lampe *f* tubulair; tube *m* fluorescent
tweezers brucelles *fpl*
twisted strand wire core âme *f* câblée
twisted strands (of wire) brins *mpl* torsadés
two-phase, four-wire alternating current courant *m* alternatif diphasé à quatre conducteurs
two-pin bipolaire *adj*
two-pin socket prise *f* bipolaire (2P)
two-pin socket with earth prise *f* bipolaire (2P + T)
two-pole; double pole bipolaire *adj*
two-way connecting block domino *m* bipolaire
two-way on/off switch interrupteur *m* de va-et-vient (often shortened to 'va-et-vient')
two-wire connector borne *f*

unit élément *m*
up-stream amont (en); amont (à l')
UTE UTE (Union Technique de l'Électricité)
utiliser of electricity récepteur *m*

variable control variateur *m*
verify (to) vérifier *v*
very low tension/voltage TBT; T.B.T.; très basse tension *f*
visible apparent,-e *adj*
volt volt *m*
voltage tension *f*; voltage *m*
voltage limiter limiteur *m* de tension
voltmeter voltmètre *m*

wall convector heater convector *m* mural
wall insert (switch) box boîte *f* d'encastrement
wall lamp applique *f*; applique *f* électrique
wall light applique *f*
wall lighting éclairage *m* par appliques
wall socket prise *f* murale
wall-plug cheville *f*

warning light lampe *f* témoin
washing machine lave-linge *m*
waterproof étanche *adj*
watertight étanche *adj*
watt watt *m*
wattage puissance *f*; consommation *f* en watts
wattmeter wattmètre *m*
winding enroulement *m*
wire fil *m*
wire a house (to) poser *v* des fils dans une maison
wire cable câble *m* métallique
wire colour couleur *f* des conducteurs; (see 'colour of wires')
wire connector with screws barrette *f*

wire cutter coupe-fil *m*; cisaille *f*; cisailles *fpl*
wire cutters pince *f* coupante en bout
wire rope câble *m* métallique
wire stripper outil *m* à dégainer les câbles; pince *f* à dénuder
wire-stripper, automatic pince *f* à dénuder automatique
wire varnish removing tool pince *f* gratte-laque
wiring câblage *m*
wiring installation installation *f* électrique
wiring-up montage *m*

Y-connection couplage *m* en étoile

12. PLASTERER

accomplishment exécution *f*
additive additif *m*; adjuvant *m*
adhesive cement (eg for plaster blocks) mortier *m* adhésif
angle bead; angle fishplate éclisse *f* cornière
apply (to) étaler *v*
apply a textured paint (to) crépir *v*

binding serrage *m*
blade lame *f*
board plaque *f*
board, ceiling fire-resistant plaque *f* coupe-feu
board, combined plaster and expanded polystyrene plaque *f* de plâtre + polystyrène
board, combined plaster and glass wool plaque *f* de plâtre + laine de verre
board, combined plaster and mineral wool plaque *f* de plâtre + laine de roche
board, ribbed plaque *f* nervurée
board, staff plaque *f* de staff

board, thin ceiling plaque *f* mince
botch (to) gâcher *v*

carry out (to) exécuter *v*
carrying out exécution *f*
case coffre *m*
ceiling plafond *m*; plafonnage *m*
ceiling boarded with panel strips plafond *m* lambrissé
ceiling boarding/shuttering coffrage *m* de plafond
ceiling light plafonnier *m*
ceiling material plafonnage *m*
ceiling on counter-laths plafond *m* sur contre-lattes
ceiling on laths plafond *m* sur lattes
ceiling ornaments plafonnement *m*
ceiling rose rosace *f*
ceiling, boarded plafond *m* en lambris; plafonnage *m*
ceiling, coffered plafond à caissons *m*
ceiling, false faux plafond *m*
ceiling, intermediate faux plafond *m*

ceiling, panelled plafond *m* lambrissé
ceiling, panelled/boarded plafond *m* en lambris
ceiling, reed-lath plafond *m* sur canisse
ceiling, suspended faux plafond *m*; plafond *m* suspendu
ceiling, traditional plafond *m* traditionnel
coat couche *f*; enduit *m*
coat, coupling couche *f* d'accrochage
coat, finishing couche *f* de finition; enduit *m* de finition
coat, first plaster couche *f* d'approche; gobetis *m*
coat, floating enduit *m* de lissage
coat, initial couche *f* d'approche; gobetis *m*
coat, jointing enduit *m* pour joints
coat, polymer based textured enduit *m* plastique
coat, priming couche *f* d'impression
coat, render gobetis *m*
coat, roughing-in gobetis *m*
coat, setting couche *f* de finition
coat, smoothing enduit *m* de lissage
coat, thin couche fin *f*
coating enduit *m*
coating knife couteau *m* à enduire
coating palette palette à enduire *f*
coating, textured enduit *m* coupé
coffering coffrage *m*
combing ratissage *m*
compaction (of plaster) serrage *m*
completing the joints exécution *f* des joints
construct a ceiling (to) plafonner *v*
constructor of ceilings plafonneur *m*
contract (to) contracter (se) *v*; rétracter (se) *v*
copper wire fil *m* de cuivre
cornice corniche *f*
corrosion corrosion *f*
counter-lath contre-latte *f*
counter-lath (to) contre-latter *v*
coving corniche *f*
coving, plaster corniche *f* en plâtre
coving, polystyrene corniche *f* en polystyrène
coving, polyurethane corniche *f* en polyuréthane
coving, wood corniche *f* en bois
crack fente *f*; fissure *f*

deaden (to) hourder *v*
deadened beam poutrelle *f* hourdis
deadening hourdis *m*
deafen (to) hourder *v*
deafening hourdis *m*
dilate (to) dilater (se) *v*
do (to) exécuter *v*
draughtproof (to) calfeutrer *v*
draughtproofing calfeutrage *m*; calfeutrement *m*
dressing (a surface) dressage *m*
dry (to) sécher *v*
dry out (to) sécher *v*
drying; drying out séchage *m*

embed (to) sceller *v*
end of setting fin *m* de prise
expand (to) gonfler *v*; dilater (se) *v*
expanded metal trellis métal *m* déployé

fastener agrafe *f*
fill (to) calfeutrer *v*
fill in (to) reboucher *v*
fill in again (to) reboucher *v*
fill in with plaster raccord *m* au plâtre
filler reboucheur *m*
filling bourrage *m*; calfeutrage *m*; calfeutrement *m*
filling in raccord *m*
filling up bouchage *m*; rebouchage *m*; rebouchement *m*
fine fin, fine *adj*
finish fini *m*
fissure fente *f*; fissure *f*
fixing accrochage *m*
float taloche *f*; palette *f* à enduire
float (to) talocher *v*
form (for plaster) coffre *m*
form hollows (to) creuser (se) *v*
formwork coffrage *m*
frame; framework ossature *f*
framework, hidden ossature *f* cachée
framework, metal (eg of a suspended ceiling) ossature *f* métallique
fulfilment exécution *f*

glass fibre fibre *f* de verre
glued calico strip bande *f* calicot collée
gripping accrochage *m*
groove (eg on a surface) saignée *f*
groove (to) rainurer *v*
gypsum gypse *m*
gypsum-quarry plâtrière *f*

hang up (to) suspendre *v*
hanging accrochage *m*
hatchet, plasterer's hatchette *f* de plâtrier
hawk, plasterer's taloche *f*
hawk, pointed plastic taloche *f* plastique
  pointue
hook agrafe *f*; crochet *m*
hook, suspension crochet *f* de suspension
hooking accrochage *m*

interior wall facing doublage *m*

jack cric *m*; vérin *m*
jack, hydraulic vérin *m* hydraulique
jack, lifting cric *m*
jack, timber cric *m* de charpentier
join raccord *m*
joint filler pâte *f* à joints; pâte *f* de
  remplissage
jointing coat enduit *m* pour joints
jointing tape; scrim bande *f* à joint
joist spacing; joist interval entraxe *m* des
  solives
jute jute *m*

key accrochage *m*
keying accrochage *m*
knife, coating couteau *m* à enduire
knife, palette couteau *m* à enduire; couteau *m*
  à palette
knife, smoothing couteau *m* plaquiste

lagging lattis *m*
larry or trowel (plasterer's) gâche *f*
lath latte *f*
lath, counter- contre-latte *f*

lath, counter- (to) contre-latter *v*
lath (to) latter *v*
lath hammer hatchette *f* de plâtrier
lathing lattage *m*; lattis *m*
lathing, close lattage *m* jointif
lathing, expanded metal lattis *m* métallique
lathing, metal lattis *m* métallique
lathing, reed lattis *m* abris; lattis *m* en
  roseaux rond
lathing, reinforced lattis *m* armé
lathing, round-reed lattis *m* abris
lathing, spaced lattage *m* espacé; lattis *m*
  espacé
lathing, split-reed lattis *m* canis; lattis *m* en
  roseaux refendus
laths tied with twisted wire lattis *m* mécanique
laths, wire-tied lattis *m* armé
lathwork lattis *m*
lattice of wood strips held together with
  galvanised wire baccula *m*
lattice work treillis *m* métallique
layer enduit *m*
layer of plaster, initial couche *f* d'approche
layer of rough plaster on a lattice hourdis *m*
level (to); make level (to) égaliser *v*
lime chaux *f*
lime, quick/slaked chaux *f* vive/éteinte
lime putty mastic *m* à la chaux
lining coffrage *m*; doublage *m*

make level (to) égaliser *v*
make smooth (to) lisser *v*
mason's tubular shore/stay étai *m* de maçon
  tubulaire
mesh maille *f*
mesh of metal lath trellis maille *f* d'un treillis métallique
metal trellis treillis *m* métallique
mix (to) gâcher *v*
moulding moulure *f*

overlap; overlapping chevauchement *m*

paint, wall and ceiling peinture *f* murs et
  plafonds

palette knife couteau *m* à palette
partition cloison *f*
plaster plâtre *m*
plaster (to) plâtrer *v*
plaster base support *m* du plâtre
plaster block (used for partitions, etc) carreau *m* de plâtre
plaster coat applied with a sprayer enduit *m* plâtre projeté mécaniquement
plaster for moulding plâtre *m* à mouler
plaster for outside use plâtre *m* pour les enduits extérieurs
plaster for plaster bricks plâtre *m* à briqueter
plaster for spraying plâtre *m* à projeter
plaster of Paris plâtre *m* de moulage
plaster over (to) boucher *v*
plaster rendering crépi *m*
plaster support support *m* du plâtre
plasterwork les plâtres
plaster to give smooth finish plâtre *m* de surfaçage
plaster up (to) boucher *v*
plaster, coarse plâtre *m* gros
plaster, fair faced enduit *m* lisse de plâtre
plaster, filling-in plâtre *m* à modeler
plaster, fine plâtre *m* fin
plaster, finishing coat plâtre *m* fin; enduit *m* de lissage plâtre; couche *f* de finition
plaster, first-coat plâtre *m* gros
plaster, modelling plaster plâtre *m* à modeler
plaster, ordinary plâtre *m* courant
plaster, rendering coat plâtre *m* gros
plaster, setting coat plâtre *m* fin
plaster, single-coat enduit *m* monocouche
plaster, smoothing coat enduit *m* de lissage plâtre
plaster, standard plâtre *m* courant
plaster, thick/thin coating of enduit *m* au plâtre épais/fin
plaster, very high hardness plâtre *m* THD (très haute dureté)
plaster, coarse plâtre *m* gros
plasterboard placoplâtre™ *f*; plaque *f* de plâtre
plasterboard nail pointe *f* pour plaque de plâtre
plasterboard with cardboard facing

plaque *f* cartonnée
plasterboard with honeycomb core plaque *f* à âme alvéolée
plasterer plâtrier *m*
plasterer's brick (hollow brick) brique *f* plâtrière
plasterer's float taloche *f*; palette *f* à enduire
plasterer's hatchet hatchette *f* de plâtrier
plasterer's hawk (board) taloche *f*
plasterer's putty mastic à *m* la chaux
plasterer's scraper grattoir *m* de plâtrier; riflard *m*
plastering plâtrage *m*; plâtrerie *f*
plasters, special-purpose plâtres *f* spéciaux
plasterwork plâtrage *m*; plâtrerie *f*
plug (to) boucher *v*
pug (to) hourder *v*
pugging hourdis *m*
put in a ceiling (to) plafonner *v*
putty, lime mastic *m* à la chaux
putty, plasterer's mastic *m* à la chaux

quick/slaked lime chaux *f* vive/éteinte

raking ratissage *m*
ready for use prêt *adj* à l'emploi
render (to) crépir *v*
render (with) (to) enduire *v* (de)
rendering enduit *m*
restopping rebouchage *m*; rebouchement *m*
retract (to) rétracter (se) *v*
rib nervure *f*
rib (to) nervurer *v*
rough-walling hourdis *m*
roughcast (rendering) crépi *m* intérieur
roughcast (to) crépir *v*
rubbing down ponçage *m*

sanding (down) ponçage *m*
scraper, plasterer's grattoir *m* de plâtrier; riflard *m*
scratcher taloche *f* à pointes
seal (to) sceller *v*
setting (plaster, cement) prise *m*
setting accelerator accélérateur *m* de prise

setting retarder ralentisseur *m* de prise
setting, end of fin *m* de prise
setting, start of début *m* de prise
sharp (blade) bien affilé; fin, fine *adj*
sheet plaque *f*
sheet metal casing coffrage *m* en tôle
shore/stay, mason's tubular étai *m* de maçon
  tubulaire
shrink (to) contracter (se) *v*; rétracter (se) *v*
shuttering coffrage *m*
slab plaque *f*
smooth (to); make smooth (to) lisser *v*
smoothing lissage *m*
smoothing palette palette *f* à enduire
smoothing tool couteau *m* plaquiste
spanning chevauchement *m*
split fente *f*
spread (to) étaler *v*
staff (a mixture of tow and plaster) staff *m*
staple agrafe *f*
steel strip feuillard *m* d'acier
stemming bourrage *m*
stop up (to) calfeutrer *v*
stopper reboucheur *m*
stopping bouchage *m*, rebouchage *m*;
  rebouchement *m*
stopping material reboucheur *m*
stopping up calfeutrage *m*; calfeutrement *m*
stopping up again rebouchage *m*; rebouchement *m*
strip lame *f*
stuff (to); pack (to) bourrer *v*
stuffing bourrage *m*
suspend (to) suspendre *v*
suspended suspendu,-e *adj*
suspender crochet *f* de suspension; suspente *f*
suspender, steel or iron strip feuillard *m*
  d'acier
suspending suspension *f*
suspension suspension *f*
suspension arrangement dispositif *f* de suspension
suspension piece dispositif *f* de suspension;
  suspente *f*
swell (to) dilater (se) *v*; gonfler *v*

tamping bourrage *m*
tape, jointing; bande *f* à joint
taping the joints exécution *f* des joints
temper (to) (plaster) gâcher *v*
tempering gâchage *m*
textured wall paint crépi *m* interieur
thick/thin coating of plaster enduit *m* au
  plâtre épais/fin
thin fin, fine *adj*
three coat plastering enduit *m* en trois
  couches
tightening serrage *m*
tow filasse *f*
trellis, metal treillis *m* métallique
trowel truelle *f*
trowel, berthelet truelle *f* berthelet
trowel, finishing platoir *m*
trowel, jointing truelle *f* à joint
trowel, oval-ended smoothing platoir *m* bout
  ovale
trowel, plasterer's truelle *f*; gâche *f*
trowel, pointing truelle *f* langue de chat
trowel, rectagular platoir *m*
trowel, scratch taloche *f* à pointes
trowel, toothed truelle *f* bretellée; truelle *f*
  berthelet
trowel, triangular truelle *f* triangulaire

underside of a floor sous-face *f* d'un
  plancher

vermiculite vermiculite *f*

wall and ceiling paint peinture *f* murs et
  plafonds
wall paint, textured crépi *m* intérieur
wallboard plaque *f* de plâtre
waste (to) gâcher *v*
wire netting treillis *m* métallique
wire netting with intersections protected by
  ceramic buttons treillis *m* céramique
wrinkle (to) creuser (se) *v*

13. PAINTER AND DECORATOR

abrasive abrasif *m*
abrasive disc disque *m* abrasif
abrasive sheet feuille *f* abrasive
accessory accessoire *m*
acrylic paint peinture *f* acrylique
additive additif *m*; adjuvant *m*
adhesion adhérence *f*
adhesive tile mortar mortier *m* colle
  carrelage
anti-corrosion primer apprêt *m* anti-
  corrosion
antirust (paint) antirouille *f*; also *adj*
antirust paint peinture *f* antirouille
arris arête *f*
artisan artisan *m*

bare surface surface *f* nue
beeswax cire *f* d'abeilles
bicoloured bicolore *adj*
bitumastic paint peinture *f* bitumineuse
blemish souillure *f*
blend (to) mélanger *v*
blowlamp lampe *f* à souder; chalumeau *m*
boat varnish vernis *m* bateau
body corps *m*
boiled linseed oil huile *f* de lin cuite; huile *f*
  de lin bouillie
brush brosse *f*; pinceau *m*
brush (to) brosser *v*
burn off (to) (paint) décaper *v* au chalumeau

cement mastic *m*
cement or plaster rendering crépi *m*
cement, adhesive colle *f*
ceramic wall tile carreau *m* de faïence
cladding revêtement *m*; matériau *m* de
  revêtement
clean (to) nettoyer *v*; décaper *m*
cleaner nettoyant *m*
cleaning nettoyage *m*; nettoiement *m*;
  décapage *m*
cleansing nettoyage *m*; nettoiement *m*
coat couche *f*; enduit *m*
coat (to) revêtir *v*; enduire *v*
coating revêtement *m*

coating; coat enduit *m*
coating knife couteau *m* à enduire
coating material matériau *m* de revêtement
coating with masonry paint crépissage *m*
colour couleur *f*; coloris *m*
comb for tile adhesive peigne *f* à colle
  carrelage
cover (to) tapisser *v*; revêtir *v*; enduire *v*
cover with masonry paint (to) crépir *v*
covering revêtement *m*
covering material matériau *m* de revêtement
crack fissure *f*
cracking fissuration *f*
crackle (fine cracks) craquelure *f*
craftsman artisan *m*
cutting knife couteau *m*
cutting knife with fixed blade couteau *m* à
  lame fixe
cutting knife with retractable blade couteau *m* à lame retractable
cutting tool with disposable blades
  cutter *m*

decorate (to) décorer *v*
decoration décoration *f*
decorator (interior) décorateur *m*; décoratrice *f*
denatured alcohol alcool *m* dénaturé
detergent détergent *m*
detergent floor cleaner shampooing *m*
  parquet
distemper badigeon *m*
distemper (to) badigeonner *v*
double layer; double coat bi-couche *f*
draught-excluder bourrelet *m*
draughtproof (to) calfeutrer *v*
draughtproofing calfeutrage *m*; calfeutrement *m*
drill foret *m*
drill, impact foret *m* à percussion
drill, rotary/twist foret *m* hélicoïdal
drying time temps *m* de séchage
durable durable *adj*

edge arête *f*
embossed (wallpaper) expansé,-e *adj*
emulsion paint peinture *f* emulsion
emulsion paint roller rouleau *m* laqueur
souple
enamel peinture *f* laquée; peinture *f* vernissante
expanded expansé,-e *adj*
exterior paint peinture *f* extérieure

face (to) revêtir *v*
facing revêtement *m*
fade (to) pâlir *v*; perdre *v* son éclat; décolorer (se) *v*
fill (to) calfeutrer *v*
filler reboucheur *m*; calfeutrage *m*; calfeutrement *m*
filling in rebouchage *m*
finish fini *m*; finition *f*
finishing finition *f*
finishing coat or layer couche *f* de finition
fissure fissure *f*
fittings; fitments garniture *f*
flat brush pinceau *m* plat
floor covering revêtement *m* du sol
floor paint peinture *f* sol
floor tile carreau *m* de carrelage; carreau *m*
par terre
floor tiles; floor tiling carrelage *m* de sol
frieze frise *f*

general purpose scissors ciseaux *mpl* multi-
usages
glass cloth; glass fabric toile *f* de verre
glass drill foret *m* pour le verre
gloss lustre *f*
gloss brillant,-e *adj*
gloss paint peinture *f* brillante
glue colle *f*
gluing collage *m*
grout enduit *m* de jointoiement; coulis *m*
grout (to) mastiquer *v*
grouting for tiles ciment *m* joint
carrelage

hacking knife couteau *m* à démastiquer
hammer drill marteau-perforateur *m*

hanging tenture *f*
hole cutter coupe-trou *m*
house painter peintre *m/f* en bâtiment

imitation tile wall covering revêtement *m*
mural imitation carrelage
inside intérieur *m*; also *adj*
interior intérieur *m*; also *adj*
interior coating enduit *m* intérieur
interior designer ensemblier *m*
interior paint peinture *f* intérieure
interior rendering enduit *m* intérieur

jacket garniture *f*

knife blade lame *f* de couteau

lac laque *f*
lacquer laque *f*
lacquer (to) vernir *v*
lacquered laqué,-e *adj*
lacquering vernissage *m*
lagging garniture *f*
lay a wooden or parquet floor (to) parqueter *v*
layer couche *f*
layer ready for covering (*eg* with tiles)
couche *f* de revêtement
level (to) aplanir *v*
light roller rouleau *m* léger
line (to) revêtir *v*; tapisser *v*; maroufler *v*
lining revêtement *m* enduit
lining material matériau *m* de revêtement
lining paper (wall) papier *m* à tapisser
linseed oil huile *f* de lin
long lasting durable *adj*

machine for applying masonry paint
machine *f* à crépir
make ready (to) apprêter *v*
marble marbre *m*
marine varnish vernis *m* marin
masking tape papier-cache *m* adhésif
masonry paint crépi *m*; peinture *f* crépi
masonry paint roller rouleau *m* crépi
mastic gun pistolet *m* à mastic
material; materials matériau *m*;

matériaux *mpl*
matt mat,-e *adj*
methylated spirit alcool *m* à brûler; alcool *m* dénaturé
mix (to) melanger *v*
multiple coatings; multicoat multicouche *adj*

new neuf, neuve *adj*
non-drip antigoutte *adj*

obstruction obstruction *f*; bouchon *m*; bouchage *m*

paint peinture *f*
paint (to) peindre *v*
paint roller rouleau *m* à peinture
paint stripper décapant *m*
paint the woodwork (to) peindre *v* les boiseries
paintbrush brosse *f*
painter peintre *m/f*
painter and decorator peintre-décorateur *m*
painting peinture *f*
painting pad tampon *m* à peindre
paintwork peinture *f*
palette knife couteau *m* de peintre; couteau *m* à palette
pane (window) vitre *f*; carreau *m*
paperhanger's brush brosse *f* de tapissier; balai *m* à encoller
parquet floor; wooden floor parquet *m*
paste (to) maroufler *v*; encoller *v*
paste colle *f*
pasting knife couteau *m* à maroufler
pavement pavage *m*
paving pavage *m*
pick out (to) (with another colour paint) réchampir *v*
picking out (with another colour paint) réchampissage *v*
plug (to); plug up (to) boucher *v*
plugging; plugging up bouchage *m*
plugging and filling prior to wallpapering bordage *m*
prepare (to) apprêter *v*
prepasted préencollé,-e *adj*

prime (to) (surface for painting) apprêter *v*; primer *v*; imprimer *v*
priming coat couche *f* d'impression; première *f* couche
protect (to) protéger *v*
protective coating peinture *f* protectrice
protective coating for marble protection *f* des marbres
protector and brightener for marble entretien *m* et brillant des marbres
pumice ponce *f*
pumice stone pierre *f* ponce
putty mastic *m*
putty (to) mastiquer *v*
putty knife couteau *m* à mastiquer

raw linseed oil huile *f* de lin crue
refurbish (to) remettre *v* à neuf
render (to) crépir *v*
rendering crépi *m*; enduit *m*
rendering crépissage *m*
renovate (to) remettre *v* à neuf
repaint (to) repeindre *v*
ridge arête *f*
roll (eg of wallpaper) rouleau *m*
roller rouleau *m*
roof paint peinture *m* toiture
roughcast crépi *m*
roughcast (to) crépir *v*
roughcasting crépissage *m*
roughness aspérité *f*
round brush with shaped bristles pinceau *m* rond à réchampir
rubber squeegee raclette *f* caoutchouc

sand (to) décaper *v* au papier de verre; poncer *v*
sandblast (to) décaper *v* à la sableuse
sanding décapage *m*; ponçage *m*
sandpaper papier *m* de verre
satin finish satiné,-e *adj*
satin-finish paint peinture *f* satineé
scrape (to) gratter *v*
scraper grattoir *m*
screed laid as floor surface chape *f* d'usure
screed layed as base for floor covering chape *f* de revêtement

scrub (to) brosser *v*
seal (to) sceller *v*; boucher *v*
sealant enduit *m* étanche
sealing bouchage *m*
seam roller (wallpaper) roulette *f* pour écraser les joints de papier peint
self-smoothing fix and grout (for floor tiles) ragréage *m* autolissant
set of tools ensemble *m* d'outils; outillage *m*
setting coat couche *f* de finition
shade coloris *m*; couleur *f*; teinte *f*
shave-hook grattoir *m* triangulaire
shellac laque *f*
shellac (to) laquer *v*
shine lustre *f*
shiny finish brillant,-e *adj*
size; sizing (sealing) apprêt *m*
skimming coat couche *f* de finition
smooth (to) lisser *v*
smooth out (to) aplanir *v*
smooth surface surface *f* lisse
spatula spatule *f*
spirit of turpentine essence *f* de térébenthine
sponge éponge *f*
sponge rubber caoutchouc *m* mousse
stain souillure *f*; tache *f*
stain (tint) teinte *f*
stain (to) teinter *v*
stop up (to) boucher *v*; calfeutrer *v*
stoppage bouchage *m*
stopping knife couteau *m* à mastiquer
stopping putty mastic *m* calfeutrement
stopping up bouchage *m*; calfeutrage *m*; calfeutrement *m*
strip (to) (eg paint) décaper *m*
stripping (eg paint) décapage *m*
stripping knife couteau *m* à décaper
substance corps *m*
surface superficie *f*; surface *f*; revêtement *m*
surface cracking faïençage *m*

tapestry tapisserie *f*
tar-brush brosse *f* à goudronner
teak oil huile *f* de teck
textile-type wall covering revêtement *m* mural textile
textured paint peinture *f* crépi, crépi *m*

textured wall paint crépi *m*
tile carreau *m*
tile (to) carreler *v*
tile adhesive, paste form colle *f* carrelage en pâte
tile chisel ciseau *m* pour carreaux
tile cleaner décapant *m*
tile clippers pince *f* à rogner
tile cutter coupe-carreaux *m*
tile cutting pliers pince *f* coupe carreaux
tile drill foret *m* pour carreaux
tile floor carrelage *m*
tile-spacers croisillons *mpl*
tiled floor carreau *m*
tiles; tiling carrelage *m*; carrelage *m* de revêtement
tint teinte *f*
top coat couche *f* de finition
turpentine térébenthine *f*
twist drill foret *m* hélicoïdal
two coats of paint peinture *f* à deux couches
two-colour; two-tone bicolore *adj*

unbroken surface surface *f* nue
undercoat sous-couche *f*
unevenness aspérité *fo*
upholsterer tapissier *m*
upholstery tapisserie *f*

varnish vernis *m*
varnish (to) vernir *v*
varnishing vernissage *m*
vinyl wallpaper papier *m* peint vinyl

wall and ceiling paint roller rouleau *m* "murs et plafonds"
wall covering tapisserie *f*; revêtement *m* mural; textile *m* mural; tenture *f* murale
wall textile textile *m* mural
wall tile carreau *m* au mur
wall tiles; wall tiling carrelage *m* mural
wallpaper papier *m* peint; papier *m* de tenture; tapisserie *f*; papier *m* à tapisser; textile *m* mural
wallpaper (to) tapisser *v*
wallpaper cutting ruler règle *f* à couper le papier peint

wallpaper decorator tapissier *m*; tapissière *f*
wallpaper paste colle *f* à papier-peint
wallpaper pasting machine machine *f* à encoller le papier peint
wallpaper pasting table table à tapisser *f*
wallpaper trimmer molette *f* de tapissier
wallpapering dry brush brosse *f* à étaler
wallpapering paste brush brosse *f* à encoller le papier peint
washable wallpaper papier *m* peint lavable et lessivable
wax cire
wet paint! peinture *f* fraîche!; attention à la peinture! *f*
white gloss (finish) laqué blanc *adj*
white spirit white spirit *m*
whitewash badigeon *m*
whitewash (to) badigeonner *v*
whitewash (to) (*eg* a wall) chauler *v*
window squeegee raclette *f* vitre
wire brush brosse *f* métallique; brosse *f* en fil de fer
wood polish, liquid cire *f* liquide bois
wood stain teinte *f* pour bois
wooden floor parquet *m*

14. COLOURS

amber ambré,-e *adj*
aquamarine bleu-vert *adj*
azure azur *m*
azure azuré,-e *adj*

beige beige *adj*
bicoloured bicolore *adj*
black noir,-e *adj*
blue bleu,-e *adj*
blue, navy bleu marine *adj*
blue, peacock bleu paon *adj*
blue, royal bleu roi *adj*
blue, sky bleu ciel *adj*
blue, slate bleu ardoise *adj*
blue-green bleu vert *adj*
bluish bleuâtre *adj*
bright brillant,-e *adj*
■ **bright colour** = brillante couleur
brilliant brillant,-e *adj*
■ **brilliant colour** = brillante couleur
brown brun,-e *adj*; marron *adj*
brownish brunâtre *adj*

cerise cerise *adj*
cherry-red rouge-cerise *adj*
colour couleur *f*; coloris *m*
crimson pourpre *adj*

dark foncé,-e *adj*; sombre *adj*
■ **dark blue** = bleu foncé
■ **dark green** = vert sombre
delicate tendre; tendresse *adj*
■ **delicate or soft rose** = rose tendre/ tendresse

emerald emeraude *adj*

fuchsia colour fuchsia *adj*

gilded doré,-e *adj*; d'or
gilt doré,-e *adj*; d'or
golden doré,-e *adj*; d'or
grained granité,-e *adj*
granite granité,-e *adj*
■ **granite grey** = granité gris
green vert,-e *adj*
green, apple vert pomme *adj*
green, bottle vert bouteille *adj*
green, emerald vert emeraud *adj*
green, grey(ish) vert-de-gris *adj*
green, jade vert jade *adj*
green, olive vert olive *adj*
greenish verdâtre *adj*
grey gris,-e *adj*
grey, blue- gris-bleu *adj*

colours

grey, mist gris brume *adj*
grey, pearl gris perle *adj*
grey, steel gris acier *adj*
greyish grisâtre *adj*

hue couleur *f*; nuance *f*; teinte *f*

-ish -âtre *suff*
■ bluish = bleuâtre = bleu+âtre

lavender lavande *adj*
light clair,-e *adj*; pâle *adj*
■ light grey = gris clair
lilac lilas *adj*

marble marbré,-e *adj*
marbled marbré,-e *adj*
■ marbled beige = marbré beige
maroon bordeaux *adj*
mauve mauve *adj*
mauvish violacé,-e *adj*
mottled marbré,-e *adj*

navy blue marine *adj*; bleu marine *adj*

orange orange *adj*

pale pâle *adj*
■ pale blue = bleu pâle
pastel pastel *adj*
■ pastel green = vert pastel
pink rose; rosé,-e *adj*
pinkish rosâtre *adj*; rosé,-e *adj*
primary colours couleurs fondamentales *fpl*
purple pourpre *m*; violet,-ette *adj*
purplish violacé,-e *adj*

red rouge *adj*
red, cherry cerise *adj*
reddish rougeâtre *adj*

salmon colour saumon *adj*
sand colour sable *adj*
shade coloris *m*; nuance *f*; couleur *f*; teinte *f*
■ shade card = carte *f* de coloris
silver (colour) argenté,-e *adj*
silvery argenté,-e *adj*
sky-blue azur *m*; azuré,-e *adj*; bleu ciel *adj*
slate-coloured ardoisé,-e *adj*
soft tendre *adj*; tendresse *adj*
■ soft or delicate rose colour = rose
tendre/tendresse
speckled moucheté,-e *adj*
■ speckled blue = bleu moucheté
straw coloured jaune paille *adj*; paille *adj*

tint teinte *f*; couleur *f*
turquoise turquoise *adj*
two-tone bicolore *adj*

ultramarine bleu outremer *adj*

violet pâle violet,-ette *adj*; parme *adj*

white blanc, blanche *adj*
white, ceruse blanc cerusé *adj*

yellow jaune *adj*
yellow, canary jaune canari *adj*
yellow, golden jaune d'or *adj*
yellow, lemon jaune citron *adj*
yellowish jaunâtre *adj*

[Note: French colours, when used alone, usually function as nouns]